Here are your

1996 SCIENCE YEAR Cross-Reference Tabs

For insertion in your WORLD BOOK

Each year, SCIENCE YEAR, THE WORLD BOOK ANNUAL SCIENCE SUPPLEMENT, adds a valuable dimension to your WORLD BOOK set. The Cross-Reference Tab System is designed especially to help you link SCIENCE YEAR's major articles to the related WORLD BOOK articles that they update.

How to use these Tabs:

First, remove this page from SCIENCE YEAR.

Begin with the first Tab, **Archaeology**. Take the A volume of your WORLD BOOK set and find the **Archaeology** article. Moisten the **Archaeology** Tab and affix it to that page.

Glue all the other Tabs in the appropriate WORLD BOOK volumes. Your set's Ci-Cz volume may not have an article on **Compact disc**. Put the **Compact disc** tab in its correct alphabetical location in that volume—near the **Comoros** article.

SCIENCE Year

1996

The World Book Annual Science Supplement

A Review of Science and Technology
During the 1995 School Year

World Book, Inc.

a Scott Fetzer company

Chicago • London • Sydney • Toronto

The Year's Major Science Stories

From the race to find the first known breast cancer gene to the opening of an enormous ancient tomb in Egypt, it was an eventful year in science and technology. On these two pages are the stories *Science Year* editors picked as the most memorable, exciting, or important of the year, along with details on where to find information about them in this book.   The Editors

◀ Powerful earthquake

A Jan. 17, 1995, earthquake in Kobe, Japan, killed more than 5,000 people, highlighting the dangers of severe earthquakes. In the Science News Update section, see GEOLOGY and GEOLOGY CLOSE-UP.

Deadly Ebola outbreak

An outbreak of the fatal infection caused by the Ebola virus left more than 220 people dead by mid-June 1995 in the African nation of Zaire. In the Science News Update section, see PUBLIC HEALTH.

Gene for breast cancer ▶

A heated scientific race ended in September 1994, when an international team of geneticists announced they had pinpointed the first known gene that causes breast cancer. In the Special Reports section, see HUNTING FOR CANCER GENES. In the Science News Update section, see GENETICS.

Rendezvous in space

U.S. astronauts and Soviet cosmonauts took part in a series of historic cooperative missions in space in 1995. In the Science News Update section, see SPACE TECHNOLOGY CLOSE-UP. ▼

World Book, Inc.
525 W. Monroe
Chicago, IL 60661

ISBN: 0-7166-0596-1
ISSN: 0080-7621
Library of Congress Catalog Number: 65-21776
Printed in the United States of America.

Archaeological finds ▲
Two stunning finds thrilled archaeologists in 1995—the discovery in France of 300 prehistoric cave paintings, including the oldest known, and the opening of a huge tomb apparently built for the sons of the ancient Egyptian pharaoh Ramses II. In the Science News Update Section, see ARCHAEOLOGY and ARCHAEOLOGY CLOSE-UP.

Comet impacts with Jupiter
Comet fragments collided spectacularly with Jupiter in July 1994, in what some scientists called the astronomical event of the century. In the Special Reports section, see WHEN WORLDS AND COMETS COLLIDE. In the Science News Update section, see ASTRONOMY.

Oldest human ancestor
Anthropologists in September 1994 reported the discovery of fossils belonging to the oldest known human ancestor, a species that lived more than 4 million years ago. In the Science News Update section, see ANTHROPOLOGY. ▼

DNA fingerprinting on trial
The highly publicized trial of former football star O. J. Simpson in Los Angeles, Calif., in 1995 spotlighted the use of genetic testing in modern criminal cases. In the Special Reports section, see NEW TOOLS OF THE FORENSIC SCIENTIST.

Contents

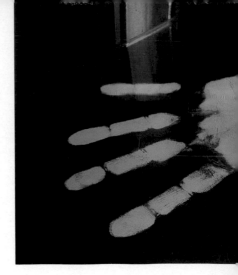

Page 165

Page 172

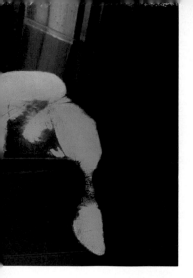

Science News Update 194

Twenty-eight articles, arranged alphabetically, report on the year's major developments in all areas of science and technology, from "Agriculture" to "Space Technology." In addition, six Close-Up articles focus on especially noteworthy developments:

Page 257

Science You Can Use 305

Five articles present various aspects of science and technology as they apply to the consumer.

World Book Supplement 329

Three new or revised articles from the 1995 edition of *The World Book Encyclopedia*: **Electronics; Heredity;** and **Marine Biology.**

Page 262

Index 353

A cumulative index of topics covered in the 1996, 1995, and 1994 edition of *Science Year.*

Cross-Reference Tabs

A tear-out page of cross-reference tabs for insertion in *The World Book Encyclopedia* appears before page 1.

Staff

Editorial Advisory Board

Contributors

Ackland, Len, B.A., M.A.
Director,
Center for Environmental Journalism,
University of Colorado at Boulder.
[Special Report, *The Radiation Question*]

Anthony, Caitlin, B.A.
Books Resource Manager,
Science News Magazine.
[*Books of Science*]

Asker, James R., B.A.
Space Technology Editor,
Aviation Week & Space Technology
Magazine.
[*Space Technology; Space Technology (Close-Up)*]

Bakker, Robert T., B.S., Ph.D.
Curator,
Tate Museum.
[Special Report, *Pterodactyls—Flying Marvels of the Mesozoic*]

Baskin, Yvonne, B.A.
Free-Lance Science Writer.
[Special Report, *Engineering the Globe: A Fix for the Environment?*]

Black, Harvey, A.B., M.S., Ph.D.
Free-Lance Science Writer.
[*Agriculture* (Close-Up)]

Bolen, Eric G., B.S., M.S., Ph.D.
Professor,
Department of Biological Sciences,
University of North Carolina,
Wilmington.
[Science Studies: *Saving the Earth's Species; Conservation*]

Brett, Carlton E., Ph.D.
Professor,
Department of Geological Sciences,
University of Rochester.
[*Fossil Studies*]

Cain, Steve, B.S.
News Coordinator,
Purdue University School of Agriculture.
[*Agriculture*]

Chiras, Dan, B.A, Ph.D.
Adjunct Professor of
Environmental Policy and
Management,
University of Denver.
[*Environmental Pollution*]

Cosgrove, Daniel J., Ph.D.
Professor of Biology,
Pennsylvania State University.
[*Biology*]

Ferrell, Keith
Editor-in-Chief,
OMNI Magazine.
[*Computers and Electronics; Science You Can Use, CD-ROM's: Multimedia Computing on a Silver Platter*]

Goldsmith, Donald, Ph.D.
President, Interstellar Media.
[Special Report, *When Worlds and Comets Collide*]

Goodman, Richard A., M.D., M.P.H.
Adjunct Professor,
Division of Epidemiology,
Emory University.
[*Public Health*]

Graff, Gordon, Ph.D.
Free-Lance Science Writer.
[*Chemistry; Science You Can Use, Environmentally Kinder Coolants*]

Hay, William W., Ph.D.
Professor of Geology,
University of Colorado at Boulder.
[*Geology; Geology (Close-Up)*]

Haymer, David S., M.S., Ph.D.
Associate Professor,
Department of Genetics and
Molecular Biology,
University of Hawaii.
[Special Report, *Hunting for Cancer Genes; Genetics*]

Hellemans, Alexander, B.S.
Free-Lance Science Writer.
[*Physics (Close-Up)*]

Hester, Thomas R., Ph.D.
Professor of Anthropology
and Director, Texas Archeological
Research Laboratory,
University of Texas, Austin.
[*Archaeology*]

Hobbs III, Horton H., B.A., M.S.,
Ph.D.
Professor of Biology,
Wittenberg University.
[Special Report, *The Fragile Wilderness of Caves*]

Hussar, Daniel A., B.S., M.S., Ph.D.
Remington Professor of Pharmacy,
Philadelphia College of Pharmacy and
Science.
[*Drugs*]

Klein, Richard G., Ph.D.
Professor of Anthropology,
Stanford University.
[*Anthropology*]

Kolberg, Rebecca, B.S., M.A.
Free-Lance Science Writer.
[*Science You Can Use, The Chemistry of Cosmetics*]

Kowal, Deborah, M.A.
Adjunct Professor,
Division of International Health,
Emory University.
[*Public Health*]

Limburg, Peter R., B.A., M.A.
Free-Lance Science Writer.
[Special Report, *Hurricanes– Whirlwinds of Change*]

Lovejoy, Thomas E., Ph.D.
Counselor to the Secretary for
Biodiversity and Environmental
Affairs,
Smithsonian Institution.
[Science Studies, *Saving the Earth's Species*]

Lunine, Jonathan I., B.S., M.S.,
Ph.D.
Associate Professor of Planetary
Sciences,
University of Arizona.
[*Astronomy*]

March, Robert H., Ph.D.
Professor of Physics,
University of Wisconsin.
[Special Report, *Found—The Top Quark; Physics*]

Morrill, John H., B.S., M.P.
Manager,
American Council for an Energy-
Efficient Economy.
[*Science You Can Use, Windows to Keep Comfort High, Energy Use Low*]

Moser-Veillon, Phylis B., Ph.D.
Professor,
Department of Nutrition and Food
Science
University of Maryland.
[*Nutrition*]

Myers, Norman, B.A., M.A., Ph.D.
Visiting Fellow, Green College,
University of Oxford.
[Science Studies, *Saving the Earth's Species*]

Peterson, Ray G., B.S., Ph.D.
Research Oceanographer,
Scripps Institution of Oceanography,
University of California at San Diego.
[*Oceanography*]

Pimm, Stuart L., B.A., Ph.D.
Professor of Zoology,
University of Tennessee.
[Science Studies, *Saving the Earth's Species*]

Raven, Peter H., A.B., Ph.D.
Director,
Missouri Botanical Garden.
[Science Studies, *Saving the Earth's Species*]

Schroeder, Don, B.A., B.S.
Technical Editor,
Car and Driver Magazine.
[Special Report, *Cars for the Year 2000 (and Beyond)*]

Sforza, Pasquale M., B.Ae.E., M.S., Ph.D.
Professor and Head of Aerospace Engineering,
Polytechnic University.
[*Energy*]

Snow, John T., Ph.D.
Dean,
College of Geosciences,
University of Oklahoma.
[*Atmospheric Sciences*]

Snow, Theodore P., B.A., M.S., Ph.D.
Professor of Astrophysics,
University of Colorado at Boulder.
[*Astronomy; Astronomy (Close-Up)*]

Stephenson, Joan, B.S., Ph.D.
Associate Editor,
JAMA.
[*Medical Research*]

Tamarin, Robert H., B.S., Ph.D.
Professor and Chairman,
Biology Department,
Boston University.
[*Ecology*]

Teich, Albert H., B.S., Ph.D.
Director,
Science and Policy Programs,
American Association for the Advancement of Science.
[*Science and Society*]

Terr, Lenore C., A.B., M.D.
Clinical Professor of Psychiatry,
School of Medicine,
University of California at San Francisco.
[*Psychology*]

Thornton, John I., Ph.D.
Professor of Forensic Science,
University of California at Berkeley.
[Special Report, *New Tools of the Forensic Scientist*]

Wischnia, Bob, B.A.
Senior Editor,
Runner's World Magazine.
[Science You Can Use, *Selecting Athletic Shoes, Scientifically*]

Woods, Michael, B.S.
Science Editor,
The Toledo Blade.
[*Engineering; Biology* (Close-Up)]

Page 54

Page 60

Page 95

When Worlds and Comets Collide

BY DONALD GOLDSMITH

The spectacular comet strikes on Jupiter
in 1994 showed that the solar system
can be a very dangerous place.

T he greatest collision between a planet and another celestial object ever witnessed by scientists happened in July 1994. For six
days, Jupiter was bombarded by pieces of a disintegrated comet
named Comet Shoemaker-Levy 9. One after another, more than 20
comet fragments slammed into Jupiter's dense atmosphere at speeds
of about 60 kilometers (37 miles) a second, creating enormous fire-
balls easily visible through telescopes on Earth.

The impacts thrilled planetary scientists and amazed the world. But
they also served as a reminder that the solar system can be a dangerous
place. Earth, too, has been struck many times in the past by huge objects hurtling down from space. Scientists think that a mammoth collision with a large comet or asteroid about 65 million years ago may
have led to the demise of the dinosaurs. And in 1908, more than 2,000
square kilometers (770 square miles) of forest near the Tunguska
River in central Siberia were leveled by an immense atmospheric blast
caused by an object—probably a meteor—less than 100 meters (330
feet) in diameter.

Scientists say that what has happened to Earth in the past will happen again in the future. The only question is when.

In fact, astronomers recently thought they had identified a large comet that could pose a danger to Earth a little more than a century from now. In 1992, an international organization of astronomers said the comet, named Swift-Tuttle, would come close to the Earth in August 2126. Scientists estimated the odds of a collision at 1 in 10,000. Fortunately, further calculations showed that there was no danger of an impact after all. But there are many other bodies orbiting out in space. It is possible—not likely, but possible—that Earth will be hit sometime in the next 100 years by some large object that astronomers haven't yet discovered.

Such threats seemed too remote for nonscientists to worry about until the Jupiter collisions suggested to some government leaders that catastrophic strikes from space should perhaps be taken a bit more seriously. On July 20, 1994, the day the first chunks of Comet Shoemaker-Levy plowed into Jupiter, the Science Committee of the United States House of Representatives instructed the National Aeronautics and Space Administration (NASA) to begin tracking any comets, asteroids, or meteoroids—pieces of asteroids—that might someday hit the Earth. NASA officials also named a six-member panel to study the possibility of developing an early-warning system for objects on a collision course with our planet. Meanwhile, some scientists debated how such bodies might best be destroyed or deflected into a safe orbit.

Although asteroids and large meteoroids are just as likely as comets to strike the Earth, a comet would be apt to cause more damage than a rocky body the same size, because comets, on average, travel at greater speeds. (See OTHER THREATS: ASTEROIDS AND METEORS.) But a comet would at least give us fair warning of its coming. Even with the unaided eye, a large comet can be seen from many millions of kilometers away, its misty tail glowing in the night sky. With their telescopes, astronomers would probably be able to predict a collision with a comet at least a year in advance.

From evil omens to dirty snowballs

People have always marveled at comets, and for most of human history they have feared them as well. Because comets appeared unpredictably in the skies, many cultures regarded these celestial visitors as omens of disaster—plagues or the overthrow of kingdoms, not the kind of devastation we now know they can bring.

In times past, no one knew what comets were. The ancient Greek philosopher Aristotle believed they were gaseous objects in Earth's atmosphere, and for centuries nobody could prove him wrong. In the late 1500's, however, the Danish astronomer Tycho Brahe made detailed observations of several comets and showed that their motions placed them well beyond the atmosphere of the Earth.

More than a century later, in the early 1700's, the British scientist Edmond Halley concluded that a comet seen in 1682 was the same one astronomers had observed in 1531 and 1607. Halley predicted the comet would return to the skies again in 1758. When the comet reappeared on schedule, it was named for Halley. In later years, astron-

Terms and concepts

Coma: A thin halo of gas and dust around the solid core of a comet, created by the evaporation of icy material.

Comet nucleus: The small icy and dusty core of a comet.

Comet tail: A stream of very thin gas and dust pushed away from the coma of a comet by the pressure of light and charged particles from the sun.

Kuiper Belt: A disk-shaped reservoir of comets believed to exist just beyond the outermost planets. The belt is thought to be the source of most short-period comets.

Long-period comet: A comet that, because of its very large orbit, takes 200 years or more to return to the inner solar system.

Near-Earth object (NEO): A comet or other large body whose orbit crosses Earth's orbit.

Oort Cloud: A spherical reservoir of comets surrounding the solar system that extends for trillions of kilometers. The cloud is thought to be the source of long-period comets.

Short-period comet: A comet with an orbital period of less than 200 years.

The author: Donald Goldsmith is the president of Interstellar Media in Berkeley, Calif., and the author of many books on astronomy.

Tail

Nucleus

Coma

To sun

Icy visitors from space

Comets are icy bodies that enter the inner solar system from more distant regions of space, circle around the sun, and then—in most cases—depart.

The visible parts of a comet include the coma—a hazy cloud of gas and dust that can be up to 100,000 kilometers (60,000 miles) in diameter—and a long thin tail. The tail, which may stretch for 100 million kilometers (60 million miles), consists of gas and dust from the coma that is pushed away from the comet by the pressure of radiation and particles from the sun. The core of a comet, hidden by the coma, is the nucleus, a compact mass of ice, frozen gases, and dust that is typically 1 to 10 kilometers (0.6 to 6 miles) across. The coma and tail appear as warmth from the sun evaporates material in the outer layers of the nucleus.

Oort Cloud

Orbit of Pluto

Kuiper Belt

Comets are thought to come from two regions called the Kuiper Belt and the Oort Cloud. The Kuiper Belt is a disk-shaped reservoir of icy nuclei that begins just beyond the orbit of Pluto. The Oort Cloud is a spherical region of space that extends for trillions of kilometers. Comets enter the inner solar system after the gravity of another body, such as a passing star, nudges them into a new orbit that takes them close to the sun.

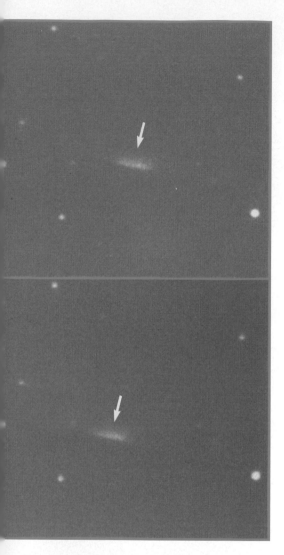

omers determined that Halley's Comet, which returns at intervals of about 77 years, may have been the comet recorded in various historical records and works of art dating back as far as 240 B.C.

Modern observations of comets have revealed that they are essentially large, dirty snowballs. A comet consists primarily of water ice and various amounts of frozen gases, including carbon dioxide, methane, and ammonia, mixed with rocky material and dust. Most of the mass of a comet is contained in a solid core called the *nucleus*, typically 1 to 10 kilometers (0.6 to 6 miles) in diameter.

Huge reservoirs of comets

Astronomers think that comets were among the first objects to form in the solar system, created from the same cloud of gas and dust that gave birth to the sun and planets some 4.6 billion years ago. The outer portions of the cloud condensed into a crowded disk of icy bodies. Over the eons, gravitational interactions between these icy objects caused most of them to take up different orbits, eventually dispersing them into a huge spherical region. This vast reservoir of comet nuclei is called the *Oort Cloud*, named after the Dutch astronomer Jan Oort, who first deduced its existence in 1950. Astronomers think the Oort Cloud extends about halfway to the nearest star, a distance of trillions of kilometers. The objects in the Oort Cloud are so distant that not even our best telescopes can see them.

Also in 1950, a Dutch-born American astronomer, Gerard Kuiper (pronounced *KOY per*), theorized that much of the original disk of comet nuclei remains as a smaller and more densely packed reservoir of comets within the vast Oort Cloud. This region, Kuiper speculated, is still disk-shaped and begins just beyond the outermost planets. The region became known as the *Kuiper Belt*, but for years there was no evidence that it actually exists. Observations in the 1990's, however—including images made in 1995 by the Hubble Space Telescope— have erased most doubts about the Kuiper Belt. Several dozen icy objects orbiting beyond the planets have now been discovered.

Astronomers are certain that the number of comets visible from Earth is just a minuscule fraction of the comets in the Kuiper Belt and Oort Cloud. They think those two regions contain sever-

First sight of a dangerous comet
Comet Shoemaker-Levy 9, the comet that struck Jupiter, was discovered in March 1993 by astronomers at the Mount Palomar Observatory in California. When examining astronomical photographs taken on different nights, *above,* they noticed a small, hazy object, arrows, that had changed position against the background of stars. Calculations of the object's speed showed that it was a comet and not an asteroid— asteroids, on average, move slower than comets. Further observations revealed that the comet was in orbit around Jupiter and would strike the giant planet in July 1994.

A series of violent impacts on Jupiter

In a previous circuit around Jupiter, Comet Shoe-maker-Levy 9 was torn apart by the planet's gravity into more than 20 fragments, which lined up in orbit like a string of pearls, *above*. The comet chunks crashed into the far side of Jupiter over a period of six days. A sequence of photographs, *right,* shows an explosion flaring up on the rim of Jupiter. To the right of the explosion is the glowing site of an earlier impact. The bright object to the left of the planet is one of Jupiter's moons.

Moon of Jupiter

Comet impact

al trillion comet nuclei. We see only those relatively few comets whose orbits have been altered, perhaps by the gravitational influence of a nearby star or even of another comet, sending them into the inner solar system.

Most of the time, when a comet is orbiting far from the sun, it consists of nothing but the nucleus. But when a comet moves toward the inner parts of the solar system, it starts to assume its more familiar appearance. When the comet nears the orbit of Jupiter, the sun's heat causes the frozen gases in the outer layers of the nucleus to start evaporating, producing a large cloud of thin gas and dust called a *coma*. The coma, which surrounds and blocks astronomers' view of the nucleus, can be more than 100,000 kilometers (60,000 miles) across.

When the comet gets about as close to the sun as the Earth is, the pressure of sunlight and of the solar wind—a stream of fast-moving particles moving outward from the sun—pushes the gas and dust away from the coma. This effect creates a long *tail* that may stretch for 100 million kilometers (60 million miles), always pointing away from the sun.

After a comet circles around the sun and begins to head toward the outer reaches of the solar system, its tail shrinks and its coma dissipates. Soon, the nucleus is all that remains until its next trip into the inner solar system.

Each time the comet returns, evaporation causes its mass to decrease by about 1 percent, and eventually there will be nothing left of it. How long it takes a comet to evaporate away to nothing depends on its size and its orbit. Some comets, such as Halley's Comet, are known as *short-period comets* because they make return trips in less than 200 years. Astronomers think short-period comets come from the Kuiper Belt. *Long-period comets,* on the other hand, have orbital periods that take them out of the inner solar system for centuries, and some will not return again for thousands or even millions of years. These comets probably come from the Oort Cloud. Most long-period comets have lost only a small amount of their mass, so they tend to be larger and brighter than short-period comets.

A rare spectacle on Jupiter

Astronomers believe that the Kuiper Belt was the original home of the comet that smashed into Jupiter. The comet was discovered in March 1993 by American astronomers Eugene Shoemaker, Carolyn Shoemaker, and David Levy at the Mount Palomar Observatory in California. The astronomers were looking for new comets by comparing photographs of regions of the sky taken on different nights. If they noticed that a tiny, faint object had changed position against the background of stars, they would identify it as a comet or an asteroid. The object's speed would reveal which of the two it is, since comets move faster than asteroids.

Studying photographic images they had made of a portion of the night sky, Levy and the Shoemakers noted what appeared to be a "squashed comet." Further observations confirmed that the object was indeed a comet and that it looked squashed because it was broken into fragments. The pieces of the comet were hurtling through space one after another, lined up like pearls on a string.

By studying the path of Shoemaker-Levy 9, astronomers determined that the comet was in orbit around Jupiter and had probably been orbiting the giant planet for 60 to 100 years. But what had broken it into pieces? Physicists and planetary scientists theorized that when the comet passed close by Jupiter in July 1992, the planet's tremendous gravity had pulled the icy nucleus apart. Further calculations revealed that the comet fragments would smash into the far side of Jupiter in July 1994.

When the collisions came, they were spectacular. The largest comet fragments, which may have been more than 3 kilometers (2 miles) in diameter, created particularly stupendous displays, igniting huge atmospheric blasts, some of them thousands of kilometers across.

Because all the impacts occurred on Jupiter's far side, just over the planet's rim as seen from Earth, no telescope—not even the Hubble Space Telescope—could see the collisions as they occurred. Only the *Galileo* spacecraft, on its way to a rendezvous with Jupiter in December 1995, was able to photograph some of the comet strikes directly. Observers on Earth could see the impact sites about 30 minutes after each

Aftermath of a mighty blast

More than 20 years after being flattened by a mysterious atmospheric explosion in 1908, a forest near the Tunguska River in central Siberia was still a scene of devastation, *above*. Much of the forest never grew back and is today devoid of trees, *left*. The blast occurred when an object less than 100 meters (330 feet) in diameter exploded with the force of a large hydrogen bomb high in the air above the remote area. A small comet was long considered a prime suspect in the event, but astronomers now think the explosion was caused by a rocky object from space called a stony meteor.

Other Threats: Asteroids and Meteors

In addition to comets, the solar system contains two other kinds of objects that can strike Earth with devastating effect: large rocky bodies called asteroids and smaller ones called meteoroids.

Like comets, asteroids and most meteoroids are chunks of debris left over from the formation of the solar system about 4.6 billion years ago. Astronomers believe that asteroids formed in the same way that the planets and their moons did, as dust particles in the rotating cloud of gas and dust that became the solar system collided and stuck together. Unlike comets, which consist mostly of ice, frozen gases, and dust, asteroids and meteoroids are composed of rock and varying amounts of iron-nickel alloy.

Most asteroids are in a band between the orbits of Mars and Jupiter, an area known as the asteroid belt. Scientists estimate the number of asteroids at more than 30,000. The largest, Ceres, is about 970 kilometers (600 miles) in diameter, and there are more than 1,100 asteroids with diameters of at least 30 kilometers (19 miles). The term *meteoroid* refers to the smallest asteroids—those less than about 100 meters (330 feet) wide. The asteroid-belt meteoroids, of which there are millions, were created when asteroids collided with one another and broke into smaller pieces. A meteoroid that enters Earth's atmosphere is called a *meteor*, and a meteor that strikes the ground is known as a *meteorite*.

Most asteroids and large meteoroids have stable orbits in the asteroid belt and pose no danger to Earth. But well over 1,000 of these objects, including several asteroids as large as 8 kilometers (5 miles) in diameter, may have orbits that cross

Earth's orbit. These are potentially serious threats to our planet. The likelihood of a collision with an asteroid or meteoroid is about the same as that of an impact from a comet the same size. Impacts with smaller objects are far more common than with big ones.

Because asteroids and meteoroids are made of rock and metal, their average density is about three times greater than that of comets. An asteroid or meteoroid therefore has triple the mass and triple the *kinetic energy* (energy of motion) of a same-sized comet moving at the same speed.

Objects from the asteroid belt, however, tend to approach Earth with considerably less speed than some comets, because asteroids orbit the sun in the same direction as the Earth. An asteroid moving toward Earth is usually overtaking our planet, or being overtaken by it. A typical intruder from the asteroid belt thus has a relative velocity of about 16 kilometers (10 miles) a second as it enters Earth's atmosphere.

Comets, which orbit in all directions, are usually moving two or three times as fast as asteroids and large meteoroids, relative to the Earth. Because the energy released by an impact increases in proportion to the square of the object's velocity, a comet colliding with Earth would probably cause far more damage than an asteroid of the same mass.

Nevertheless, an impact with an asteroid, or with a meteoroid more than a few hundred meters across, would cause tremendous damage to our planet. Even a somewhat smaller meteoroid would destroy everything within a radius of tens of kilometers. [D. G.]

An iron meteorite weighing about 300,000 tons created Meteor Crater in Arizona about 50,000 years ago. The crater is 1,275 meters (4,180 feet) wide.

collision occurred, as Jupiter's rapid rotation (once every 10 hours) carried them into view. But several fiery plumes of gas—the tops of the largest explosions—were visible at the time of impact as they rose above the planet's rim.

Jupiter consists primarily of gases, so the impacts caused no long-term damage. The only noticeable effects were a few dark blotches in the atmosphere that persisted for several months and could still be seen as stretched-out atmospheric streaks in 1995.

When Earth gets pummeled

If our own planet had been the target of Comet Shoemaker-Levy 9, the outcome would have been much different. Earth, too, would have survived the bombardment, but scientists say that the collisions would have caused widespread devastation and greatly damaged the planet's complex web of life.

The extent of the destruction that would result from a comet striking the Earth at a typical speed of about 50 kilometers (30 miles) a second would depend on the size of the comet. A strike by a comet 10 kilometers (6 miles) or so in diameter would be truly catastrophic, equivalent to a billion 1-megaton hydrogen bombs exploding all at once. Besides the immediate effects of the impact, trillions of tons of pulverized debris would be thrown into the atmosphere, where it would blot out the sun for months. Much of the planet's vegetation would die, and with it much of the human and animal life that depends on it. Civilization itself might well be destroyed, and whatever scattered remnants of humanity survived—if any did—would sink into a prolonged dark age.

That is the magnitude of the collision many scientists believe occurred 65 million years ago, when the last of the dinosaurs and many other species of animals vanished forever from the Earth. Geologists think they may have identified the ancient crater produced by that event off the coast of Mexico's Yucatán Peninsula.

Fortunately, such collisions are rare. The geological record of impact craters on Earth shows that a 10-kilometer-wide object strikes our planet, on average, only once every 100 million years.

Strikes by smaller bodies are more frequent, simply because small objects in the solar system are much more numerous than large ones. The best-preserved impact crater made within the last few tens of thousands of years—Meteor Crater in Arizona—was created by a relatively small object. About 50,000 years ago, an iron meteorite about 30 meters (100 feet) in diameter smashed into the Arizona desert to produce the crater, a depression more than 1.2 kilometers (0.75 mile) across and about 175 meters (575 feet) deep. Despite the meteorite's fairly small size, it struck with the explosive force of 20 million tons of TNT.

The blast that gouged out Meteor Crater was comparable to the Tunguska explosion of 1908. Scientists estimate that a comet or meteor collision of that size occurs once every 200 to 300 years, on the average. One reason we don't have more impact craters on Earth is that many objects rapidly disintegrate in the atmosphere, just as happened in Siberia. Only very large or very hard objects make it all the way to the ground. Moreover, it is all but certain that the great majority of strikes have occurred in the ocean, because more than 70 percent of the planet is covered with water. But the scarcity of impact craters on land is due largely to erosion. As centuries pass, wind and water slowly obliterate all traces of most craters.

Contemplating catastrophe

Although a Tunguska-sized explosion over a populated area would be a calamity, the destruction would be limited to a relatively small area. Many scientists and government leaders are more concerned about the possibility of a collision with a larger body, one with a diameter of 1 kilometer (0.6 mile) or more. An object that size hits the Earth at least once every million years or so, on the average.

At a speed of 50 kilometers a second, a comet that size would hit the Earth with a *kinetic energy* (energy of motion) equivalent to 1 million 1-megaton hydrogen bombs, or 1 trillion tons of TNT. Experts say the destruction and loss of life resulting from such a collision would surpass anything humanity has ever experienced from a single event.

Flashing through Earth's atmosphere in about two seconds, the comet would smash into the ground with incredible force and explode in an immense fireball. The shock wave from the blast would level virtually everything for a radius of more than 100 kilometers. Within much of that area, the heat of the fireball would reduce the debris to ashes and shapeless blobs of melted stone and metal. Beyond the ring of total destruction, damage from the shock wave and heat would be severe to moderate for another 1,000 kilometers (600 miles).

The collision would produce a crater at least 20 kilometers (12 miles) across and several kilometers deep. The force of the impact would hurl molten material long distances, igniting forest fires, and eject an immense volume of dust and vaporized rock into the atmosphere. The dust and gas would spread around the planet and obscure the sun.

The atmospheric darkening would be much less severe than would result from a truly enormous impact such as the one that occurred 65 million years ago, but it would still be significant. The atmospheric effects from a 1-kilometer-comet strike might cause widespread crop failures and starvation. So even if we had adequate warning of the collision and evacuated the areas most apt to be devastated, these secondary effects could still cause great loss of life.

But what about the more likely possibility that a comet would hit in the ocean? Unfortunately, that too would be a disaster. Although a comet strike far out at sea might spare cities from being flattened or burned, the collision would still do plenty of damage.

After its plunge through the atmosphere, the comet would plow through several kilometers of seawater in a fraction of a second, breaking apart from the force of the impact. Still moving at immense speed,

Opposite page: A comet 1 kilometer in diameter striking the Earth would cause immense devastation, especially if it hit in an urban area. Traveling at a speed of perhaps 50 kilometers (30 miles) a second, the comet would streak through Earth's atmosphere in about two seconds and slam into the ground, producing a huge explosion. The shock wave and heat from the blast would destroy everything within a radius of more than 100 kilometers (60 miles). The impact and explosion would dig a crater at least 20 kilometers (12 miles) wide and throw huge amounts of dust into the atmosphere.

the comet would burrow into the sea floor and explode, creating a crater more than 10 kilometers in diameter and spewing material in all directions. Vast amounts of steam and vaporized rock would be thrown upward before the parted water could rush back to cover the hole in the sea floor.

The worst effect of an ocean strike might be the resulting tidal wave. The comet's sudden displacement of a huge volume of water, together with the titanic blast on the sea floor, would create a tidal wave a kilometer or more in height that would surge outward at almost 1,000 kilometers an hour. Many low-lying coastal cities would be submerged.

To protect the planet

Because a collision with a comet would have such terrible consequences, experts say it's worth considering how such a disaster might be prevented. Some astronomers have proposed the construction of a network of telescopes dedicated to searching the solar system for all near-Earth objects (NEO's), objects whose paths cross Earth's orbit and which are large enough—1 kilometer or more in diameter—to cause large-scale damage. Such a system would most likely enable scientists to identify all these threats, which astronomers think may number 2,000 or more. At present, only about 100 are known.

NASA's six-person panel was expected to recommend the development of just such a system, probably to be called Spaceguard. NASA already has a much more limited program, the Spacewatch survey, which uses a telescope at the Kitt Peak National Observatory near Tucson, Ariz., to watch for NEO's. Spacewatch observations are detecting about 30 new NEO's a year, ranging in size from about 6 meters (20 feet) to 6 kilometers (3.7 miles) in diameter. A similar project is being carried out at Mount Palomar.

In 1995, NASA and the Air Force were also funding the development of improved electronic detectors, known as charge-coupled devices (CCD's), to increase the light-gathering ability of telescopes. The more sensitive CCD's would give small instruments the resolving power of considerably larger telescopes, making it possible to use many existing telescopes to search for NEO's. Once astronomers identify an NEO, they can chart its orbit and predict its future motions.

It may thus be possible to find and catalog every potentially dangerous asteroid, large meteoroid, and known comet. But a new short-period comet making its first trip around the sun would pose an unforeseen danger. Likewise, a long-term comet returning from a million-year circuit through the Oort Cloud might sneak up on us by surprise. Experts say we must be particularly on the lookout for these previously unknown comets.

Unfortunately, detecting a comet on a collision course with Earth will undoubtedly be easier than preventing the impact. So far, scientists and engineers have proposed several schemes, but all involve considerable risk.

One solution is to send nuclear-armed rockets into space to blow up

Opposite page: A 1-kilometer-wide comet landing in the ocean would bore through several kilometers of water in a fraction of a second and break apart as it embedded itself deep in the sea floor. There, it would explode, blasting steam and vaporized rock out through the tunnel it had drilled in the sea before the parted waters had time to come back together. The impact and explosion would gouge a crater more than 10 kilometers wide in the seabed and generate a tidal wave at least 1 kilometer in height that would submerge coastal cities over a wide area of the planet.

the comet or nudge it into a new orbit. Such a mission would require extremely accurate calculations. Astronomers would have to be absolutely certain that the object was sure to strike the Earth—otherwise, the nuclear explosion might change what would have been a near-miss into a direct hit. And spaceflight engineers would have to give the rockets just the right trajectory and explode the warheads at precisely the right time to get the desired effect.

Attempting to destroy the comet outright could be a chancy proposition, however. If we were to simply blow it into large pieces, those chunks might rain down over a large region of the Earth. Calculations indicate that such an outcome could be worse than a single large collision. To be successful, engineers would have to make sure that the comet was completely pulverized. Simply altering the object's orbit might be a safer bet. That could be done by detonating warheads close enough to the object to affect its motion but not break it apart.

The farther away a comet could be intercepted, the easier it would be to push it into a safe orbit. Only a small change in the object's path would make a large difference over a distance of several billion kilometers, just as moving a rifle barrel a couple of millimeters can be the difference between hitting a far-off target dead center or missing it completely. Thus, early detection of a comet on a collision course with Earth would give engineers a tremendous advantage in diverting it.

With enough warning, it might even be possible to avoid explosive devices altogether. Some scientists have proposed sending astronauts to an approaching comet or asteroid to mount powerful rocket engines on it or even fit it with a huge "solar sail." The latter would be a giant reflector made of metallic foil, which would capture the pressure of sunlight the way a sloop's sails catch the wind, slowly easing the object into a new orbit. But such schemes assume a warning time measured in years. If we discovered a comet just months away from hitting the Earth, nuclear-tipped rockets might be the only feasible solution.

Thankfully, astronomers say we probably have plenty of time to weigh our options. Even though comets and asteroids have crashed into our planet many times in the past, the long intervals between the largest impacts make it likely that the next big one won't arrive for thousands more years. Still, the experts caution, we would do well to keep a close watch on the skies, especially for the smaller objects that arrive more frequently. But on the rare occasion that a major comet makes its majestic way around the sun, the odds will be good that we can simply sit back and enjoy the show.

Opposite page: In what some experts say might be our best hope for defending against a comet heading for Earth, rockets tipped with nuclear warheads intercept the comet while it is still far off in space. The warheads explode hundreds of meters away from the comet, diverting it into a safe orbit without destroying it. An attempt to blow a comet into tiny fragments might instead break it into a number of large chunks that together could be more destructive than a single massive object.

For further reading:

Eicher, David J. "Death of a Comet." *Astronomy*, October 1994, pp. 40-45.
Goldsmith, Donald W. *Nemesis: The Death-Star and Other Theories of Mass Extinction.* Walker Books, 1985.
Hall, Louis B. *Searching for Comets.* McGraw-Hill, 1990.
Tyson, Peter. "Cometbusters." *Technology Review*, February/March 1995, pp. 22-30.

Ecologists are discovering that hurricanes play vital ecological roles by encouraging some species, harming others, and renewing the natural landscape.

Hurricanes—
Whirlwinds
of Change

BY PETER R. LIMBURG

A satellite image captures Hurricane Andrew as it strikes the Bahamas and Florida in August 1992, *above*. Three views of a Puerto Rican forest damaged by Hurricane Hugo in September 1989 show regrowth 1 month, 3 months, and 17 months after the storm (*left, top to bottom*).

Terms and concepts

Climax species: A plant or animal species whose population is relatively stable in the absence of disturbance.

Climax state: The final stage of development in an ecosystem marked by a stable equilibrium among plant species and the animals dependent upon them.

Forest gap: An opening in the dense canopy of leaves of a forest created when a large tree falls over or a hurricane strikes. The increased sunlight and warmth favor pioneer species, because they are the first plants to take over an area after a disturbance.

Hurricane: A powerful whirling storm that begins over tropical regions in either the North Atlantic Ocean or eastern North Pacific Ocean and whose wind speeds reach 119 kilometers (74 miles) per hour or more. Such a storm in the western Pacific Ocean is called a typhoon, and one in the Indian Ocean is called a cyclone.

Pioneer species: Plants that are the first to move into an area where disturbance has occurred.

Storm surge: A series of high waves formed by a combination of a hurricane's strong winds and low atmospheric pressure over the sea.

The author:
Peter R. Limburg is a free-lance writer specializing in articles on nature.

Hurricanes unleash monstrous, destructive forces. Tremendous winds flatten forests. Torrential rains flood farmland. Huge waves surge onto shore, washing away almost everything, natural or constructed, along vast stretches of coastline. In a few hours, billions of dollars worth of property becomes rubble.

Hurricane Hugo, which struck the West Indies and Southeastern United States in September 1989, brought similar devastation. But these storm clouds also proved to have a silver lining. In the hurricane's path were forest tracts in South Carolina and Puerto Rico that ecologists had been studying for years. Thus, quite by accident, Hugo gave scientists the opportunity to study the impact of a hurricane not in the usual, human terms of lives lost and property damaged, but from nature's point of view.

After all, hurricanes are a fact of life for wilderness areas in the Caribbean and the Southeastern United States. Were the storms truly catastrophes for all the plants and animals that live in the area? Or did some species actually benefit? And what about the long-term effects of a hurricane? Was the health of an ecosystem harmed, or perhaps improved? Finding the answers to these questions would not only deepen scientists' understanding of the workings of nature, but also provide information that conservationists could use to protect endangered plants and animals in the path of future hurricanes.

Armed with extensive data about life in the forest before Hugo, scientists began studies in a relatively new area of ecological research. Some researchers embarked on studies to determine how quickly an ecosystem rejuvenates after a hurricane. Others examined how the mix of plant and animal species changed during the process. When Hurricane Andrew cut a path across south Florida in 1992, marine biologists seized the opportunity to find out how coral reefs are damaged and reborn after a hurricane. Ecologists studied damaged areas in Everglades National Park to determine how the presence of cities, farms, and other human construction impacted the recovery process.

By 1995, scientists had begun to develop a number of surprising insights. It appears that hurricanes are not catastrophes to all of the creatures in their path—some species undergo population booms after the storm. And scientists are also finding that healthy ecosystems bounce back with amazing speed. Wilderness areas close to cities and farms, on the other hand, may suffer so much from pollution and other environmental problems that a hurricane could sound the death knell for some species.

Studying Hurricane Hugo's effects in South Carolina

One of the prime areas for studying damage caused by Hurricane Hugo was the Francis Beidler Forest in South Carolina, where about 700 hectares (1,700 acres) were damaged. The Beidler Forest is owned and managed by the National Audubon Society, one of the largest conservation organizations in the world. Before Hugo struck, scientists had accumulated extensive data on plant and bird life in Beidler.

After the hurricane, researchers at Beidler set out small observation plots at sites ranging from the severely damaged to the untouched. The biologists tagged and recorded the damage to all trees above a certain size, usually 2.5 centimeters (1 inch) in diameter when measured about 1.3 meters (4.5 feet) above the ground. They estimated the amount of destruction to the upper part of the forest—the so-called *canopy*—by using a long tube-and-mirror device that operates similar to a periscope on a submarine. Through a series of mirrors, the device reflects back to the viewer a view of the canopy. Scientists also inventoried low-growing shrubs and plants and measured the diameter of felled tree trunks, branches, and twigs.

The researchers found that some tree species at Beidler were much more vulnerable to hurricane damage than others. Before the hurricane, baldcypress and tupelo trees grew in swampy lowlands. Only one or two feet higher, on the banks of the swamps and streams, ash and red maple grew in the slightly drier soil. Higher still, on the sandy ridges, stood oaks and pines. Hugo knocked down the oaks, which have shallow root systems, as if they were bowling pins. The loblolly pines and tupelos were snapped off or blown down by the strong winds. But the cypresses stood firm, propped up by their dense, strong wood and massive buttress-shaped trunk. Their slender branches, stripped of needles by the wind, also helped them survive by offering little wind resistance.

Spruce pines, on the other hand, remained standing but soon died. Biologists speculated that the trees had suffered fatal damage belowground caused by the intense wind. Violent shaking can set up vibrations in the tree that damage the fine hairlike structures in the root system. Without their fine roots and root hairs, the trees cannot absorb needed water or nutrients. Disease-causing agents can also enter a tree through broken roots.

Other trees left standing suffered from the loss of leaves. Losing leaves may seem trivial, since new ones normally sprout. However, generating new leaves weakens a tree, making it more vulnerable to infestation by disease and insects. And in the months after a hurricane, disease-causing microbes and insects become more populous in the environment, because many species thrive on the decaying, woody debris that litters the ground.

Five years later: A forest renewed

The leaf loss seemed to benefit the ecosystem as a whole, however. After Hugo felled trees and stripped leaves from some of those left standing, more sunlight was able to stream in to warm the soil and the air. When biologists rechecked the plots at the Beidler forest five years after the hurricane had struck, the scientists found that seeds of sun-loving, fast-growing plants called *pioneer species* had sprouted in the open areas.

Some of the pioneer species were nonwoody plants such as wild flowers. Others were shrubs that formed a woody undergrowth. The pio-

Nature's Powerful, Whirling Sea Storms

A hurricane is a powerful, whirling storm that begins over the ocean and whose wind speeds reach 119 kilometers (74 miles) per hour or more. Properly speaking, however, the word *hurricane* refers only to those storms that occur in tropical regions over the North Atlantic Ocean or eastern North Pacific Ocean. When such storms occur in the western Pacific Ocean they are called *typhoons*. Those in the Indian Ocean are termed *cyclones*.

All of these storms begin simply as a large area of warm air over warm ocean water. The mass of warm air is a low pressure area, because as the warm air rises, a weak vacuum is created beneath it. The atmospheric pressure is lower there than in the surrounding area. Air outside the warm air mass moves into the low pressure zone, creating wind. The greater the difference in pressure, the stronger the wind.

Earth's rotation makes the low pressure area take on a spin as it moves away from its origin. A low spins slowly at first, then gains speed as it travels over warm ocean currents.

Warm moist air from near the surface rises into the spinning air mass. The air cools as it rises, and the moisture in it condenses. The process creates clouds, which form a wall up to 15,200 meters (50,000 feet) high. The wall surrounds the center of the storm, called the eye. The eye is usually about 32 kilometers (20 miles) in diameter

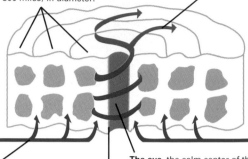

A hurricane contains a central zone called the eye surrounded by swirling bands of clouds that bring torrential rain and violent winds. The hurricane forms where warm, moist air rushes into an area of low air pressure over the ocean.

Rainbands are formed as warm, moist air sucked into the low pressure zone rises, cools, and forms clouds. The series of bands of clouds can measure 320 to 480 kilometers (200 to 300 miles) in diameter.

Cooled air spreads out horizontally along the top of the hurricane.

Warm, moist air rushes in to replace the upward spiraling air.

The eye, the calm center of the storm, is typically about 32 kilometers (20 miles) in diameter.

The eyewall borders the eye. In the eyewall, warm air spirals upward, creating the hurricane's strongest winds—with speeds of 120 kilometers (70 miles) per hour or more.

and is free of rain and clouds. But in the wall, violent air currents, called microbursts, blow up and down, creating powerful thunderstorms. Clouds and winds spiral out from the wall as far as 240 kilometers (150 miles) in all directions.

Most of the hurricanes that strike eastern North America and the Caribbean islands originate off northwestern Africa in a region called the intertropical convergence zone. In this zone, two wind systems blow steadily past each other in opposite directions. Between them, lows tend to

neer species provided shelter for the seedlings of the trees that survived the hurricane in little islands of vegetation.

By 1994, biologists saw extensive regrowth. The broken tupelos had sprouted new branches from their trunks. Clearings as small as about 1,000 square meters (10,900 square feet) contained thousands of cypress seedlings, each 1 to 2.5 meters (4 to 8 feet) tall. Damaged areas on higher ground were filled with dense vegetation too thick to walk through. The plants were so thick that even deer could not penetrate the area, which protected any pine seedlings that had sprouted in the undergrowth.

Researchers who studied the animal life of the forest found that many of the animals that survived the storm were greatly stressed by form. The spin of the developing hurricane is intensified by the opposing winds.

Typhoons originate between the Marshall Islands and the Philippines. Cyclones appear to begin over a warm section of the southern Pacific Ocean east of the Fiji Islands, off the northwestern coast of Australia.

Hurricanes in the Northern Hemisphere form in summer, when the convergence zone is north of the equator. As Earth tilts away from the sun, winter begins in the north, and the convergence zone moves down below the equator into the Southern Hemisphere. The change brings hurricane season to nations south of the equator.

Hurricanes in the Northern Hemisphere usually begin by traveling from east to west, then gradually head northwest, north, and finally northeast. In the Southern Hemisphere, the storms turn southwest, south, and finally southeast.

The path of an individual hurricane is irregular and very unpredictable, however. It may suddenly veer off course or stall in one spot for several days. The irregularity of the path is due to other winds. They push and tug at a hurricane and force it to change direction or hover over one area.

When a hurricane heads toward shore, it can cause great damage not only because of the strong winds but also because of the storm surge. A storm surge is a series of high waves produced by the winds and low atmospheric pressure. In a region about 80 to 160 kilometers (50 to 100 miles) from the center of the storm, the surge may raise the level of the sea. Hurricane Andrew struck the Miami, Fla., area with a storm surge 5.15 meters (16.9 feet) high. The Great Labor Day Hurricane of 1935 spawned a surge of nearly 9.15 meters (30 feet). On a flat, low-lying coastline, such as that of South Carolina and Florida, the surge may wash hundreds of meters inland.

Eventually, the hurricane will pass over a large land mass or cold ocean water. Then, as it no longer gets heat energy and moisture, the whirlwind of destruction loses force and dies.   [P. L.]

Powerful whirling storms form over oceans in several tropical regions around the world (shaded areas). Such storms are called hurricanes when they occur over the North Atlantic Ocean or eastern North Pacific Ocean. When the storms occur in the western Pacific Ocean, they are called typhoons, and in the Indian Ocean, they are termed cyclones.

the aftermath. Populations of insect species that fed on the leaves and juices of living plants were reduced severely, as were those of other insects and spiders that preyed on the plant-feeders. Bird species that ate fruit, nectar, or seeds departed for better feeding grounds. Mammals such as deer, mice, and raccoons left for nearby undamaged areas. In short, the animals that depended on green vegetation for their food had to find a new habitat or starve. The animals that relied on vegetation for shelter had to seek protection elsewhere or get picked off by predators.

But some animals thrived and multiplied in the new conditions. For insects such as wood-boring beetles that feed on dead and dying trees, the litter of branches and tree trunks on the forest floor provided a

Wide-ranging destruction

The tremendous force of a hurricane can turn forests into leafless matchsticks and coral reefs into scarred monuments to the storm's fury. Fish and other animals may die by the thousands.

A 1995 view of a bleached, dead star coral patch in the Caribbean Sea, *above,* testifies to a hurricane's long-range effects. Seven years earlier, Hurricane Gilbert's churning waves and sand caused the damage.

In 1992, Hurricane Andrew stripped the leaves from tropical hardwood trees in Everglades National Park in southern Florida, *above.* In some areas, only the tips of palm trees remained intact after the storm.

feast. The beetles' grubs, or *larvae,* in turn attracted woodpeckers and other birds.

Because researchers have monitored bird populations in the Beidler Forest for many years, scientists were able to develop detailed data on the changes in bird populations. Researchers found that by 1994, some bird species had recovered almost to the same level as before the hurricane struck, and others, such as the white-eyed vireo, had actually increased in population. This species prefers the shrubby habitat flourishing in Hugo's wake. Another species, the yellow-throated vireo, made its first appearance at Beidler after Hugo blew through, perhaps to take advantage of the exploding insect populations feeding on dead bark and leaves.

The biggest surprise appearance was the redheaded woodpecker. Whereas it had been a rarity in Beidler before 1989, the bird was the second or third most numerous woodpecker species seen in 1994. Hugo had created the bird's preferred nesting habitat: tall, dead tree trunks standing in open spaces.

Other bird species did not fare so well. There were fewer red-eyed

Thousands of dead fish litter a stretch of beach in Louisiana in the wake of Hurricane Andrew in 1992. As Andrew's floodwaters receded, they carried nutrient-rich runoff into the Gulf of Mexico. The nutrients encouraged the growth of tiny marine organisms that rapidly used up much of the oxygen in the water. The lack of oxygen suffocated the fish, biologists reported.

vireos in 1994 than before the hurricane, because Hugo had destroyed most of the mature forest that is the birds' natural habitat. The northern parula warbler, whose population was in decline before Hugo, continued to trend downward.

Hurricane research in Puerto Rico

Hurricane Hugo devastated Puerto Rico as well as South Carolina, and the storm's eye passed within 15 kilometers (9 miles) of the Luquillo Experimental Forest in the northeast. Luquillo, a tropical rain forest on a rugged mountain range crisscrossed by deep valleys and swift streams, has since become a major site for research on the ecological effects of hurricanes.

Biologists in Puerto Rico found that the windward slopes of the forest bore most of Hugo's destructive force. After the storm, the landscape appeared covered by a jumble of giant matchsticks. In one area where 36 species of trees had stood before the hurricane, only eight species remained afterward. For four of these species, only one or two trees survived. The mahogany and other nonnative trees that had been planted in Luquillo for study were all destroyed.

In general, biologists found that large trees sustained more damage than small trees, probably because the wind had more surface to push against. Oddly, many more trees were knocked down in the valleys than on the exposed ridges. Scientists theorize that trees in the protected conditions in the valley may have grown more quickly than those on the windy ridges. The valley trees thus may not have developed the strong root systems that anchored the trees on the ridges. A unique rooting habit was probably responsible for the survival of the tabonuco tree, one of two tree species in the forest that endured the hurricane particularly well. The tall tabonuco tree grows in groups of 2 to 14 specimens, their roots intertwined to form a firm underground anchor. The roots of some tabonucos wrap around rocks beneath the soil, providing even stronger anchorage.

The other tree species that survived Hugo well, the sierra palm, was aided by leaves that fall off easily. By the time the hurricane's strongest winds began to blow, the palm leaves had fallen, and the wind pushing against the bare trunks was rarely able to knock the trees over. After the storm, each sierra palm quickly produced new leaves from the bud at the top of its trunk.

Within a few weeks, many of the other damaged trees sprouted new growth. However, over the following two years, many of those trees died. The researchers believe the delayed mortality was almost certainly due to the loss of fine roots coupled with the loss of leaves.

In the newly created gaps in the Luquillo forest, grasses and seedlings of native pioneer species quickly sprang up. Among the seedlings were the cecropia tree, a pioneer species that at maturity attains a height of 15 meters (50 feet). Scientists estimated that 16,000 cecropia seedlings had sprouted per 1 hectare (2.5 acres). By 1994, the number had dropped to about 10,000 per hectare. The seedlings of slower growing trees had begun to crowd out the cecropias, just as the cecropias had shaded out the grasses within a year after Hugo's wrath.

A mixed fate for the forest's animal life

To assess the hurricane's effect on insect populations, researchers first looked for a species of *walkingstick* (a wingless insect that looks like a twig) that had been under study at Luquillo for years along with several species of plant-eating snails. Apparently, the study animals had literally been blown away by the storm. They were so scarce that study could resume on only one snail species.

On the other hand, seven months after the hurricane, a population explosion among several species of butterfly caterpillars occurred in the most severely damaged areas of the forest. The caterpillars multiplied in response to abundant food—succulent new leaves. By 1995, the numbers of most species had dropped back to prestorm levels, possibly because parasitic wasps and flies that infest the caterpillars were keeping the population in check.

Researchers found that the numbers of young frogs dropped sharply after the hurricane—a troubling discovery because frogs are a key species in the food web of Luquillo. They eat vast numbers of insects and are eaten in turn by birds, snakes, and huge spiders. But only one year after the hurricane, the population of adult frogs had grown to four times its level before the storm, though the adult frogs were smaller than normal. The exploding insect populations could apparently support more frogs to maturity, but at the cost of reduced adult size.

Of all the animals in the forest, the endangered Puerto Rican parrot was the species biologists were most concerned about. Before Hugo passed through, the species had dwindled to about 47 birds living in the wild. Immediately after the storm, researchers spotted only 25 or 26. By 1995, however, after several years of good hatches, the parrot population appeared to be recovering.

Examining the Everglades after Hurricane Andrew

Hurricane Andrew, a narrow, intense storm, turned south Florida into a third major site for hurricane research in 1992. In Andrew's path were mangrove forests along the east and west Florida shore. These forests contain mangrove trees that protect the shore from erosion by trapping sediment among their spidery, interlacing roots. Many fish, shellfish, and other sea creatures find shelter and breed among the mangrove roots, and birds come to feed on these animals. Raccoons prey on the eggs and nestlings of the birds and catch crabs scuttling around the root mass.

Scientists found that Andrew did little damage to the mangroves on the eastern shore of Florida. These trees are a dwarf variety that grows only 1.5 meters (5 feet) tall. They were nearly submerged in water, and so they were protected from the winds. On the west coast, however, the mangroves are a taller variety, and many were snapped off and died. Researchers speculated that others died because their roots became covered by storm-borne sediment containing poisonous sulfur compounds given off by decaying organic debris.

In the Everglades, biologists found that the native tropical hardwood trees withstood Andrew's winds relatively well. Although they lost leaves and branches, most of the trees remained standing and soon regenerated their missing parts. The pines did not do as well. In some locations as many as 30 percent of the pines were killed. In others, only 3 percent died. But even in the worst-hit areas, 70 percent of the damaged pines recovered.

Scientists were keenly interested in the hurricane's effect on a key component of the Everglades ecosystem, a dense mat of algae and other microbes called *periphyton*. Small fishes and crustaceans, such as crawfish and freshwater shrimp, hide from predators in this mat. Some also find prey there. After the hurricane, the periphyton was greatly reduced, and there were far fewer resident fish and shrimp. In only a year, however, the periphyton and the animals that depend on it had become reestablished in most locations.

One of the most important Everglades species—the alligator—was partially affected by the storm. Alligators are valuable to some life in the Everglades chiefly because they create small ponds as they wallow in the muck. The wallows are refuges for certain fish in the dry season, and the fish are food for egrets and other wading birds. Birds and mammals can drink at the wallows if shallower ponds and channels dry

Hurricane damage and recovery

Hurricanes' strong winds, torrential rain, and rough seas cause characteristic damage to marine, shoreline, and inland ecosystems. Five years after a hurricane, however, many animal species have reappeared, and many plants have regenerated.

In a coastal ecosystem

Before a hurricane (near right): On a North Carolina coast, turtles nest on the beach, and sand dunes rise at the high-tide mark. Farther inland, oaks and pines teem with birds and squirrels. The dense shade allows only a few woody shrubs and ferns to grow on the forest floor.

Immediately after a hurricane (middle): Strong winds and waves have leveled the sand dunes, enabling the water to wash farther inland. Many trees are uprooted or snapped off. Many animals are gone, having fled the storm or been killed by flying branches and other debris.

Five years later (far right): Waves wash up on a beach that has retreated inland, and dunes are reforming at a new high-tide mark. Surviving trees have grown new bushy limbs. Woodpeckers nest in the dead pines. Wild flowers and grasses thrive in the abundant sunlight.

In a marine ecosystem

Before a hurricane (near right): In a reef off the Florida coast, corals grow in shallow warm water, providing small fish with protection against predators.

Immediately after a hurricane (middle): Churning water has broken pieces of branching coral and overturned round "head" corals. Dead fish, mussels, and seaweed have been thrown out of the water onto the beach.

Five years later (far right): Fish swim among new growth on the branching coral, and seafans and seaweed grow among patches of dead coral.

up. Adult alligators seemed to survive the storm well, but the flooding destroyed many eggs and hatchlings. Seasonal floods and predators normally claim a significant percentage of alligator eggs and young. Therefore, researchers are not yet certain whether Andrew's toll was enough to cause a dip in the number that normally reach maturity.

The birds of the Everglades apparently escaped the hurricane with little loss. Eggs were not in jeopardy because the nesting season was over when the storm hit. Moreover, most of the young birds apparently were able to cope with the stress.

Devastation and recovery at a coral reef

Andrew also brought an opportunity to study the devastation and recovery of coral reefs, the underwater limestone formations created by colonies of tiny coral animals and plants. Coral reefs form the basis of marine ecosystems containing fishes, starfish, and other sea animals. A hurricane's strong winds churn up waves that break off branches of treelike corals, such as elkhorn and staghorn, and overturn massive "head" corals, species that form structures resembling boulders. The force of the waves buries some living corals in sediment, suffocating them, and fatally blasts others with suspended sand. Churning water slams the broken pieces of coral into the reef, breaking off more coral in a chain of destruction. Sponges and soft corals are ripped loose and carried away by currents.

After Andrew swept through southern Florida, scientists from the University of Miami and other institutions donned scuba gear to lay out observation plots on coral reefs that had been in the hurricane's path. The researchers returned to the plots periodically to record the coral colonies that died and to note the species that showed signs of regeneration. The scientists also kept track of the species of seaweed, algae, sponges, and sea fans that moved into dead patches of coral. The newcomers prevent coral regeneration, because coral larvae need a bare, hard surface on which to attach themselves.

The scientists found to their surprise that Andrew did relatively little damage to the reef, probably because of the relatively small width of the storm. Andrew overturned fewer than 5 percent of the massive coral heads, though it damaged more than 90 percent of the branched elkhorn coral colonies, and 30 percent of these were shattered completely. Researchers found living coral colonies thriving right next to devastated areas. The reef appeared undamaged below the depth of 6 meters (20 feet), partly because Andrew's winds did not churn water below this point and partly because few of the vulnerable branching corals grow below that depth.

The elkhorn coral seemed to thrive after the hurricane, however. Fragments of elkhorn coral survive best when the coral animals in them can cement themselves on dead coral, preferably dead elkhorn coral, though they can also attach to certain mollusk shells and hard-packed sand. In 1993, a year after Andrew struck, scientists found that the broken elkhorn fragments had cemented themselves to the hard-

Making matters worse

A year after Hurricane Andrew whirled through Florida's Everglades National Park, scientists found that while some areas rebounded, the presence of human beings increased the devastation elsewhere.

West of the Everglades, pine trees flourish a year after the storm, *left.* Abundant ground water enabled the trees to recover relatively quickly from Andrew's onslaught. Within the Everglades, most pines regenerated due to adequate ground water, and they survived infestations of bark beetles, which park workers collect for counting, *below.*

East of the park, near the city of Homestead, *left,* the pines died. The nearby city had drawn down ground water supplies, and the water-starved trees were too weak to survive the bark beetle infestation.

packed bottom. By 1994, some had grown about 10 centimeters (4 inches). The elkhorn fragments were growing so well that some researchers think this coral species may rely mainly on hurricane disturbance for propagation.

Seeing hurricanes in a new light

From elkhorn coral in the sea to woodpeckers, caterpillars, and pioneer plants on land, many individual species appear to be short-term beneficiaries of a hurricane, scientists have discovered, and relatively few native species seem to suffer long-term harm. These findings indicate that nature may view a hurricane as a blessing. Without hurricanes, ecologists now think, many pioneer species might disappear forever, and with them the animals that depend on them for food and shelter.

By opening the door for species that might not otherwise be able to gain a foothold, hurricanes may ensure that an ecosystem contains a diverse mix of species. And an ecosystem that contains many different native species is healthier than one in which only a few predominate. A forest with dozens of tree species, for example, is likely to have at least some species capable of surviving a drought, disease, or infestation of pests.

This view of hurricanes complements scientists' relatively new ideas about the importance of change to an ecosystem. Many biologists used to think that the natural state of a wilderness was its so-called climax state, such as a magnificent forest dominated by large, old trees of a single species. Proponents of this view see volcanic eruptions, hurricanes, and fires caused by lightning as disasters because these events destroy the climax state of the ecosystem. The newer view is that all ecosystems continually undergo transformation and that catastrophic events are simply the necessary agents of change.

How the human presence magnifies damage

What may indeed be a disaster, however, is the fact that human activity can prevent an ecosystem from recovering naturally from a hurricane. If a hurricane flings a ship onto a reef, live coral may be not only crushed but also poisoned, by the oil or gasoline leaking from the fuel tanks. And when hurricane flooding overwhelms the waste disposal plants of coastal cities, raw sewage flows into rivers and bays and ultimately can kill marine animals.

The torrential rain from Hurricane Andrew, for example, flushed vast quantities of organic matter from surrounding farmlands and residential lawns into Biscayne Bay. The sudden, rich bounty of nutrients sparked a plankton bloom that threatened to choke out the sea grasses and sponges on the bottom of the bay. The plankton multiplied so rapidly that all the available oxygen in the water was depleted. Scientists saw schools of fish at the surface of the water trying to get oxygen directly from the air. Hundreds of fish died. Near the mouth of a drainage canal into the bay, lobsters attempted to climb the retaining wall to escape from the polluted water, according to observers.

Hurricane damage may also help a troublesome plant or animal species gain a foothold in new areas. Ecologists fear, for example, that the hurricane damage in Biscayne Bay may allow cattails—a nonnative marsh plant—to multiply faster than the native sawgrass and crowd it out. And Andrew's strong winds blew seeds of the Brazilian pepper tree from a dense infestation of the plants within the Everglades to the banks of the freshwater streams that drain from the Everglades. Scientists fear that the fast-growing invader will choke out the mangroves on the fringe of the Everglades.

In at least one case, however, a hurricane will help restore a human-dominated ecosystem to its more natural state. After Hugo devastated nearly three-quarters of South Carolina's 101,171-hectare (250,000-acre) Francis Marion National Forest, the United States Forest Service (USFS) decided that parts of the damaged forest should be restored to the area's original longleaf pine ecosystem. Such an ecosystem had dominated the Atlantic and Gulf coasts when European settlers arrived in the 1600's. Over the centuries, logging and development reduced the number of longleaf pines by about 95 percent. Today, fast-growing loblolly pines and sweet gum trees planted by the lumber industry are the dominant species.

The new 10-year plan designed by the USFS emphasizes ecology over the demand for timber, according to Marion Forest officials. The longleaf pines are more disease-resistant than the current species, and they will form the basis of a more diverse ecosystem that includes shrubs, grasses, and wild flowers. The longleaf pine ecosystem is also the preferred habitat for endangered red-cockaded woodpeckers. USFS scientists hope that the woodpecker population will increase as the longleaf ecosystem becomes established.

Clearly, society will continue to regard hurricanes as natural disasters and calculate their damage in human terms. Hugo wreaked an estimated $7 billion in property damage, and Andrew, $20 billion to $25-billion. The sight of such vast destruction makes it difficult to believe that anything good can come of a hurricane. But by discovering more about how nature rebuilds, researchers hope to identify ways to turn hurricane damage into scientific opportunity.

For further reading:

Boucher, Douglas H. "Growing Back After a Hurricane." *BioScience,* March 1990, pp. 163-166.
Graham, Frank, Jr. "Matchsticks!" *Audubon,* January 1990, pp. 44-51.
Levin, Ted. "Survival of the Wettest: In the Everglades, Andrew Was a Win-Win Situation." *Audubon,* November/December 1992, pp. 22-25.
Twist, Clint. *Hurricanes and Storms.* Macmillan Children's Book Group, 1992.

Cars for the Year 2000 (and Beyond)

The internal combustion engine has its advantages, but engineers predict that cleaner, more efficient cars will soon be taking to the road.

BY DON SCHROEDER

Imagine it is the year 2025, and you are stuck in a traffic jam. Ahead of you is a vintage 1995 car that jolts memories of your first few years of driving. How different cars were back then. Nearly all had bodies made of steel. Most cars weighed between about 1,000 and 2,000 kilograms (2,000 and 4,000 pounds) and ran on gasoline, which was the only fuel most service stations sold. All cars seemed pretty much the same: They all had four wheels and a gasoline engine. You drove the same car to commute to work, to make a quick trip to the grocery store, or to travel across the country.

What seemed advanced and sophisticated back then seems almost laughably simple compared to what you drive now. Your car weighs only about 600 kilograms (1,300 pounds), and it's made mostly of recyclable, reinforced plastics. A small hydrogen engine in the trunk charges a rack of batteries that provide electricity to power the car. Instead of an instrument panel, the car displays the readings as ghostly

Terms and concepts

Ethanol fuel: An alternative to gasoline produced by fermenting starch or sugar crops, such as corn or sugar cane. Ethanol produces fewer harmful emissions than gasoline but requires relatively large amounts of energy to produce.

Fuel cell: An advanced, virtually emission-free engine that uses electrochemical reactions between hydrogen and oxygen to produce electricity to power a motor.

Hybrid electric vehicle: A vehicle that combines an internal combustion engine with a battery-powered electric motor.

Hydrocarbons: Compounds made of hydrogen and carbon. Gasoline is a mixture of hydrocarbons.

Methanol fuel: An alternative fuel to gasoline made by reforming natural gas, coal, wood, or even the methane gas produced during garbage decomposition. Methanol burns more cleanly than gasoline, but it is toxic and expensive to produce.

Ozone: A molecule made of three oxygen atoms. In Earth's lower atmosphere, ozone is a component of smog.

Regenerative braking: A technology in which a battery-charging generator is powered by the energy of the motion of a car during braking.

The author:
Don Schroeder is the technology editor at *Car and Driver* magazine.

numbers that appear on the windshield. A small red light indicates your car's position on a glowing map in the windshield to the right of the instruments. Looking at the windshield map, you're reminded of the old fold-out paper maps. You can't remember the last time you saw one.

A scenario like this might seem hard to imagine, in light of the less dramatic changes consumers have seen in cars since the mid-1960's. But the automobile industry is currently facing pressures that make continued reliance on the tried-and-true car designs unlikely.

Some of that pressure stems from the continuing problem of automobile pollution. In the United States alone, according to the Environmental Protection Agency, highway vehicles produce 44 percent of the nation's air pollution, releasing more than 64 million metric tons (70 million short tons) of chemical pollutants per year. Those pollutants include nitrogen oxides, which mix with chemicals in Earth's atmosphere to cause acidic precipitation, commonly called *acid rain.* Another automobile pollutant is carbon monoxide, a poisonous gas that can reduce the supply of oxygen to body tissues. Unburned *hydrocarbons* (compounds containing hydrogen and carbon) can mix with nitrogen oxides in the presence of sunlight to form ozone, a main component of smog. Finally, cars and trucks are responsible for 20 to 25 percent of the excess carbon dioxide the United States releases into the atmosphere each year. Many scientists believe that rising levels of this heat-trapping gas will cause a *global warming,* a rise in Earth's average surface temperature that could cause widespread, disruptive climate changes.

Aside from causing pollution, cars and trucks increase our reliance on foreign sources of oil. In 1993, highway vehicles burned more than 50 percent of the petroleum consumed in the United States. Our appetite for petroleum has made the United States highly dependent on other countries for petroleum imports. Unstable supplies or price shocks can lead to economic problems in the United States and political tensions abroad.

Since the 1960's, the U.S. government has been pushing the automobile industry to make cleaner, more fuel-efficient cars. In 1966, the federal government began placing strict controls on allowable tail pipe emissions, which eventually resulted in the appearance of the catalytic converter, a muffler-shaped device that cleans exhaust by combining the pollutants with special metals that, when heated, change the pollutants to carbon dioxide and water. Another improvement was the evaporative recovery system, which continuously collects gasoline fumes from the gas tank and fuel system and stores them in a charcoal cannister to be burned in the engine.

In 1995, federal laws allowed new cars to emit only 4 percent of the pollutants that most cars emitted in 1960, and light trucks were allowed only 10 percent of 1969 emission levels. Computerized diagnostic systems mandated for 1996 cars will help reduce pollution further

The two-stroke engine

Designers trying to create a smaller, lighter automobile are focusing on the two-stroke cycle engines used in lawn mowers and motorcycles. The two-stroke design reduces weight and engine size, increasing fuel economy compared with the four-stroke cycle engines that power today's cars. The drawback to most current two-stroke technology is that the engine is polluting because it cannot be used with standard pollution-control devices such as catalytic converters. An experimental two-stroke car designed by the Orbital Engine Company of Australia, *left*, weighs about 90 kilograms (200 pounds) less than a comparable four-stroke car and is about 12 percent more efficient.

A two-stroke gasoline auto engine, *right*, resembles a standard four-stroke gasoline engine in many ways. But the two-stroke cycle engine needs only two strokes of the pistons to produce power. The first stroke occurs when the piston rises to compress a mixture of fuel and air that has already entered the top of the cylinder through the intake port, *below*. In the second stroke, *below right*, the spark plug ignites the compressed fuel-air mixture, and the explosion pushes the piston down. As the piston uncovers the exhaust port, the burned gases escape, and the new fuel-air mixture enters the cylinder through the intake port.

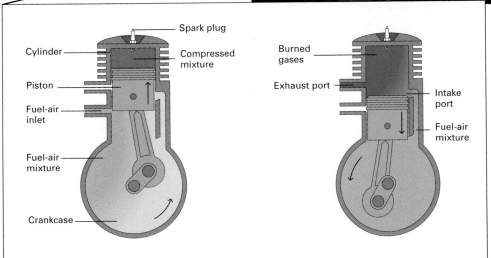

Spark plug

Cylinder

Compressed mixture

Piston

Fuel-air inlet

Fuel-air mixture

Crankcase

Burned gases

Exhaust port

Intake port

Fuel-air mixture

The battery-powered electric car

Battery-powered electric cars emit no pollution from the tail pipe, making them "zero emission" vehicles of the type mandated by law in California by 1998. The major drawback of the cars is their limited range. Engineers have not developed a practical battery that can travel more than about 160 kilometers (100 miles) before it needs recharging.

The General Motors Corporation introduced the Impact battery-powered electric car, *left*, in 1990. Such cars require frequent battery charging, *above*. The battery chargers convert regular alternating current to direct current so that batteries can run off household electricity.

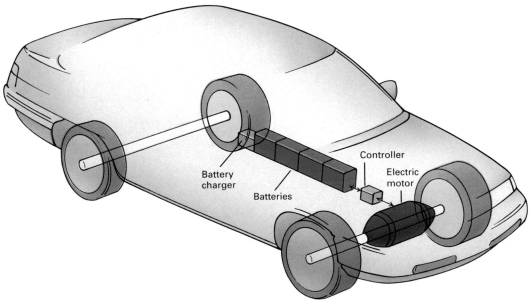

Controller

Battery charger

Electric motor

Batteries

A typical battery-powered electric car uses a pack of 12-volt batteries to provide electricity to run an electric motor, which provides the power to make the car go. An electronic controller regulates the flow of current to the motor and the speed of the car as demanded by the driver.

A hybrid car

A combination of internal combustion engine and battery-powered electric technology holds promise as a design for the car of the future. This design, called a hybrid car, would provide many of the emissions benefits of a battery-powered car but with a greater traveling range.

The German automaker BMW developed an experimental series hybrid car called the E-1, *above*, in 1993. The E-1 operates as a battery-powered electric vehicle. An on-board gasoline engine can fuel a generator that recharges the batteries as the car moves. BMW engineers claim that the on-board generator can extend the E-1's range by about 100 kilometers (60 miles).

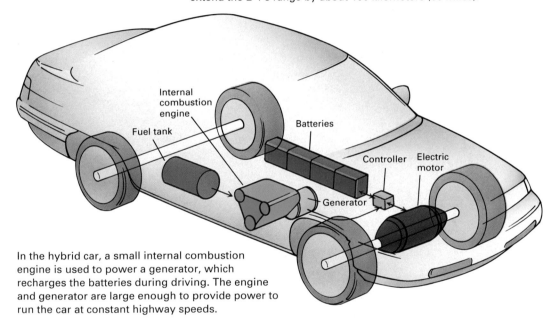

In the hybrid car, a small internal combustion engine is used to power a generator, which recharges the batteries during driving. The engine and generator are large enough to provide power to run the car at constant highway speeds.

by monitoring the condition of the engine and catalytic converter.

Spurred by federal mandates, manufacturers have also increased automobile fuel-efficiency over the years. In 1965, the typical new car sold in the United States could travel little more than 6 kilometers per liter of gasoline (14 miles per gallon). Since then, the mileage for average new cars has doubled, to more than 12 kilometers per liter (28 miles per gallon in the 1994 model year.

But none of these advances have tackled the major problem with current automobile design. As a mode of transportation, steel-bodied cars with internal combustion engines are simply not very efficient. Even in the most advanced internal combustion engines, only about 15 to 30 percent of the energy contained in the gasoline ends up turning the car's wheels. The rest of the energy exits through the radiator or exhaust pipe as heat or is lost through friction as engine parts rub against each other. Vehicles also achieve low fuel mileage because they are so heavy. Even with the lightest models, transporting a driver requires burning enough gas to move an additional 10 times the driver's weight in iron, steel, rubber, and glass. The poor energy efficiency translates into higher than necessary pollution emissions, because the more gasoline a car must burn, the more pollution it produces.

Automakers will have to tackle these problems in order to meet the latest government mandates. The strictest legislation affects California, the state with the most severe air pollution problems in the United States. One California requirement is that by 1998, 2 percent of the cars each manufacturer sells in the state must emit no air pollution at all. By 2001, these so-called "zero-emission vehicles" must account for 5 percent of new vehicle sales. By 2003, the portion jumps to 10 percent. New York and Massachusetts officials have also announced plans to require zero-emission vehicles before the year 2000.

The federal government is also pushing for better fuel economy. A major national initiative is the Partnership for a New Generation of Vehicles, a collaboration between the U.S. government and domestic automakers announced by the Administration of President Bill Clinton in September 1993. Through the partnership, the government will promote the development of a "supercar" that gets at least 34 kilometers per liter (80 miles per gallon).

Given the need to rethink the basic design and operation of automobiles, industry observers believe that advanced, even radical, technologies are on the way. As of 1995, automotive designers were working on several alternatives—electric cars; hybrid cars, which use both electricity and gasoline; cars that burn fuels other than gasoline; cars with lawnmower-type "two-stroke" engines; and even three-wheeled cars that burn less fuel because of their light weight. Some designs will prove to be more practical than others, and as engineers test prototype cars, they will gain a better understanding of which new technologies are likely to be acceptable to the public. For now at least, the only way to predict the shape of the new breed of cars is to look at the designs under development, consider their advantages and disadvantages, and try to imagine how they might be used singly or in combination to create the cars we'll be driving in the next century.

Instead of burning gasoline or another fuel, electric cars are powered by electricity. In a typical electric car, electricity flows from the batteries through a device called a controller that adjusts the current going to an electric motor. The motor provides the power that turns the wheels.

Battery-powered electric cars have not yet appeared on major manufacturers' showroom floors, however. Most of the few thousand battery-powered cars now on the road are standard gasoline-powered cars that individuals or companies converted to electric propulsion. Nearly all these cars store electricity in banks of at least 12 conventional lead-acid batteries, the type of battery used to start cars with gasoline engines.

Mass-produced electric cars will have an advantage over the conversions. The mass-produced cars will include lighter body materials, special tires with low rolling resistance, and lower aerodynamic drag. A broader range of battery types, including nickel-hydride, sodium-sulfur, and lithium-ion should also be available. Sophisticated designs for current controllers will also allow regenerative braking, a technique for recharging the batteries while the car is slowing down on the road. During braking, the drive motor acts as a generator, which converts the mechanical energy of the car into electrical energy that recharges the battery. The generator applies a braking force to the wheels in place of that regularly applied by the brakes.

The main advantage to battery-powered electric cars is that they do not burn fuel. That means the cars emit no pollution from the tail pipe, and their widespread use could dramatically reduce world dependency on petroleum for transportation. Another advantage is that battery-powered cars are quiet. Finally, in industrialized nations, widespread use of battery-powered cars would not require major changes in the distribution of energy. Sources of electric power are plentiful in the United States, and the cars could be recharged overnight, when the demand for electricity and its cost are lowest.

As a car of the future, however, the battery-powered electric car has some serious drawbacks. A major problem is that today's batteries cannot store enough energy to power the cars for very long distances between recharges, which can take hours. Today's best battery-powered cars have maximum ranges of 160 kilometers (100 miles), a figure that drops significantly if the car's air conditioning, heater, or headlights are turned on. And unlike a gasoline-powered car that is nearing empty, a battery-powered electric car slows dramatically when its battery is running down.

Electric cars in the mid-1990's were expensive as well, because they were produced in small quantities. Even with subsidies from the government or the car industry, battery-powered cars cost between $2,000 and $20,000 more than a new gasoline-powered car when first introduced. When electric cars are mass-produced and batteries are fully developed, experts expect that owning an electric car will cost about the same as a gasoline-powered car, however. At typical electricity prices, battery cars are roughly half as expensive to drive per mile as the typical gasoline-powered economy car. This does not include the cost of periodic battery replacement, which should become less frequent as battery technology matures.

Finally, although battery-powered cars are considered "zero-emission vehicles," discarded batteries may leak toxic chemicals if disposed of improperly. Lead-acid batteries are currently the only viable power source for electric cars, and mining and producing lead for batteries can cause lead pollution. Lead is a *neurotoxin* (an agent that damages

A hydrogen-powered car

Hydrogen offers environmental advantages over gasoline as a fuel for automobiles with internal combustion engines, because the combustion of hydrogen emits only nitrogen oxide and water vapor. Hydrogen's density is far less than gasoline's, however, so special techniques, such as compressing the gas, absorbing it in other substances, or liquefying it, would be necessary. Storing sufficient fuel on board would be a big problem.

An operator connects gas lines to storage tanks, *above,* in order to fuel Mazda Motor Company's hydrogen-powered HR-X hydrogen car, *left.*

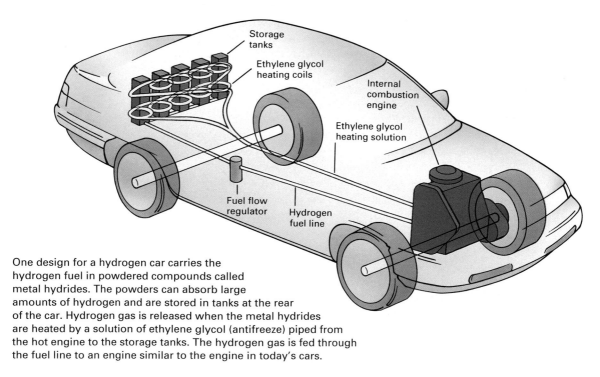

Storage tanks

Ethylene glycol heating coils

Internal combustion engine

Ethylene glycol heating solution

Fuel flow regulator

Hydrogen fuel line

One design for a hydrogen car carries the hydrogen fuel in powdered compounds called metal hydrides. The powders can absorb large amounts of hydrogen and are stored in tanks at the rear of the car. Hydrogen gas is released when the metal hydrides are heated by a solution of ethylene glycol (antifreeze) piped from the hot engine to the storage tanks. The hydrogen gas is fed through the fuel line to an engine similar to the engine in today's cars.

nerve cells) and can delay mental development and stunt physical growth in children. And pollution will be produced at the power plant that generates the electricity stored in the battery. Most U.S. electric power plants burn coal as fuel, in the process emitting sulfur dioxide, nitrogen oxides, and carbon dioxide. However, electric power plants emit no hydrocarbons or carbon monoxide pollution, as gasoline-powered cars do.

One new design overcomes the problem of the limited range of battery-powered cars by including an engine-powered generator that burns a fuel such as gasoline to produce electricity on-board the car. The engine-generator is much smaller than the engine in a present-day gasoline car, because its primary duty is to recharge the battery while the car is on the road. It provides limited electrical power to accelerate the car. That power comes from the battery.

Designs for such "hybrid" electric vehicles are configured in one of two ways—series and parallel. In a series hybrid, the engine powers a generator, which charges the batteries. The batteries in turn power the car's motor. In a parallel hybrid, the engine has a direct mechanical link to the wheels, helping the electric motor power them. In both cases, the engine is big enough to propel the car on its own only at constant speed, not during acceleration.

Automobile designers say that a carefully designed hybrid electric car would emit little pollution while maintaining the range of the standard internal combustion engine car. Further, the hybrid design could reduce costs, because a large number of expensive high-tech batteries are not needed to maintain acceptable power and range.

The major disadvantage to the hybrid vehicle technology is that the engine creates some pollution, though much less than a normal-sized internal combustion engine that operates all the time. But because the hybrid emits some pollution, the vehicle is not capable of meeting legal requirements for zero tail pipe emissions.

Internal combustion engines—whether they also assist electric motors—appear to be headed for a revolution in any case, in the form of alternative fuels. Two of the most likely liquid alternatives are alcohols: methanol and ethanol. Both are usually mixed with a small amount of gasoline to form gasohol.

Methanol is produced primarily from natural gas, but it can also be made from coal, wood, and even the methane gas produced by garbage decomposition. Methanol's *energy density*—the amount of energy released per liter when it burns—is about half that of gasoline. A methanol vehicle would require about twice as much fuel as a standard gasoline-powered car in order to travel an equal distance.

Ethanol is made from fermenting starch and sugar crops, such as corn and sugar cane. The energy it releases per liter is about two-thirds that of gasoline.

Alcohol-powered cars would have similar driving characteristics to gasoline cars, but would offer some advantages. By replacing gasoline,

Ford's experimental Synthesis-2010 auto employs aluminum in place of much of the steel that makes up standard automobile bodies. The lighter aluminum saves hundreds of pounds, saving fuel and reducing pollution.

alcohols would lessen the nation's dependence on petroleum imports. And, in general, alcohol-fueled engines emit fewer pollutants than do gasoline-fueled engines, particularly unburned hydrocarbons and carbon monoxide.

But there are notable disadvantages to these fuels. Methanol is more toxic to human beings than gasoline, and it is more easily absorbed into the skin. Methanol-powered cars emit substantial amounts of formaldehyde, a smog-inducing compound. Alcohols are also much more corrosive than gasoline to rubber, plastic, aluminum, magnesium, and lead—materials commonly used in automobile fuel systems.

Finally, there are cost and distribution concerns. Methanol is slightly cheaper to produce per gallon than gasoline, but there is no existing network to distribute it in large quantities. Ethanol is nearly twice as expensive to produce as gasoline, and it takes more energy to make ethanol from corn than the ethanol produces when it's burned. Vast amounts of land would be required to grow corn for ethanol production, and some economists claim that "ethanol farms" would reduce the amount of corn grown for food and thus raise food prices.

Two other alternative fuels are compressed natural gas (CNG) and liquefied petroleum gas (LPG). For use in combustion engines, both fuels offer advantages over gasoline.

CNG's benefits are many. Because a gas mixes more readily with air than a liquid (such as gasoline), CNG burns more cleanly in the engine's combustion chamber. That reduces tail pipe emissions. Natural gas is also one of the safest fuels to handle, because it needs very particular conditions in which to ignite with air. Because internal combustion engines need only a minimum of modifications to run on CNG, the additional cost of a CNG-fueled car would be only a few hundred dollars. Finally, CNG reserves in the United States are plentiful: The

American Gas Association estimates that enough CNG exists in the contiguous 48 states to fuel U.S. cars well into the 2000's.

Although CNG is about one-third less expensive than gasoline on an equivalent energy basis, the fuel has some disadvantages. Because of its lower density, CNG provides only a quarter of the energy of gasoline. Also, as with alcohol fuels, distributors would have to build a retail distribution network before CNG could become popular as a gasoline alternative. And, filling up a CNG tank at high pressure would be a time-consuming and cumbersome task.

Liquefied petroleum gas (LPG), commonly known as propane, shares many of the characteristics of CNG. It is the most popular alternative fuel in current use, powering more than 250,000 automobiles and trucks in the United States. A by-product of crude oil refining, propane costs about one-third less than the gasoline produced along with it. Propane offers the emission advantages of CNG and better range than CNG—about equivalent to that of methanol. But propane is not as abundant as CNG, and since it is a by-product of petroleum refining, it does not help reduce U.S. dependency on petroleum. Finally, like CNG, propane requires a pressurized system for fuel storage in the car, as well as at the filling station.

A more futuristic fuel source is hydrogen gas. As a motor vehicle fuel, hydrogen can be burned in the internal combustion engine in a manner similar to CNG and propane. Hydrogen's major advantage over the other fuels is that it burns more cleanly, since it does not contain carbon. The only tail pipe emissions from hydrogen combustion are small amounts of nitrogen oxides.

Many technical difficulties surround the use of hydrogen, however. Today's internal combustion engines would need significant—and costly—reengineering to run properly on hydrogen gas. And gaseous hydrogen offers even less energy per unit volume than CNG at the same pressure, so the range of a hydrogen car is severely limited. Storing hydrogen on-board the car presents a serious problem.

A more likely use of hydrogen is as a fuel for advanced, batterylike devices for electric cars. These devices, called fuel cells, combine oxygen and hydrogen to generate electricity. Like batteries, fuel cells contain positive and negative electrodes and an *electrolyte* (conductive material) between the two electrodes. Hydrogen enters one electrode and oxygen enters the other. The hydrogen forms *ions* (electrically charged atoms) that pass through the electrolyte to the other electrode to react with the oxygen to form water. The breakup of the hydrogen molecules releases electrons, which travel to the oxygen electrode by way of the motor as an electric current to power the car.

Because fuel cells generate little heat, they convert the hydrogen fuel to electrical energy with an efficiency of more than 50 percent—a rate much higher than that of an internal combustion engine using hydrogen as a fuel. Fuel cells also produce essentially zero pollution. Research on fuel cells was in the early stages in the mid-1990's.

Another design approach to achieving low pollution and high fuel economy is to modify the combustion engine itself. One such change involves reducing the number of strokes of the engine's pistons from four per cycle to two. All internal combustion engines rely on pistons within cylinders to produce the power to turn the car's wheels. Fuel and air enter the cylinders through intake valves, and the high pressure caused by igniting the fuel-air mixture moves the pistons up and down in what is known as the power stroke. The pistons turn a crankshaft, which transfers the engine's output power to the wheels through the transmission.

Passenger car engines today are four-stroke designs, with only one stroke actually powering the car. The other three strokes are needed to produce the power stroke. One stroke pulls a mixture of air and fuel into the cylinder, and one compresses the mixture before the power stroke. The fourth stroke exhausts gases and other by-products of combustion from the cylinder after the power stroke.

Smaller piston engines, such as those in motorcycles and lawnmowers, are designed for a two-stroke cycle. Like four-stroke engines, two-stroke engines have compression and power strokes. But the intake of the air-fuel mixture and the expulsion of the exhaust gases take place at the same time, at the end of the power stroke.

Because of the port arrangement, the two-stroke engine needs no valves at the top of the cylinder, so the engine can be made as much as 30 percent lighter than a four-stroke engine. Furthermore, a power stroke occurs with each revolution of the crankshaft rather than with every other revolution, as in a four-stroke. This means that smaller cylinders can be used for the same power output in a two-stroke engine, again reducing weight and engine size and increasing fuel economy.

While the two-stroke engine may conserve fuel, it has problems meeting the emissions standards set for four-stroke engines. When a two-stroke engine idles, its exhaust is much cooler than that of a four-stroke. Part of the problem is the relatively cool exhaust, which inhibits emission control because catalytic converters work effectively only with hot emission gases. Until engineers solve the emission problem, the two-stroke can be considered a possibility only for the distant future.

Lightweight body
Nearly all automobile engineers agree that the bodies of the next generation of cars will be made of lightweight but strong materials such as Kevlar, plastic, and fiberglass. By reducing the weight of the car, these composite materials would help conserve fuel.

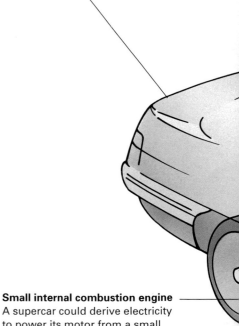

Small internal combustion engine
A supercar could derive electricity to power its motor from a small internal combustion engine that operates a generator. The engine would be used primarily to extend the range of the battery and could be designed to burn cleaner-burning gasoline, ethanol, methanol, compressed natural gas, liquefied petroleum gas, or hydrogen.

The makings of a supercar

The "supercar" that many engineers envision for the future is expected to have many advantages over today's cars. Although no standard design has yet emerged, the supercar will probably consist of a combination of many of the technologies now under development. Engineers predict that the car will travel 80 miles or more per gallon (34 kilometers per liter), weigh about half as much as today's cars, and still provide the safety, comfort, and performance that people expect from automobiles.

Energy storage

Energy storage would come from advanced batteries or a flywheel, a lightweight but strong wheel that spins at high speed due to the car's momentum. The spinning flywheel operates a generator, which supplies electricity directly to the motor or to a battery pack.

Improved aerodynamics

A more aerodynamic shape would reduce wind resistance and improve fuel efficiency.

Fuel cell

Fuel cells could also provide electricity for the motor. Fuel cells harness chemical energy by combining hydrogen and oxygen in the presence of an *electrolyte* (conductive material). Fuel cells are much more efficient than internal combustion engines and produce virtually no pollution.

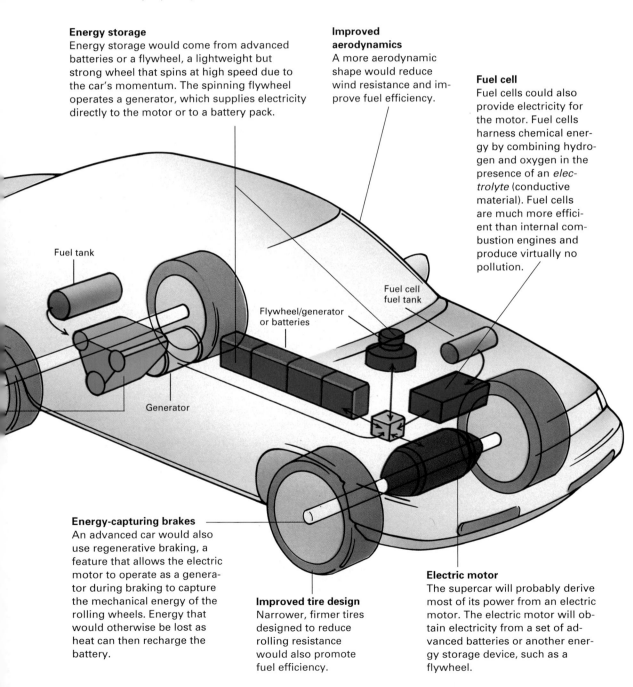

Fuel tank

Fuel cell fuel tank

Flywheel/generator or batteries

Generator

Energy-capturing brakes

An advanced car would also use regenerative braking, a feature that allows the electric motor to operate as a generator during braking to capture the mechanical energy of the rolling wheels. Energy that would otherwise be lost as heat can then recharge the battery.

Improved tire design

Narrower, firmer tires designed to reduce rolling resistance would also promote fuel efficiency.

Electric motor

The supercar will probably derive most of its power from an electric motor. The electric motor will obtain electricity from a set of advanced batteries or another energy storage device, such as a flywheel.

Aside from the efficiency of the engine or fuel cell, the weight of the car is a major factor in determining how much energy it uses and how much pollution it produces. Much of the weight of existing cars is in the steel components. Steel offers many benefits—it is reusable, relatively inexpensive, and easily shaped and molded—but it is relatively heavy. In their search for lighter materials for auto bodies and chassis, engineers have found two alternatives with reasonable costs: aluminum and plastic composites.

Aluminum can be easily formed into body panels, and it weighs only about half as much as steel. Not all of the car's weight is in the body, of course, but substituting aluminum for steel there could result in a significantly lighter car. In 1994, for example, Chrysler produced an experimental Neon with an aluminum body that weighed about 20 percent less than a standard steel-bodied model.

A few aluminum-bodied cars are already being produced in low volumes, such as the Acura NSX and the Audi A8. But making aluminum bodies for high-volume production—hundreds of thousands of cars per year instead of one-tenth that amount—creates another set of challenges. For one thing, refining aluminum creates more pollution than making steel. And welding aluminum to form a body requires much more energy than steel welding. That's because aluminum conducts heat much more effectively than steel does, and so heat from the welding torch spreads throughout the metal part, rather than being concentrated at the site of the weld. Aluminum is also three to four times more expensive than steel.

Car bodies do not have to be made of metal at all, however. For years, sports- and specialty-car manufacturers have been using an alternative to steel or aluminum—plastic composites. These materials consist of fibers bound with plastic or resin for extra strength. With sophisticated composites, engineers can arrange strong carbon fibers in individual body parts for optimum strength. As with aluminum, plastic composites save weight. A carbon-fiber composite part can be made as strong as a steel one at one-half to one-third the weight.

Another way to sharply reduce body weight is to design a car that has one fewer wheel. Prototypes of three-wheeled car designs weigh about 25 percent less than a similarly sized four-wheel car. Due to their smaller frontal area, three-wheeled cars are also often more aerodynamic than four-wheelers. Designs for three-wheeled cars come in two forms—those with a single wheel in front, and those with the single wheel in back.

Safety concerns have dampened some enthusiasm for three-wheelers. Handling three-wheeled cars can be tricky, and they tend to roll over more easily than four-wheeled cars.

On today's roads, any type of smaller and lighter car is at a disadvantage to larger and heavier ones in an accident, and that makes safety an issue for any design that requires a lighter car. Car designers say that careful engineering can overcome many of the safety problems, however. Body parts made of composites, for instance, are capable of distributing crash forces to give passengers even more protection than they would have in steel-bodied cars.

According to industry observers, the most exciting possibilities in new car development are created by combining a composite body with other new technologies. Engineers working on the Partnership for a New Generation of Vehicles project, for example, are hoping to create a "supercar" that combines elements such as a hybrid power train with regenerative braking, plus a composite plastic body.

Unfortunately, developing any single technology requires investments of billions of dollars. And new designs may not be immediately profitable, because car buyers are reluctant to accept vehicles that are different and do not match the performance and convenience of their present cars in all respects. These factors make it likely that most new cars of the next dozen years will be steel-bodied, with four-stroke internal combustion engines that run on gasoline.

But the new cars will come. Thanks to the California mandate, mass-produced battery-powered cars should be a reality at least by the year 2000. Automotive experts predict the hybrid electric car will be even more popular, because it will be available at lower cost and offer better range and performance than battery-powered cars. For internal combustion engines, compressed natural gas is expected to be the most widely used alternative to gasoline. Alcohol fuels are also likely to be in widespread use, as engineers design more cars to operate on varying mixtures of alcohol and gasoline.

It's more difficult to make predictions about which, if any, of these technologies will endure and lead to the car of tomorrow. But one thing is certain: As designs continue to change, today's technology will become more and more unfamiliar.

For further reading:

Lovins, Amory B. and L. H. "Reinventing the Wheels." *Atlantic Monthly,* January 1995.

McCosh, Dan. "Emerging Technologies for the Supercar." *Popular Science,* June 1994.

Riley, Robert Q. *Alternative Cars in the 21st Century: A New Personal Transportation Paradigm.* Society of Automotive Engineers, 1995.

Sperling, Daniel. *Future Drive.* Island Press, 1995.

Wilkerson, Stephan. "Our Next Car?" *Audubon,* May-June, 1993.

Through discoveries of tracks and fossil bones, scientists are finding that the pterodactyl was a well-adapted creature with sophisticated powers of flight.

Pterodactyls—
Flying Marvels
of the Mesozoic

BY ROBERT T. BAKKER

I magine that you're a pterodactyl, walking on a warm, sandy beach in the area that is now Wyoming, 90 million years ago in the Cretaceous Period. You feel the rippled sand press against your sharp hand claws, three on each forefoot. Your four long, straight hind claws leave a fork-like mark on the beach each time you take a step. You waddle quickly as you work your way up a low sand dune, elbows and knees swinging outward through wide arcs. You look like a combination of a giant toad and a fruit bat, awkward and sprawling in your gait.

When you reach the crest of the dune, you pause. You feel the offshore breeze blowing over your snow-white fur. The wind grows stronger. You crouch down, bending at the elbows and knees. Then you leap straight up.

In one massive, coordinated contraction, your huge chest muscles thrust your arms down, and your legs push off against the ground. As your body hurtles upward, you snap your wings open, and their immense white surfaces catch the breeze. You are airborne.

Opposite page: An artist's rendering of pterodactyls on a beach is based on fossil tracks made millions of years ago and discovered in the American West in the early 1990's.

The time of the pterodactyls

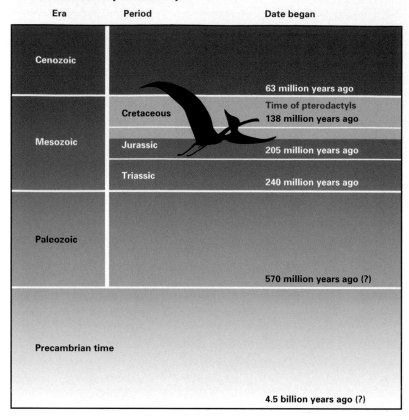

Era	Period	Date began
Cenozoic		
		63 million years ago
Mesozoic	Cretaceous	Time of pterodactyls 138 million years ago
	Jurassic	205 million years ago
	Triassic	240 million years ago
Paleozoic		
		570 million years ago (?)
Precambrian time		
		4.5 billion years ago (?)

Pterodactyls flourished in the late Jurassic Period and the Cretaceous Period. This was also a time of dinosaurs, sea creatures, small mammals, and the first birds.

The author:
Robert T. Bakker, a paleontologist, is a curator at the Tate Museum in Casper, Wyo., and the author of *The Dinosaur Heresies* (1986) and *Raptor Red* (1995).

You ascend hundreds of feet in an upward spiral, scanning the shallow water below for a telltale sign of prey. You see lizardlike plesiosaurs, 6 meters (20 feet) long, using their penguin-style flippers to chase ammonites, the armor-plated ancestors of squid. Sea turtles with wide, flat bodies probe the sandy sea-bottom for clams.

But your huge, birdlike eyes are searching for something else. Suddenly you spy surface ripples caused by a school of mackerel-sized fish. You lower your left wing tip and begin a steep, banking turn. You zero in on the dark form of your target. You fold your wings against your body. You become a streamlined missile, hurtling straight down into the school of fish.

With a splash, you pierce the water, your head and neck as rigid as a strong spear. "Thwunk!" Your muzzle tip skewers a fat fish as you plunge underwater. You extend your wings to a half open position and rise triumphant to the surface.

Is this what life must have been like for a pterodactyl? Yes, according to new research into the anatomy and behavior of these extinct flying beasts. Fossils of pterodactyls were first dug up at the end of the 1700's, but the interpretation of their way of life suffered because scientists didn't recognize the creature's remarkable mixture of birdlike and batlike features. Now, in the mid-1990's, we have a much better picture of pterodactyls as living animals. Fossil hunters have discovered pterodactyl trackways at a dozen locations in the Western United States, and anatomists have scrutinized perfectly preserved skeletons that show every joint in the wing, neck, and body. The scientific evidence shows that pterodactyls must have been exceptional aerialists with powers of flight that were superior in some aspects to those of modern birds.

Pterodactyls (pronounced *tehr uh DAK tuhls)* lived during the Mesozoic Era, which began 240 million years ago and encompassed the Triassic, Jurassic, and Cretaceous Periods. They belonged to an extinct group of flying animals known as pterosaurs, fossils of which have been found on every continent except Antarctica. There were two major kinds of pterosaurs—rhamphorhynchoids and pterodactyls. Rhamphorhynchoids developed first, but were later dwarfed in size and variety by the pterodactyls. The largest flying animal ever known was a pterodactyl, *Quetzalcoatlus* (named after the Aztec god, Quetzal-

First views of pterodactyls
A fossil of *Pterodactylus antiquus, below,* found in a limestone quarry in Bavaria, Germany, in the mid 1700's, was the first pterodactyl fossil examined by scientists. In 1817, a German scientist drew a batlike recreation of another early pterodactyl fossil find, *right.*

An 1863 woodcut shows pterodactyls as ugly, repulsive flying creatures. Early scientists thought that the pterodactyl probably had limited flight power and perhaps swooped down on prey from cliffs.

coatl), with a wingspan of nearly 12 meters (40 feet). Some species of pterodactyls, however, were as small as sparrows.

Almost 100 different species of pterosaurs have been identified, but scientists think there must have been many more. Most pterosaur remains were preserved in coastal sands that later turned to rock, yielding the fossil skeletons found in our day. For this reason, our knowledge of these magnificent creatures is mainly limited to pterodactyls that lived near the sea, even though some species would have made their home inland.

The early view of pterodactyls—flying fiends

The pterodactyl as we know it today was an extraordinary beast, elegant in design. But for most of the last two centuries, pterodactyls have been portrayed as ugly, evil, and repulsive. The first pterodactyl remains were found in a limestone quarry in Bavaria, Germany, in the late 1700's. In 1809, French anatomist Georges Cuvier bestowed the name *Pterodactylus* (meaning *wing finger*) on the fossil and decided the creature's closest living relatives would be reptiles.

Almost since that day, illustrators began depicting pterodactyls as flying fiends—part bat, part bird, part crocodile—covered with dark leathery skin. The flying-devil image of pterodactyls became standard in popular writing as well as in science texts. In the 1912 novel *The Lost World,* the English author Sir Arthur Conan Doyle imagined explorers

Ornithodesmus lived 130 million to 120 million years ago. Its wingspan was 5 meters (16.4 feet).

Pterodactyl fur
The skin on an unusually well-preserved pterodactyl skeleton, *left,* found in what is now the country of Kazakhstan shows faint impressions of hairlike structures. Scientists suspect that the hair may have helped the pterodactyls retain body heat.

stumbling upon a Brazilian plateau where Mesozoic creatures survived to the 1900's. Doyle's pterodactyls are hideous aerial scavengers that drip noxious drool as they swoop down to bite at the human interlopers. A giant pterodactyl in the 1933 motion picture *King Kong* was fashioned after the same image. It had black, reptilian wings, and its role in the script was to try to steal the female star, Fay Wray, by grabbing at her with its monstrous hind claws.

In the 1960's and 1970's, most museum displays and textbooks still presented pterodactyls as nightmarish beasts with batlike skin. Not only were they unappealing to look at, but these pterodactyls also were reconstructed as sloppy fliers. Pterodactyl wings were thought to be

Color for camouflage
Modern sea gulls, *right,* have white undersides so that fish in the water cannot see them swooping down from a bright sky. Since pterodactyls also fished the oceans, it is likely that they had a similar color camouflage, *below.*

Sea gull

Pteranodon ingens lived 115 million to 70 million years ago. Its wingspan was 7 meters (23 feet).

merely limp expanses of skin, making the cumbersome beasts incapable of efficient soaring flight or powerful flapping.

Snowy-white, furry pterodactyls

Finally, in the late 1970's and 1980's, perceptions of pterodactyls began to change. In the mind of fossil experts, pterodactyl hide was transformed from dark and leathery to snowy-white and furry. Part of this revolution in thinking came from rediscoveries of scientific work from the 1920's. At that time, German paleontologists found pterodactyl remains in Jurassic rocks that seemed to preserve an image of the fine structure of its skin. Using a microscope, scientists could see tiny hair-shaped structures that covered the body like fine fur. Few paleontologists believed the notion that pterodactyls had fur until 1970, when Russian experts announced their discovery of fossil specimens that indisputably showed the entire body covered with hair.

Once we accept the idea of pterodactyls as furry fliers, the next question to ask is, "What color was the fur?" We can find no clues from fossil bones or even fossil skin, but we can make a good guess based on nature's hard and fast rules of color. The rules are that an animal's coloration must do two things—provide camouflage in the native environment and help attract mates.

Under those rules, the 200-year-old tradition of showing pterodactyls with dark, batlike

Rhinoceros hornbill

Colorful crests
Males of many bird species depend upon bright colors to attract mates. The large, brightly colored bill and crest of such birds as hornbills, *above,* probably serve mainly for this kind of courtship display. The large crest of the *Pteranodon sternbergi, right,* most likely served a similar purpose—as a colorful mating billboard.

Pteranodon sternbergi fossil

skin made no ecological sense. Nearly all of our pterodactyl specimens have been dug up from sediments formed in shallow oceans, and pterodactyl teeth and muzzles appear adapted to catching fish and squid. In other words, those pterodactyls were the Mesozoic equivalent of today's oceanic birds, like gulls, terns, and albatrosses. And what color are most sea birds? White—the best camouflage for birds that swoop down on fish swimming near the surface. A snowy underside makes the bird's body invisible against the bright sky. Therefore, most pterodactyls are likely to have had white fur on their bellies, throats, and thighs.

Gnathosaurus lived 150 million years ago. Its wingspan was 1.7 meters (5.6 feet).

Pterodactyl courtship—dabs of color

According to the rules of ecology and animal behavior, ptero-dactyls may also have displayed splashes of bright color. Animals with large eyes and great powers of visual discrimination use color to communicate with each other. For example, today's bird species see a wider range of colors than humans do, and most birds use some sort of bright color patterns in the courtship season to attract mates. Dabs of red ornament the beaks of gulls, and circles of lively colors highlight the eyes of male puffins during the breeding season.

Like birds, pterodactyls must have had good vision. As long ago as the 1880's, pterodactyl skulls were found with the brain shape pre-served as an impression in the sediment filling the braincase. The fos-sils showed that the pterodactyl brain was nothing like a reptile's brain. Instead, it possessed two birdlike features. One was the presence of huge *frontal lobes,* the halves of the forebrain where higher intellectual functions are carried out. The other feature was the existence of very large *optic lobes* (vision centers in certain animal brains), proof of ex-ceptional vision. Pterodactyl brain impressions found in the 1980's confirmed the bird-style brain organization. So it would be logical to conclude that, like modern birds, pterodactyls used color for courtship.

We can also guess where the bright colors would be on a pterodactyl body. Many Cretaceous Period pterodactyls evolved huge crests that stuck out behind their foreheads. These cranial devices would not have been useful as aerial rudders or stabilizers, and female pterodactyls seem to have had smaller crests than males of the same species. The crests make ecological sense only if they were courtship billboards— features that would beckon potential mates and frighten away sexual rivals. Many modern birds sport brightly colored crests on their heads. Hornbills, toucans, and touracos are good examples. And so it is very reasonable to suppose that males of the great Cretaceous pterodactyl *Pteranodon* ("toothless flier"), for example, sported a vivid crimson crest in the breeding season.

Modern bird societies are knit together by elaborate ceremonies in which males and females "exchange vows" by performing long dance routines, with much head-bobbing, prancing, bowing, and strutting. The bird-style intelligence of pterodactyls implies that their social life

A lesson in wing anatomy: Birds, bats, and pterodactyls

For clues to the flying style of pterodactyls, experts compared ptero- dactyl wings to those of living birds and bats, the only other animals with backbones to have achieved flight.

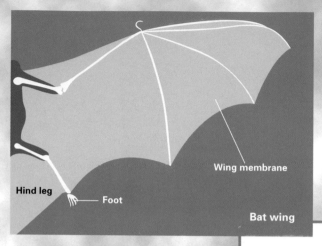

Bats fly more efficiently than birds because the hind legs are attached to the trailing edge of the wing. When a bat flaps its wings, the hind legs push up and down along with the arms. All the muscle pow- er of the rear limbs can be added to the arm power to make a stronger wing stroke.

Bat wing

Wing membrane

Hind leg — Foot

The wings of modern birds are attached to the front limb bones, and strong chest muscles are required to flap the wings up and down. When a bird is flying, its lower body, thighs, and calf muscles cannot contribute to flight power and are dead weight.

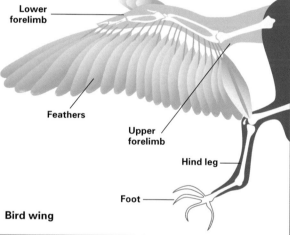

Lower forelimb

Feathers

Upper forelimb

Hind leg

Foot

Bird wing

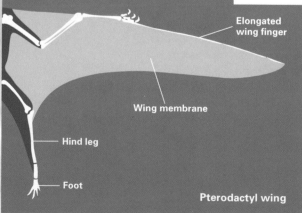

Elongated wing finger

Wing membrane

Hind leg

Foot

Pterodactyl wing

New fossil evidence indicates that ptero- dactyl wings were attached to the rear leg like bat wings. The pterodactyl thus would have been a strong flier, able to use its lower-body muscles in addition to upper- body muscles to create a powerful wing stroke. The wing itself was a membrane strengthened by a network of strong, flex- ible fibers. The membrane extended from a long fourth digit called a "wing finger."

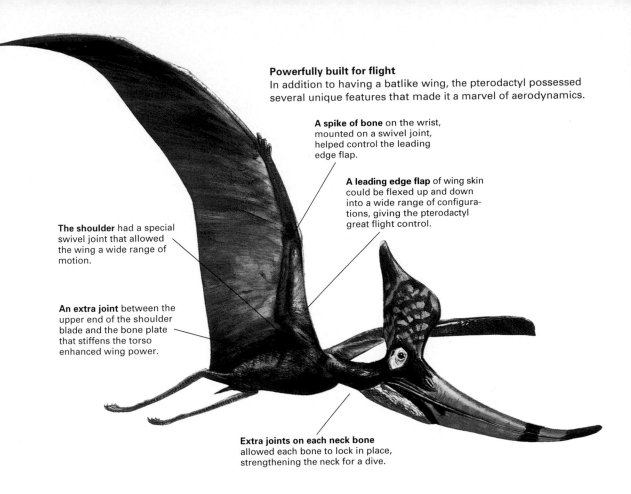

Powerfully built for flight
In addition to having a batlike wing, the pterodactyl possessed several unique features that made it a marvel of aerodynamics.

A spike of bone on the wrist, mounted on a swivel joint, helped control the leading edge flap.

A leading edge flap of wing skin could be flexed up and down into a wide range of configurations, giving the pterodactyl great flight control.

The shoulder had a special swivel joint that allowed the wing a wide range of motion.

An extra joint between the upper end of the shoulder blade and the bone plate that stiffens the torso enhanced wing power.

Extra joints on each neck bone allowed each bone to lock in place, strengthening the neck for a dive.

was complex too, and that pterodactyl courtship may have been full of instinctual choreography.

Strong wings and precise flight control

As scientists in the late 1970's and 1980's reappraised the appearance and social behavior of pterodactyls, pterodactyl flight also was reevaluated. Specimens dug up in the 1920's were examined once more, and the myth of the pterodactyl's weak, limp wings was dispelled. Fossil impressions of the wing membrane show clearly that the wing was strengthened by a network of strong, flexible fibers held together in a sheet of elastic tissue. In life, pterodactyl wings must have been tough and nearly unbreakable.

Our view of pterodactyls' abilities as a flier changed after humanity gained sufficient understanding of flight to build airplanes. We now understand that any flying machine—bird, bat, or airplane—depends upon a force called *lift*. For a body to become airborne and to stay in the air, there must be a lifting force on the wings that offsets the downward pull of gravity.

That lifting force is created when a wing is curved on the top and straight on the bottom. When such a wing slices through the air, the air that has to travel over the curve is forced to move faster than the air below the wing. The difference in air speed creates an area of low air pressure above the wing. Air under the wing tries to move into the low-pressure area, but the wing is in the way, so the air pushes up on the wing—creating lift. The larger the wing surface and the faster it slices through the air, the greater the lift.

Birds can soar and glide because their wings have a curve on the *leading* (front) edge. Airplane wings follow this design. But when airspeed is low and the wing is turned up to climb or down to land, the airflow over the leading edge may become so turbulent that air pressure no longer holds up the wing. If that happens, the flying machine will begin to drop. To combat the problem, modern aircraft have flaps on the leading edge that can be extended forward to expand the wing area and increase lift as needed.

Amazingly, pterodactyl remains show the same feature. In addition to a large wing surface and a curved leading edge, the pterodactyls had a special spike of bone on the wrist, mounted on a swivel joint. Wing-impression fossils show that this swivel bone held a leading edge flap of wing skin that could be flexed up and down into a wide range of configurations.

In airplanes, leading edge slots are another antistall device. These are holes cut into the leading edge flaps to allow air to flow smoothly over the wing at the lowest speeds. In pterodactyl wings, the leading edge flap may also have had a hole in the center, making it function as a leading edge slot.

Of bats and birds

Modern analysis of pterodactyl legs and torsos led to the conclusion that these Mesozoic aerialists may have been even more efficient fliers than modern birds. Flying birds operate under one major, built-in handicap: flight feathers are attached only to the front limb. Because the wing is supported only by the arms, the torso and hind legs are dead weight when the animal is flying. When in the air, a bird's body, thigh, and calf muscles cannot contribute to flight power. In fact, the bird hind leg is built to a totally different mechanical blueprint than is the arm. The leg is used for walking, jumping, scratching, digging, and climbing, but never for flying.

Bats, on the other hand, are more efficient fliers. Bat hind legs—and in some species, the tail—are attached to the *trailing* (rear) edge of the wing. When a bat flaps its wings, the hind leg moves up and down with the arm. That means that all the muscle power of the rear end of the body can be added to the arm power. The result is a superstrong wing stroke.

Which modern-day fliers—birds or bats—are closer in wing-leg design to pterodactyls? In the 1970's and 1980's, many experts believed that pterodactyl wings were powered only by the arms, without any contribution from the hind legs. Re-creations of the animals showed

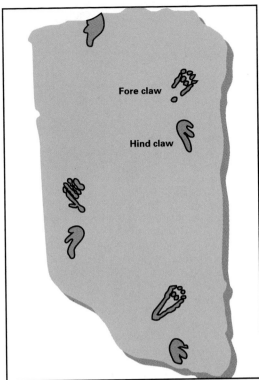

Fore claw

Hind claw

Pterodactyl tracks
A plaster cast of tracks laid down millions of years ago by a pterodactyl, *above left,* give faint clues to the anatomy of the animal that made them. The tracks show parts of four impressions of fore claws and hind claws, *above right.* The tracks indicate that the pterodactyl walked with a bat's awkward gait, *right.*

them running around on the ground like birds, supporting their body weight on their hind legs.

The discovery of fossil footprints in Colorado, Utah, and Wyoming in the early 1990's may debunk this "bird hind-leg" theory. Bird-style footprints are distinctive because only the hind feet are used for walking, and the legs are close together under the body. They do not sprawl out sideways. Bird tracks are similar to those left by meat-eating dinosaurs—such as *Allosaurus* or *Tyrannosaurus*—with the right and left hind paws hitting the ground very close to the center line of the tracks. Bats, however, leave tracks from the forefeet as well as the hind feet, and the hind feet are splayed far out to the sides.

Sprawled-out hind feet are necessary to hold out the trailing edge of the wing when the bat flies.

The newly discovered pterodactyl tracks show pterodactyls walking like giant vampire bats, with the arms and legs spread sideways. The wide spread of the hind legs is evidence that pterodactyl hind legs were attached to the wing. These tracks indicate that pterodactyls did not walk like birds.

More evidence for a bat-style locomotion comes from the tail bones of one of the largest pterodactyls, *Pteranodon*. The bones include special tail rods that probably attached to a rear wing extension running from tail tip to hind leg. And wing imprints from other pterodactyl species show that the trailing edge of the main wing was firmly anchored to the thigh and calf.

Maximizing power for flight

With this anatomy, a pterodactyl could put nearly 100 percent of its total body muscles to work when flapping its wings, the hind leg muscles working in concert with the arm muscles. Typical backboned animals have a considerable mass of muscle that helps move the backbone in the torso. In birds and bats, these trunk muscles are useless for flight. Advanced pterodactyls such as *Pteranodon* had less weighty muscles running along the backbone. Instead they had a special plate of lightweight bone that strengthened the torso and the shoulders. In this way, most of the muscle groups that could not contribute to flying were eliminated.

Any giant flying animal faces its greatest challenge when trying to take off. Large pterodactyls met the challenge with several anatomical features. First, they had many square feet of wing per pound of body weight, which meant that a single wing flap could provide plenty of upward force. Second, their sharp wing claws enabled them to climb up trees or along cliffs, so they could gain some height for the take-off. Third, a special feature of the shoulder allowed pterodactyls to gain extra downward thrust from their wings during the crucial first leap into the airstream.

That feature makes pterodactyl shoulders marvels of aeronautical engineering. Advanced species had an extra pivot joint between the upper end of the shoulder blade and the bone plate that stiffened the torso. No other backboned animal has this joint, which lets the shoulder swivel. The very long shoulder bone could swing up and back as well as down and forward, movements that would increase the power of the wing downstroke.

The great fish hunter

No matter how good the flier, hunting fish from the air isn't easy. One big problem is that when an aerial fisher swoops down and jabs its beak into the water, it can reach only those fish that are swimming close to the surface. A very few modern sea birds escape this limitation by using the plunge-diving technique. We can see the technique in the brown pelicans that fish off the California coast. These big birds circle slowly in the air until they spot their fish target. Then they dive straight down. Just before they hit the surface, they fold their wings against their sides, giving their bodies the shape of an armor-piercing bomb. The pelican penetrates the water to a depth of several feet. Then it opens its huge mouth and sucks in prey.

Giant Cretaceous pterodactyls of the *Pteranodon* family were also built to be plunge-dive bombers. The *Pteranodon* head was huge and pelican-shaped, with a long, pointed bill. But penetrating the water at high speed is dangerous—the force could twist the head right off the neck. To strengthen the neck against the shock of hitting the water, *Pteranodon* had extra joints on the underside of each neck bone that locked each bone in place. During the dive, the pointed bill, head, and neck became as rigid and deadly as a spear.

Pteranodon also had expandable lower jaws like those of today's pelicans. When the great pterodactyl plunged deep into the water, it could open its throat pouch wide and suck in fish or squid. Altogether, these pterodactyls had a plunge-diving design that was unequaled in efficiency until the pelicans themselves evolved 60 million years later.

If pterodactyl images have come a long way since *King Kong*, it's because pterodactyl science has come a long way. The creatures no longer have the reputation of being nasty and devilish. Indeed, as scientists fine-tune their knowledge of pterodactyl anatomy, the pterodactyl is becoming one of the most admired of Mesozoic species.

For further reading:
Bakker, Robert T. *The Dinosaur Heresies.* Morrow, 1986.
Rudwick, Martin J. S. *Scenes From Deep Time.* University of Chicago Pr. 1992.
Wellnhofer, Peter. *The Illustrated Encyclopedia of Pterosaurs.* Crescent Books, 1991.

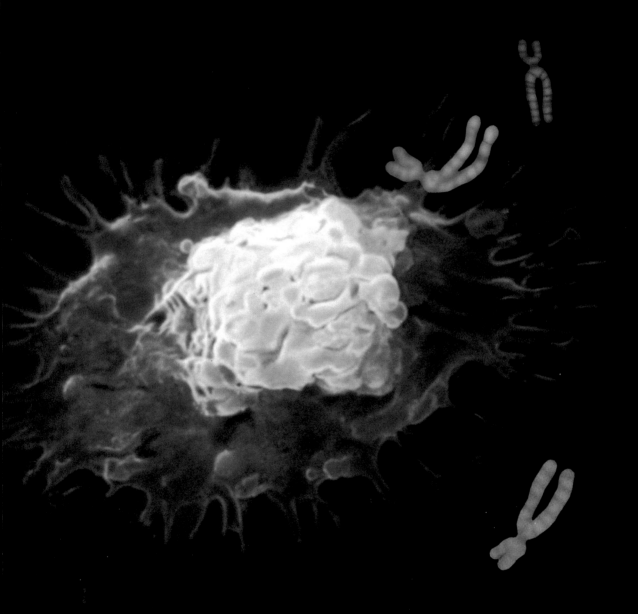

Hunting for Cancer Genes

By the mid-1990's, scientists had uncovered many of the genetic flaws responsible for the devastating disease called cancer. But much more remains to be discovered.

BY DAVID S. HAYMER

The race was on. The goal: finding the first known gene that can cause breast cancer, a devastating disease that affects an estimated 1 in 8 American women over the course of their lifetime. The race began in October 1990, when geneticist Mary-Claire King of the University of California at Berkeley identified the general location of a gene for breast cancer on one of the 23 pairs of human *chromosomes*, the threadlike structures that carry genetic information in the cell. Hundreds of scientists from around the world began working furiously to find the gene's exact location. But the chromosome region identified by King held as many as 1,000 different genes, and a series of false leads repeatedly dashed hopes of quickly homing in on the right one.

Finally, in September 1994, a team led by geneticist Mark Skolnick of the University of Utah in Salt Lake City announced they had successfully isolated the defective gene King had identified. But the race was not over yet. Hot behind that disclosure came an October 1994 announcement by a group of American, Canadian, and European researchers that they had located another gene linked to breast cancer. And still scientists keep searching. The two genes found in 1994 appear to give rise to only 5 to 10 percent of all breast cancer cases, virtually all of them in people with an inherited form of the disease. No one knows how many more breast cancer genes have yet to be found.

Previous page: Color-enhanced chromosomes surround a breast cancer tumor, both magnified many times. In reality, chromosomes are much smaller than a single cell.

The breast cancer findings were only the latest installments in a story of discovery dating from the 1970's, when molecular biologists began unraveling the connection between cancer and the genetic material that controls the function and structure of every cell in the body. Since then, researchers have identified three different types of cancer genes and have linked specific genes to more than 50 kinds of cancer. Research is still in its infancy, however. Scientists believe that many cancer genes remain to be discovered and that much must still be learned about how the errant genes cause normal cells to become time bombs.

What is cancer?

The word *cancer* actually refers to more than 100 different diseases, distinguished in part by the organ or tissue in which the cancer arises. But all types of cancer begin when something happens to a normal cell that makes it multiply out of control. In most cancers, the multiplying cells gradually form a mass called a tumor. Sometimes, the tumor grows extremely slowly or stops growing when it is smaller than the head of a pin. In other cases, the tumor grows large enough to invade and destroy nearby healthy tissue.

At some stage, the cancerous cells may leave the tumor and enter the bloodstream or *lymphatic system* (a network of nodes and vessels that carry clear fluid called lymph). Unless the cancer cells are killed by the body's disease-fighting immune system, they migrate to other parts of the body, where they can establish new tumors—a process called *metastasis*. Cancer gets its name from the Latin word for *crab* because of the crablike appearance of a tumor as it spreads. The spreading, or *malignant,* tumor is deadly because it can spawn new tumors that destroy tissue in the brain, liver, or other vital organs.

Recognizing the role of genes

Physicians first recognized that cancer had a hereditary component in the mid-1800's. The first clue was that in rare cases, many members of the same family—from grandparents to cousins—developed the disease, often at an early age. The number of cancer cases among the family members was too great to be explained by chance, and so physicians wondered if a susceptibility to cancer was being passed from generation to generation along with other physical traits.

By the early 1910's, investigators had observed differences in the appearance of the chromosomes of cancer cells and normal cells. But at that time, scientists did not understand how genes functioned, and so the genetic basis of cancer remained obscure.

That situation had changed dramatically by the mid-1900's. Researchers learned that genes are made of DNA (deoxyribonucleic acid), a molecule that resembles a long, twisted ladder formed of two parallel strands. The strands are joined by "rungs" made of a pair of chemical subunits called bases. There are four kinds of bases, each of which can pair up with only one of the others. The sequence of paired

The author:
David S. Haymer is associate professor of genetics at the University of Hawaii in Honolulu.

Terms and concepts

Cancer: A disease that involves the uncontrolled growth and division of cells.

DNA: Deoxyribonucleic acid, a biochemical molecule that holds genetic information.

Gene: A section of DNA containing coded information for producing a protein. Genes control cell functions and are the basic units of heredity.

Mutation: A change in the DNA that makes up a gene.

Oncogene: A mutated gene responsible for some kinds of cancer. In their normal form, potential oncogenes help promote cell growth.

Tumor suppressor gene: A gene that normally helps suppress cell growth. Tumor suppressor genes can cause cancer when mutated.

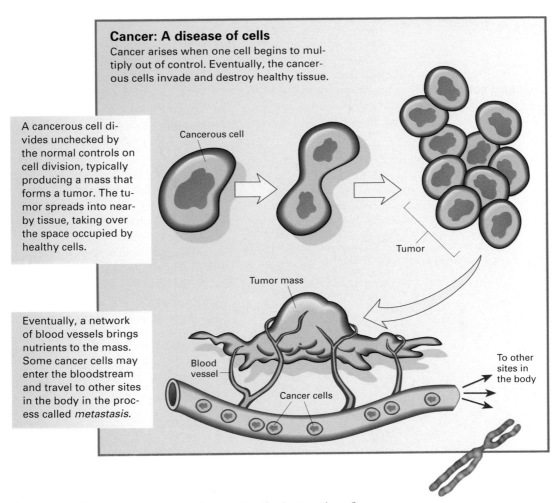

Cancer: A disease of cells

Cancer arises when one cell begins to multiply out of control. Eventually, the cancerous cells invade and destroy healthy tissue.

A cancerous cell divides unchecked by the normal controls on cell division, typically producing a mass that forms a tumor. The tumor spreads into nearby tissue, taking over the space occupied by healthy cells.

Cancerous cell

Tumor

Eventually, a network of blood vessels brings nutrients to the mass. Some cancer cells may enter the bloodstream and travel to other sites in the body in the process called *metastasis*.

Tumor mass

Blood vessel

Cancer cells

To other sites in the body

bases in each gene acts as a code that carries the instructions for production of a particular protein. Proteins give structure to many of the body's tissues and carry out the chemical processes essential to life.

Another discovery was that a cell's functions are disrupted when genes are *mutated* (changed) in some way. Mutations can occur as a result of exposure to radiation or poisonous chemicals in the environment or because errors crop up when DNA is copied in preparation for cell division. Microbes called retroviruses also can cause mutations because they insert their own genetic material into the DNA of a cell.

However they happen, some mutations lead to the production of faulty proteins that are unable to perform their normal function. In other cases, mutations can cause the production of too much of a protein. Still other mutations cause a cell to create no protein at all.

Discovery of the first cancer genes

The first known cancer gene came to light in 1970, through the study of a retrovirus known to cause cancer in chickens. Investigators were surprised to find that the virus contained an extra gene, and that the gene was responsible for the cancer. The scientists called the gene an *oncogene,* from the Greek word *onkos,* meaning *tumor.*

A more crucial finding came in 1976, when microbiologists Michael Bishop and Harold Varmus of the University of California in San Francisco observed that healthy chickens carry a slightly different form of the oncogene. This suggested that an ancestor of the virus had picked up the gene when it infected a chicken cell. In the virus, the gene had mutated. Now when descendants of the virus infected a chicken, the gene caused cells to divide uncontrollably. This discovery, which earned Bishop and Varmus the 1989 Nobel Prize for physiology or medicine, led to the realization that all animal cells contain potential cancer genes, awaiting only chance mutations to activate them.

Armed with this new understanding, researchers set about identifying human genes with cancer-causing potential. This is a daunting task. Human beings have about 100,000 different genes, and only a small number, or even one, may be involved in a single type of cancer. Each gene, moreover, can consist of several thousand base pairs—and a cancer gene may differ from its normal counterpart by only a single base.

By 1982, investigators had shown for the first time that an oncogene was at work in human cancer, finding the gene in cells taken from patients with bladder cancer. This gene, called *ras,* later turned out also to contribute to cancers of the colon, bladder, pancreas, and other organs, making it the most frequently activated known oncogene.

The next year brought an even more important finding, when researchers showed that an oncogene called *sis* codes for a growth factor, a type of protein that triggers cell division. This discovery proved what many workers in the field had suspected: The normal function of potential oncogenes is to *code for* (carry instructions for making) proteins that promote cell growth and division.

In a healthy cell, cell division involves several different proteins. The process begins when proteins called growth factors bind to proteins

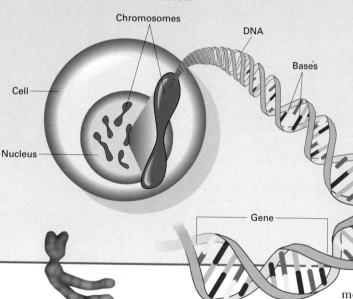

Cells and genes

The instructions that govern cell division are carried by genes, the units that transmit hereditary information and control all the functions of a cell. Genes lie on structures called chromosomes inside the cell's nucleus. The genes are made of DNA (deoxyribonucleic acid), a molecule formed of two parallel strands joined by pairs of chemical subunits called bases.

Chromosomes

DNA

Bases

Cell

Nucleus

Gene

called receptors on the cell surface. Each receptor is specially configured to receive one type of growth factor, which fits it as a key fits a lock. When the growth factor latches onto a receptor, it causes signaling proteins inside the cell to set off a complex chain of events that eventually causes the DNA to be copied and the cell to divide in two.

A mutation in one of the genes that code for these proteins can cause a cell to divide more times than it should. For example, if there is a defect in the gene for one of the signaling proteins, the cell might make abnormally large quantities of the protein. In response to the extra signaling protein, the cell and its offspring keep dividing.

In 1985, scientists discovered that a mutated signaling gene is responsible for chronic myeloid leukemia (CML), a cancer of white blood cells. In CML, portions of two chromosomes in a blood cell accidentally swap places. The swap causes part of a gene called *abl*, normally found on one of the two chromosomes, to fuse with a different gene from the other chromosome. The resulting mutated form of *abl* produces an abnormal protein that relays a continuous growth signal.

A number of oncogenes, like *abl*, make proteins involved in the signaling pathways inside the cell. Others code for growth factors, receptors, and proteins involved in DNA copying and in cell division. Scientists have uncovered about 20 oncogenes involved in human cancers.

Genes that normally suppress cancer

By the 1980's, scientists had begun to realize that oncogenes were not the only kind of genes involved in cancer. For one thing, researchers had not turned up any oncogenes common to individuals suffering from *familial* (inherited) cancers, which suggested that some other kind of mutation was at work in these diseases. A breakthrough came in 1983, when investigators found that a chunk of DNA from both chromosomes in one pair was absent or mutated in tumor cells from patients with *retinoblastoma*, an eye cancer that usually runs in families. In 1986, researchers showed that this DNA included a gene whose function is to halt cell division. Because this gene, and others like it, normally suppress the unchecked cell growth that leads to tumors, such genes came to be called *tumor suppressor genes*.

Oncogenes and tumor suppressor genes have been likened to the gas pedal and brakes on a car. Oncogenes act like a gas pedal, spurring the cell forward in its growth cycle. Tumor suppressor genes stop cell growth, just as we use the brakes to bring a car to a halt.

Tumor suppressor genes come into play at checkpoints in the life of a cell. As a cell passes through various stages of cell division, the proteins produced by tumor suppressor genes check to ensure that everything is progressing normally. If it is, the cell moves forward into the next stage, rests temporarily before moving on, or stops dividing. If cell division is not progressing as it should—perhaps because the cell's genetic material has been damaged in some way—tumor suppressor genes halt the process so the problem can be corrected. If the damage is too great to be repaired, the cell self-destructs.

Genes, proteins, and mutations

Genes regulate all cell activities, including cell division, by coding for proteins that carry out the work of the cell. If a gene is *mutated* (changed), it may produce abnormal proteins that cannot perform their job properly. Mutations also can result in too much of a protein being produced, or no protein at all. Genes can be mutated through exposure to radiation or certain chemicals, or through accidental changes that occur when DNA is copied during reproduction.

A normal gene consists of a segment of DNA made up of as many as several thousand bases. The sequence of bases in the gene *codes for* (carries the instructions for making) a specific protein.

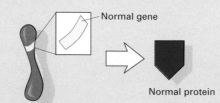

Normal gene

Chromosome

Normal protein

Sometimes, one of the bases in a gene is accidentally switched for an incorrect one. The gene may then produce an abnormal protein that does not work properly. Or the cell may not make the protein at all.

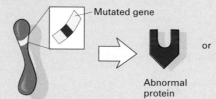

Mutated gene

Chromosome

Abnormal protein   or   Absent protein

Occasionally, parts of two chromosomes swap places during cell division. When this occurs, genes from the two chromosomes can fuse, creating an abnormal protein. Or a gene can be turned on inappropriately, producing too much protein.

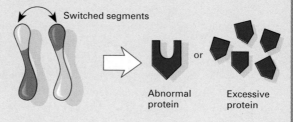

Switched segments

Abnormal protein   or   Excessive protein

Another kind of mutation results in extra copies of a gene. The extra copies may produce too much protein.

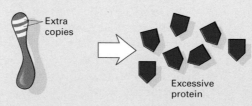

Extra copies

Excessive protein

Some mutations can result in the loss or deletion of a gene. When a gene is deleted, the protein it codes for will be absent.

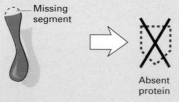

Missing segment

Absent protein

Because tumor suppressor genes put the brakes on cell growth, mutations in one or more of these genes seem essential to many, if not most, cancers. Scientists have identified at least 12 different tumor suppressor genes involved in numerous human cancers, including cancers of the lung, prostate, kidney, and bladder. The two breast cancer genes discovered in 1994 also appear to be tumor suppressor genes.

But perhaps the most important tumor suppressor gene is one that produces a protein called p53. Although p53 was discovered in 1979, researchers did not begin to understand its function, and its role in cancer, until 1990.

The pivotal studies of p53 focused on a rare inherited condition called Li-Fraumeni syndrome, named for the scientists—Fred Li and Joseph Fraumeni of the National Cancer Institute in Bethesda, Md.—who identified it in 1969. Whereas most familial cancers involve a specific type, such as breast cancer, Li-Fraumeni syndrome is unusual in that its sufferers are prone to a range of different cancers, including breast cancer, lung cancer, brain tumors, skin cancer, and leukemia. In 1990, Li, Fraumeni, and others showed that the common factor among these individuals was a defective form of the gene that codes for p53. Scientists now estimate that mutations in the p53 gene are involved in about half of all cancer cases in the United States.

Researchers do not yet understand exactly how p53 works. But studies show that, among other things, the p53 protein monitors DNA during one of the early checkpoints in cell division. If the protein detects that DNA has become damaged, it activates genes responsible for shutting down cell growth. Once the damage has been repaired, the p53 gene turns itself off, production of the p53 protein stops, and cell division continues. The p53 protein also seems to help activate the cell's self-destruct mechanism when damage proves impossible to fix. In this way, the protein prevents cells bearing potentially cancer-causing mutations from developing into tumors. But if the p53 protein is abnormal or missing because of a mutation in the gene that codes for it, cell growth continues unchecked, and cancer may result.

The role of the p53 gene in promoting cell death may help explain why efforts to combat cancer through radiation therapy or chemotherapy sometimes work for a time, then lose their effectiveness. These treatments are designed to kill cancer cells by causing massive damage to their DNA. When an altered p53 gene is not a cause of the cancer, the treatment may thus work by provoking the body's own means of suppressing tumors—production of the p53 protein. Eventually, however, the drugs or radiation may damage the p53 gene in one or more cells, stymieing those cells' impulse to self-destruct. As a result, the cells continue to divide despite the damage caused by the treatment.

Quality-control genes

To researchers' best knowledge, oncogenes and tumor suppressor genes are the only types of genes able to cause cancer directly. But scientists in the 1990's have begun to implicate another group of genes in

Three types of cancer genes

Scientists have discovered three types of defective genes that can lead to cancer. Two of the genes are involved in cell division, and the third allows mutations to build up in the cell.

An oncogene is a mutated form of a gene that normally helps stimulate a cell to divide. Oncogenes may churn out too much protein, or they may make abnormal proteins that fail to turn off when they should, causing cells to divide uncontrollably.

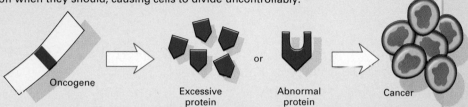

Oncogene

Excessive protein

or

Abnormal protein

Cancer

A tumor suppressor gene is a gene that normally halts the process of cell division. Mutations can cause tumor suppressor genes to stop making proteins or to make proteins that fail to work. Either case can result in unchecked cell growth.

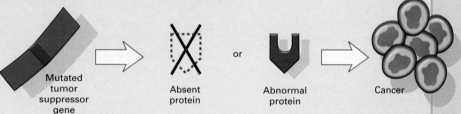

Mutated tumor suppressor gene

Absent protein

or

Abnormal protein

Cancer

A quality-control gene codes for a protein that scans DNA, searching for mistakes in the bases that make up each pair. The proteins mark places where incorrect bases appear. Other proteins then replace the marked bases with the correct ones.

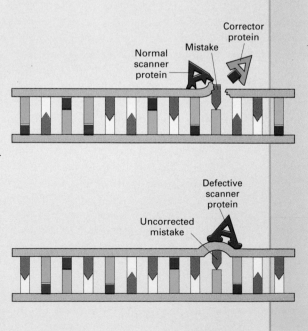

Normal scanner protein

Mistake

Corrector protein

Defective scanner protein

Uncorrected mistake

When a quality-control gene is mutated, it produces a defective protein that fails to detect mistakes in DNA. As a result, cells with faulty quality-control genes accumulate mutations rapidly. Eventually, one or more mutations are likely to create an oncogene or faulty tumor suppressor gene, setting the stage for cancer.

at least some cancers. These genes are often called "quality-control genes," because they are responsible for the repair of damaged DNA.

In 1993 and 1994, geneticists discovered the first two known quality-control genes. The researchers believe that defects in each of the two genes contribute to the most common form of inherited colon cancer, hereditary nonpolyposis colon cancer (HNPCC). Together, defects in these genes account for about 15 percent of all colon cancers.

The researchers discovered that the two genes involved in HNPCC normally work as part of a squad of genes that identify and repair errors in DNA. Both genes produce proteins that scan newly copied DNA and mark places where an incorrect sequence of bases appears. Then, other proteins replace the incorrect bases with the correct ones. When a scanner gene is defective, the protein it makes cannot do its job, and so the places needing repair are never marked. As a result, cells with defects in one of these genes are 100 times more likely to carry additional mutations than are normal cells. Eventually, chances are good that a mutation will affect one or more genes that help control cell growth, leading to cancer. Such cancers typically show up in the colon. There, millions of cells divide each day, far more than in most other organs, providing numerous opportunities for mutations to occur.

Keeping cancer from spreading

Even after a cancer has begun, however, it may be many years—if at all—before it becomes deadly. Breast cancer, colon cancer, and other cancers that form tumors may not become life-threatening until they spread to vital organs. For this to happen, a tumor must develop a system of blood vessels that will nourish the tumor cells and provide avenues by which they can travel to other parts of the body. This is not automatic, however. Because excess blood vessels can harm normal tissues, body mechanisms prevent the growth of blood vessels unless they are needed—for example, to promote healing after injury.

Beginning in the 1980's, scientists isolated several proteins that stimulate the formation of blood vessels, as well as others that inhibit their growth. Since then, researchers have learned that cells ordinarily secrete both types of proteins, but they produce inhibitors in greater numbers. As a cancerous tumor grows, the levels of the inhibitors mysteriously drop, giving the stimulators the upper hand. In the 1990's, researchers began working to identify some of the genes that produce these proteins and to study their role in the spread of cancers.

Genes that affect blood vessel growth may not be the only ones involved in metastasis, however. In May 1995, researchers reported the discovery of a gene, called KAI1, that in its normal form appears to keep prostate cancer from spreading. In laboratory experiments, the scientists transferred the KAI1 gene into prostate cancer cells from a rat, then injected these cells into mice. Other mice were injected with prostate tumor cells that lacked the gene. For reasons that the scientists do not yet understand, the mice injected with cells lacking the KAI1 gene formed up to nine times as many tumors as the other mice.

Milestones in the study of genes and cancer

Scientists began to unravel the secrets of cancer genes in the 1970's. By mid-1995, they had identified at least 20 oncogenes, 12 tumor suppressor genes, and 4 quality-control genes that contribute to human cancers. Some of the most significant discoveries are:

Gene	Type	Date located	Associated cancers
ras	Oncogene	1979	Bladder and colorectal cancer
myc	Oncogene	1982	Lung cancer
abl	Oncogene	1985	Leukemia
Rb	Tumor suppressor	1986	Retinoblastoma (an eye cancer)
Wt1	Tumor suppressor	1990	Kidney cancer
p53	Tumor suppressor	1990	Leukemia; breast, lung, skin, brain, bone, prostate, and pancreatic cancer
VHL	Tumor suppressor	1993	Renal cancer
hMSH2	Quality control	1993	Colon cancer
hMLH1	Quality control	1994	Colon cancer
BRCA1	Tumor suppressor (?)	1994	Breast and ovarian cancer
BRCA2	Tumor suppressor (?)	1994	Breast cancer

Using genes to fight cancer

Researchers hope their growing knowledge about the genetics of cancer will one day enable doctors to more easily combat the disease. A critical step in that direction has been the development of tools designed to speed up the tasks of isolating genes and identifying their DNA sequences. One of these tools, developed in 1985, is a method of gene copying called polymerase chain reaction (PCR). In PCR, DNA-copying proteins can make millions of copies of a gene within hours. PCR and other tools have in some cases brought the time it takes to isolate a gene from years to months, allowing scientists to uncover the genetic flaws behind a growing number of cancers.

Once a gene has been isolated and its DNA sequence determined, researchers can design tests to determine if people carry the faulty gene by analyzing the DNA in a sample of blood. As of 1995, at least 15 tests for such genetic flaws had been developed.

The tests, which cost several hundred dollars each, are most useful for people in families prone to the disease who wish to know whether they have inherited a specific genetic flaw. But inherited genetic defects are involved in only a minority of cancer cases. Most cancers develop because of genetic damage acquired over a lifetime, and experts say it would be extremely difficult to design a test that would encompass all the possible mutations that could result in cancer, even if all or most of them should become known.

Among scientists and physicians, a controversy rages over the use of the cancer-gene tests currently available. The controversy stems in part from fears that people who test positive will suffer mental anguish, as well as discrimination when seeking jobs and health insurance. Those concerns would be somewhat offset if physicians could provide a cancer-prone person with reliable methods to prevent the disease. Frequent checkups and lifestyle changes could benefit people at risk for some cancers, but not all.

Research into cancer genetics may have greater potential for helping doctors combat the disease once it arises. For instance, being able to test for mutations in the p53 gene would give doctors a way of knowing whether treatments such as chemotherapy or radiation will be effective against a particular tumor. If the p53 gene in the tumor cells was mutated, the gene would not be able to play its normal role in helping damaged cells self-destruct—and so the therapy would be useless.

The study of cancer genetics should also lead to the design of new, more-effective treatments. Some future treatments may target the proteins that normally stimulate or halt cell growth or repair damaged DNA. It may be possible, for instance, to make drugs that will destroy excess growth-promoting proteins and so stop a tumor in its tracks.

One of the most exciting areas of study involves using genes themselves to combat cancer, a type of treatment known as *gene therapy*. In a typical gene therapy experiment, doctors remove tumor cells from a patient, infect the cells with a harmless virus altered to carry a useful gene, then return the cells—with the new gene—to the patient. Or doctors may use a virus or some other carrier to insert a gene directly into cells without removing them from the patient.

Using gene therapy, doctors could reverse the course of cancer by going directly to the genes responsible. First, doctors would determine whether tumor cells contained a mutation in some previously identified gene—say, the gene for p53. The doctors could then supply the cells with a working copy of the p53 gene, which would instruct the abnormal cells to self-destruct. If, on the other hand, an oncogene was responsible for a tumor, doctors would furnish the cancerous cells with a gene for a protein that turns the oncogene off. By mid-1995, trials of such experimental therapies had begun on several patients.

Years of intensive work have revealed many of the secrets governing the chain of events leading to cancer. As scientists work to deepen their understanding of these events, they also face another challenge: to use this information to help reduce the terrible toll that this disease inflicts. Scientists say the chances are good that they will succeed.

For further reading:

Cavenee, Webster K., and White, Raymond L. "The Genetic Basis of Cancer." *Scientific American*, March 1995, pp. 72-79.

Varmus, Harold, and Weinberg, Robert A. *Genes and the Biology of Cancer.* Scientific American Library, 1993.

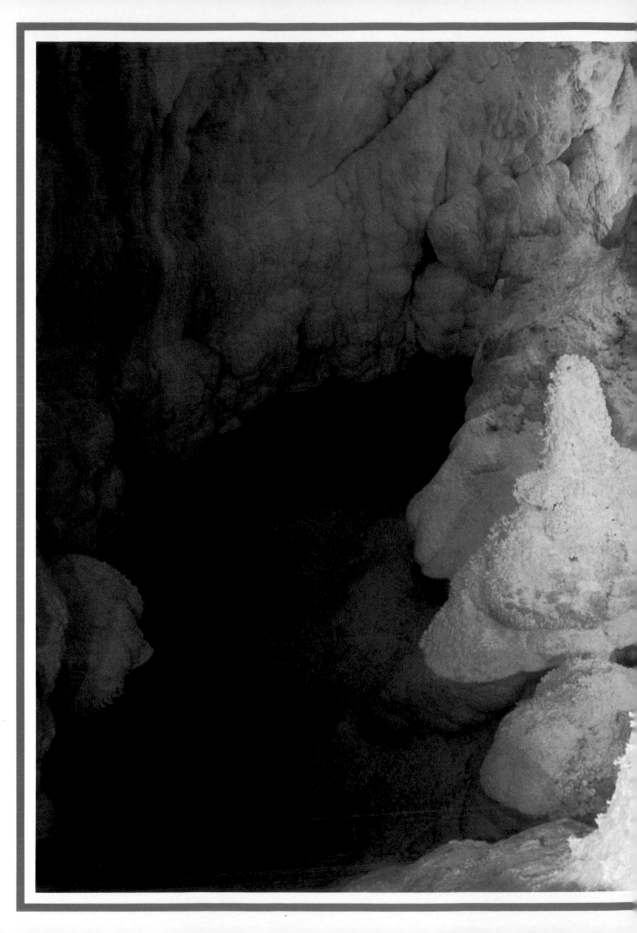

The Fragile Wilderness of Caves

Sightless creatures and fantastic formations exist in a dark universe below ground, where even the breath of human visitors can alter the delicate ecological balance.

BY HORTON H. HOBBS III

Terms and concepts

Breakdown: Large blocks of rock that have fallen from cave ceilings and walls.

Ecosystem: A community of plants, animals, fungi, and microbes, together with the soil, water, and other nonliving components of their environment.

Guano: Feces of bats, birds, crickets and other animals. Guano is an important source of food for cave animals.

Karst: A terrain resulting from limestone dissolution. Karst landscapes have caverns, rolling hills, sinkholes, and few surface streams.

Speleothems: Mineral structures of varying shapes that form as water in a cave deposits dissolved minerals on various surfaces.

Stalactite: A cone- or cylinder-shaped speleothem that hangs down from a cave ceiling, protruding boulder, or ledge.

Stalagmite: A cone- or cylinder-shaped speleothem that rises up from a cave floor or other surface directly below a stalactite.

Speleology: The scientific study of caves.

The author:
Horton H. Hobbs III is a professor of biology at Wittenberg University in Springfield, Ohio. He explores and researches caves throughout the Western Hemisphere.

I backed off the edge of the cave entrance shaft and began my descent along the nylon climbing rope into a pit of darkness. The sunny green world of Tennessee's Appalachian Mountains receded above me. When my feet touched bottom, I stood upright in the dim light and yelled "off rope" to my three caving companions, letting them know that the next person could begin the descent. After the others joined me, we shouldered our ropes and packs, adjusted our helmet lights, took one last look at the blue sky far above, and headed into the blackness of the cave.

As scientists and cave explorers, our mission was to gather temperature and humidity data from small instruments that we had placed in the cave several weeks earlier. We were also to investigate unexplored passageways in this poorly known cave and to keep a watchful eye for any cave life.

We picked our way cautiously through the cave until the lowering ceiling forced us to our hands and knees. In one place, the dwindling tunnel became a mere slit in the rock. We slithered through it, and on the other side climbed over *breakdown,* large blocks of rock that had fallen from the cave ceiling and walls.

After wading through a shallow stream about 300 meters (325 yards) into the cave, we noticed a small opening in the floor of the passageway. We checked our cave map and found that the opening was not marked. After attaching a rope to a boulder, we descended into the newly discovered pit one by one. It was a long trip, because the pit proved to be as deep as a six-story building is tall. Mineral "icicles," called stalactites, pointed down from the ceiling. Fluid-looking mineral formations called draperies hung from the walls.

At the bottom of the pit, we saw a pool of water, and in it was an extremely rare sight: a pure white crayfish with eggs attached to her underside. The eerie creature was blind as well as colorless, adapted to life in constant and complete darkness. She walked slowly along the bottom of the pool, not overly disturbed by our presence.

We left the pool and followed a winding, keyhole-shaped passage for several hundred meters, to where it ended abruptly at the edge of an opening into another chasm. Without additional rope, we would have to return another day.

The thrill of exploration

Our discoveries that day would not make headlines, unlike the December 1994 finding of a cave in France containing hundreds of drawings made by prehistoric human beings. Some experts called that discovery the archaeological find of the century. (In the Science News Update section, see ARCHAEOLOGY [CLOSE-UP].) But all new cave findings produce a sense of awe in the explorers, whether they are amateur "cavers" or *speleologists,* scientists who study caves.

Luckily, the potential for finding new underground realms is great, because the vast majority of the world's caves have been only partially explored and surveyed. Speleologists are tantalized by the possibility of discovering another Lechuguilla Cave, found near Carlsbad Caverns in New Mexico in the late 1980's. What at first seemed to be a small cave turned out be one of the longest and most spectacular caves in the world. But the scientific study of caves is so new that even ordinary caverns can yield important insights about the unique environment underground and the strange creatures that live there.

The world below ground has intrigued human beings since prehistoric times. Many thousands of years ago, our ancestors used cave entrances as shelters. In the deeper recesses, they buried their dead and painted symbols on the walls. The ancient Greeks of Mycenae, a civilization that reached its peak between 1400 and 1200 B.C., attached great importance to caves. Their myths tell of a cave as the birthplace of Zeus, chief of their gods, and of an underworld they called Hades, where a ferryman rowed the souls of the dead across the River Styx into a land of suffering and eternal grief. In ancient Japanese mythology, the sun goddess Amaterasu retired into a cave each night, plunging the world into darkness. Countless other myths and stories point to the cultural importance of caves, their chill and musty odors and eerie darkness often being associated with terrors of the grave.

The unique geology of caves

Geologically speaking, a cave is any natural opening in the ground that extends beyond the point where sunlight can penetrate. Caves occur in a variety of rock types and can range in size from a single tiny tube less than 1 millimeter (0.04 inch) in diameter to broad interconnecting passages that form a network many kilometers long and wide. Obviously, because of our size, we human beings are capable of exploring only the largest portions of caves. We can study organisms found in smaller caves only if the creatures venture into the larger regions. Because of that, we have a limited understanding of the smallest cave animals, their behavior, and their interactions within their tiny realms.

Caves form through geologic processes that typically require thousands or even millions of years. Some caves are created when earthquakes or other forces within the Earth move masses of bedrock. Other caves are made by wind-borne particles that wear deep pockets into rockfaces. Similarly, the pounding of waves coupled with the abrasive action of sand in the water scours sea caves in rocks along seacoasts.

Streams of water or *lava* (molten rock) also create caves. Ice caves in glaciers are formed by meltwater flowing beneath the ice and excavating tunnels on its way to the foot of the glacier. Caves called lava tubes can be created as lava flows down from a volcano. As it flows, the lava at the surface may cool and harden, even though the hot stream of lava continues to move beneath the surface. When the lava stops flowing, a tubular cave remains.

Most of the world's caves were created in a different process, one in which underground rock slowly dissolves. These caves, called *solution caves,* form in limestone, gypsum, dolomite, or other types of sedimentary rock that can be dissolved by acidic water over time. About 15 per-

Cave-forming forces

Different geologic forces produce caves in a variety of landscapes from seacoasts to glacier-filled valleys. The processes may take thousands, even millions, of years to hollow out rock or ice.

Acidic water

New Mexico's immense Lechuguilla cave was created by naturally formed acid that dissolved underground rock. Most of the world's caves, called solution caves, were formed by the same type of chemical action. Acidic water dripping in from above deposits dissolved minerals to create huge dripstone columns and other formations unique to solution caves.

Pounding waves

A sea cave in one of the Channel Islands off the California coast, *right,* was hollowed out by the relentless surf, aided by the scouring action of sand in the water. Sea caves are found along rocky sea coasts worldwide.

Molten lava

An Oregon cave, *above,* formed from a river of lava during a volcanic eruption. The river cooled and hardened at the surface, but the lava within remained liquid. When the lava stopped flowing, a tubular cave remained.

Melting ice

An ice cave in an Alaskan glacier, *right,* was created as meltwater flowing toward the foot of the glacier excavated a tunnel on its way downhill. Ice caves may be found wherever there are glaciers.

How a cave forms

It takes thousands of years for a solution cave to form.
Most of these caves are found in *karst,* regions containing
large deposits of limestone rock near the surface. Acidic
rainwater that seeps into the limestone forms hollowed-
out channels that enlarge into caves over time.

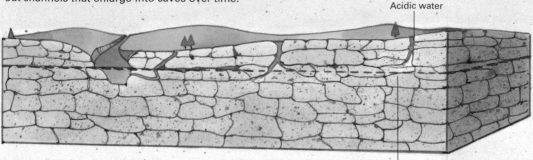

Acidic water

Level of underground water

Rainwater becomes acidic when it reacts with carbon dioxide in the air
and with organic material in the soil. The acidic water, *above,* seeps
into cracks in the limestone and begins to dissolve the rock there.

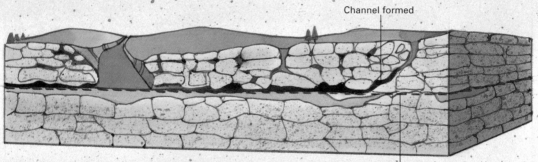

Channel formed

Level of underground water

As the water flows horizontally below the surface toward a natural
outlet, such as a river, it dissolves the limestone to form an underground channel.

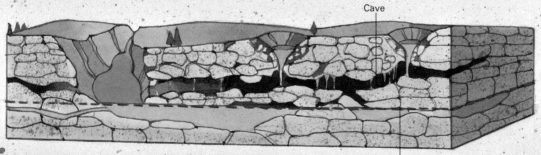

Cave

Level of underground water

Eventually, the riverbed erodes the valley so deeply that the underground water seeks a new, lower route to the river, leaving the old
channel as an air-filled cave. No longer supported by water, the walls
and ceiling of the cave begin to collapse, enlarging it in places.
Groundwater continues to drip in, forming stalactites and other mineral deposits in the cave chambers and passageways.

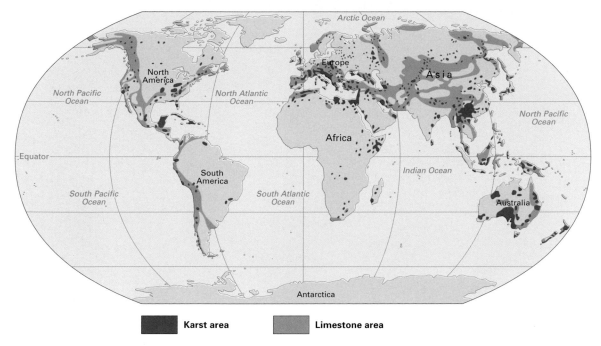

■ Karst area   **■ Limestone area**

Solution caves are typically found in regions that contain limestone or related soluble bedrock. In those areas, karst terrain develops where groundwater has dissolved some of the bedrock.

cent of the 48 contiguous states has soluble rocks at or near the surface of the ground. Such areas are known as *karst*. A karst landscape may contain many *sinkholes*, depressions caused by the collapse of bedrock.

The process by which solution caves form begins with rain. As raindrops fall, they pick up some carbon dioxide gas from the air, forming a weak solution of carbonic acid. The slightly acidic water droplets soak the ground and absorb more carbon dioxide from microbes in the soil. As the water seeps down to the underlying limestone, the acid begins to dissolve the rock, following tiny fissures. The fissures eventually enlarge and over thousands of years widen into passages and caverns. For various reasons, some passages that are normally filled with water may dry out. Without water to support them, the rock ceiling and walls collapse, further enlarging the cave.

Even after a solution cave has formed, water continues to move through it. As the water stops, starts, drips, and splashes, it deposits some of the minerals it picked up as it dissolves rock. Over time, these deposits create an array of fantastic structures called *speleothems*. The great variety of speleothems results from the different ways minerals are deposited, not because of a variety of minerals. In fact, the number of minerals found in caves is quite small. The most common is calcite, a form of calcium carbonate, the major component of limestone.

Dripping water, evaporation, flowing water, pools of standing water, even microorganisms—all produce a characteristic shape of speleothem. As water drips steadily from the cave ceiling, for example, some calcite is left behind in a circular pattern. Drop by drop, the mineral builds up on the ceiling. Over thousands of years, a huge stalactite is

Mineral magic

As water drips, flows, and evaporates inside a solution cave, minerals dissolved in the water are deposited in a fantastic array of shapes.

Deceptively appetizing, a "fried egg," *above,* and strips of "bacon," *above right,* are formations of calcite, the most common mineral found in caves. Pure calcite is white or transparent, but such impurities as iron in the dripping or flowing water can stain the calcite yolk-yellow or bacon-brown.

Gypsum crystals sprout into delicate tendrils, *above,* and crystals of selenite, a less common form of gypsum, grow in clusters that resemble nests, *left.*

Frosty sprays of gypsum hang from the ceiling of a cavern dubbed the Chandelier Ballroom in Lechuguilla cave. The fragile branches took thousands of years to form as water seeping through the cave ceiling evaporated, leaving behind huge gypsum crystals.

formed. Correspondingly, as drops of water hit the cave floor, minerals are deposited on the ground. A stalagmite begins to grow upward directly beneath the stalactite. Mighty columns form where stalactites hanging from the ceiling join stalagmites rising from the cave floor.

Slight changes in the way water moves through a passageway can create vast differences in the speleothems left behind. Smooth flowstone appears on the cave floor where water trickles and spreads over a wide surface, leaving a thin sheet of minerals. Fencelike rimstone builds up around the edges of pools as the water evaporates. Cave pearls grow where water falling into a drip pool sends droplets splashing out onto the rock nearby. The pearly formations become larger as successive layers of minerals are deposited, much as an oyster forms a real pearl by secreting a substance around an irritating grain of sand.

The formation called moonmilk resembles just what the name suggests, a white puddle on the floor of a cave. Speleologists believe the activity of some microorganism may be responsible for this unusual speleothem's milky, smooth surface.

Some of the most beautiful speleothems are *helictites*, crystal structures that spiral out of the cave floor, walls, ceiling, or even other mineral formations. Helictites get their twisted shape as a result of slight environmental changes that cause the crystals to grow first in one direction, then another.

Zones of relative light and darkness

Mineral formations are by no means the only unique feature of solution caves. For example, environmental conditions in a cave are relatively constant compared with the variations we experience on Earth's surface. In addition to being dark, a cave is comparatively silent. Its air and water temperatures fluctuate very little, and the humidity is high.

But speleologists have discovered that physical conditions in a cave do vary from place to place and from time to time. To mark those changes, scientists divide all caves into two major ecological zones—the *threshold zone*, which has some light, and the *dark zone*, which has none. The two zones are evident whether the entrance to a cave is horizontal or vertical, though in caves with a vertical entrance, the zones are not as well defined. Even submerged pits accessible only with special diving equipment will have two ecological zones because some light penetrates into the outer part of the cave.

The threshold zone extends from the entrance of the cave to the farthest place where sunlight can penetrate. The environment of the zone is controlled by the climatic and meteorological conditions on the surface outside the cave. The threshold zone of a cave near the equator, for example, has a warmer wintertime air temperature and higher humidity than a cave in the Midwestern United States. Sunlight intensity in the threshold zone varies with the time of day, season of the year, and the direction the entrance faces. A cave entrance in the deep woods receives far less sunlight on a summer afternoon than does a cave in a clearing in the same woods. But on a winter afternoon, the light reflecting off the snow through leafless tree branches might be of similar intensity in both caves.

The intensity of light marks the difference between two parts of the threshold zone—a relatively bright *entrance region* and a dimmer *twilight region* farther inside the cave. Light intensity diminishes rapidly in the twilight region.

The entire threshold zone experiences swings in temperature and humidity, less dramatic than on the surface but greater than in the cave's deeper recesses. In a temperate climate, seasonal temperatures may range from −10 °C to 30 °C (14 °F to 86 °F) in the entrance region and from 0 °C to 20 °C (32 °F to 68 °F) in the twilight region.

When we have gone so far into a cave that we no longer see any sunlight, we are in the dark zone. The part of the dark zone we come to first is called the variable-temperature region. Environmental conditions here are more constant than in the twilight region, but the temperature still fluctuates. Relative humidity increases, now ranging from 30 to 100 percent.

Finally, we come to the most remote area of the cave, the part of the dark zone called the constant-temperature region. Although the water temperature throughout a cave may fluctuate with the season, the air temperature in this part of the cave does not change. It approximates the average annual temperature at the surface. Rarely will it ever vary by more than 1 Celsius degree (2 Fahrenheit degrees). For example, although surface temperatures in southern Ohio fluctuate widely during the year, deep cave temperatures in Freeland's Cave in Adams County remain at 10 °C (50 °F).

Humidity is continuously high in the constant-temperature region, typically ranging from 80 to 100 percent. Little evaporation can take place in air already so highly saturated with moisture. Yet the air is not stagnant, because air currents continuously pass through most parts of the cave. Some caves have a distinct "suck-and-blow" cycle, as air pressure in the cave seeks to achieve equilibrium with air pressure outside the cave. In such a cycle, cold air sinks and warm air rises through shafts within the cave and at the entrance. This sets up a wind pattern that varies from day to night and seasonally.

Bears, bats, and other cave creatures

Because of the presence of sunlight, the threshold zone has the most abundant plant life of the cave *ecosystem* (the community of plants, animals, fungi, and microbes along with the nonliving features of their environment). In the threshold zone, the light is strong enough to allow ferns, flowers, and other green plants to grow. The plant species found here are the same ones that tolerate living in the shade outside the cave. Violets and lady-slippers growing on the forest floor throughout the Midwestern United States, for example, also thrive in the entrances of Midwestern caves.

Seeds of other surface plants may also wash into the cave and sprout inside. In the absence of light, they grow tall, thin, and pale and die

Life in a cave

All caves have two ecological zones, providing habitat for creatures adapted to little sunlight or to none at all. One group of animals lives in the threshold zone, which extends from the entrance to the farthest point where sunlight penetrates. More highly adapted creatures live farther inside, in a zone of complete darkness. Bats and a few other animals live in all parts of the cave.

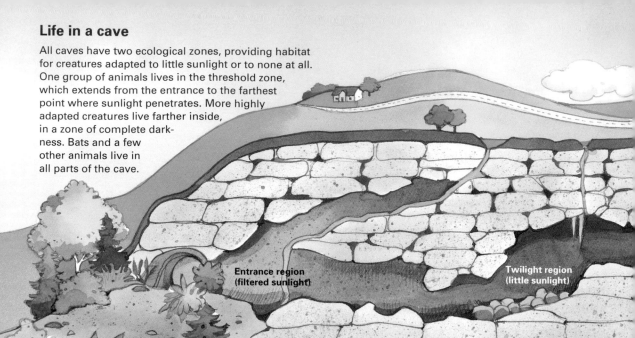

Entrance region (filtered sunlight)

Twilight region (little sunlight)

Threshold zone

A grizzly bear peers from the entrance of the cave it uses as a den. Bears may hibernate in a cave all winter but leave in the spring.

Bats roost upside down in a Texas cave. Bats may roost throughout caves during the day and fly out in search of food at night.

A mass of daddy longlegs intertwine inside the entrance of a cave in Texas. The spiderlike animals are commonly found in threshold zones, where they intercept their prey—insects flying into the cave.

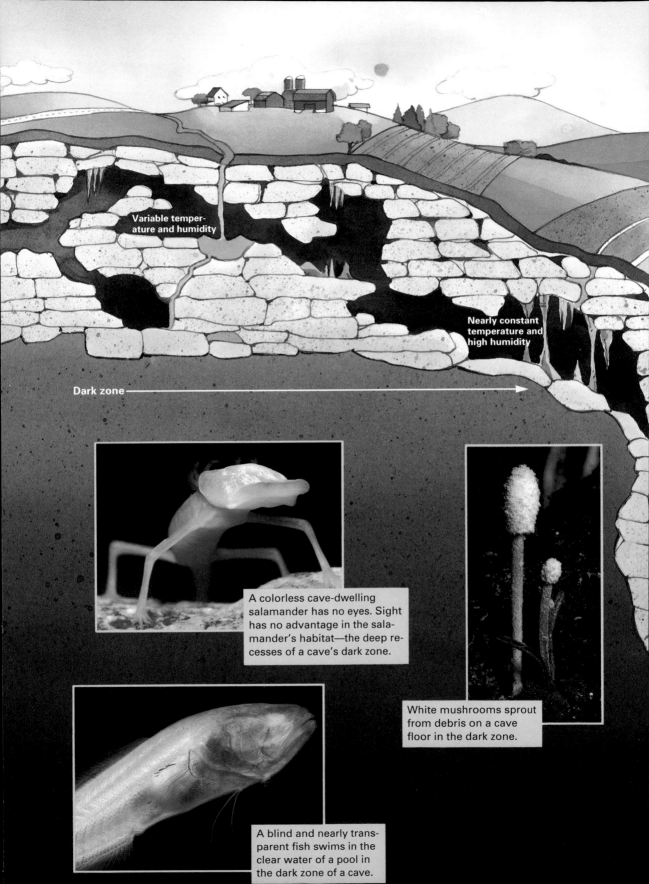

Variable temperature and humidity

Nearly constant temperature and high humidity

Dark zone

A colorless cave-dwelling salamander has no eyes. Sight has no advantage in the salamander's habitat—the deep recesses of a cave's dark zone.

White mushrooms sprout from debris on a cave floor in the dark zone.

A blind and nearly transparent fish swims in the clear water of a pool in the dark zone of a cave.

Threats to the world underground

Limestone quarried for making cement, *above,* as well as for other uses in the construction industry, can slice away entire cave ecosystems. Tourists, such as those descending into Natural Bridge Caverns in Texas, *above right,* more subtly disturb the ecological balance. Breathing and sweating alter the chemistry of the cave air, and people may accidentally, or intentionally, damage stalagmites and other formations.

long before maturing. Nevertheless, they play a role in the cave ecosystem by becoming food for other cave organisms.

In the reduced light of the twilight region, few plant species thrive. There we find mainly mosses, liverworts, and algae, which grows farther from the cave entrance than any other green plant because it can thrive in low light. In the blackness of the dark zone, even algae cannot grow. The dark zone contains no plants.

Bacteria, on the other hand, live in every part of the cave. Most of the bacteria found in caves are also seen in surface soils. Circulating air, roaming animals, human cavers, and water bring in numerous types of bacteria. Once in the cave, the microbes feed on a variety of energy sources. Some derive energy from sulfur or iron compounds, whereas others break down complex organic materials, in the process freeing up simpler compounds that feed other organisms.

Cave scientists have discovered that fungi—which range from large mushrooms to microscopic cells—grow throughout caves. Most cave fungus species originated aboveground, though some may be highly specialized forms that are permanent cave dwellers. Cave fungi grow in mud, water, living and dead organisms, and even on speleothems. Some fungus species live on the feces, called *guano,* of cave animals such as crickets or bats. Cavers must use caution when exploring caves with large bat populations, because such caves are notorious sites of a disease-causing fungus called *Histoplasma capsulatum.* The fungus causes a potentially fatal illness with symptoms similar to tuberculosis.

A researcher at a pond in Lechuguilla, *above,* gauges the health of the cave by sampling the water. Scientists have found that groundwater seeping into caves may contain contaminants from agriculture, mining operations, and urban sewerage systems.

Some cave creatures cannot exist out of the cave environment. However, many are capable of moving in and out of caves. For that reason, speleologists generally classify cave animals according to whether they spend part or all of their lives underground. Cave dwellers such as bears, bats, raccoons, and moths are incapable of living out their lives in a cave. These animals must leave to feed or mate. Scientists classify such animals as *trogloxenes.* Bats, for example, may roost in the cave during the day and fly out every night in search of food. Bears hibernate in a cave for the winter but leave the cave in the spring. Another group of cave dwellers are "accidentals," animals that accidentally wander, fall, or wash into caves and can survive there only temporarily. Fish, for example, may wash into a cave during a flood. If the newcomers cannot find a way out of the cave, they will serve as food for other cave dwellers.

Animals called *troglophiles* (cave lovers) are capable of living their life either inside a cave or outside it. Certain species of salamanders and beetles fall into this category.

But of all the cave animals, the *troglobites,* the creatures that live only underground, are the most fascinating. Troglobites are related to species that live aboveground, but the cave dwellers have evolved characteristics that suit them to their unique environment. The populations of almost all troglobitic species appear to be quite small. Some have been found in just one cave, never elsewhere in the world.

Darkness is the most obvious limitation of the troglobites' home. Coloration has no advantage if one animal cannot be seen by others, and most troglobites have little or no pigment. In the dark zone, we thus find white crayfish, pale beetles, and pink salamanders.

Having well-developed eyes is of no advantage to organisms living in the dark zone, and most troglobites have small eyes when compared with their cousins living aboveground. Many troglobitic species of crabs, shrimps, crayfishes, and fishes lack eye pigment and parts of the eye. Some cave fishes, crayfishes, and insects are completely blind.

Troglobite insects compensate for their lack of vision with anatomical features that give them a keen sense of touch. Some cave insects have antennae twice as long as their bodies. The antennae can detect cracks and uneven ground more readily than the shorter appendages of their aboveground relatives. Troglobitic insects cannot see and lack the radarlike sense of bats, and thus have little use for wings. Some species have no wings at all, and others retain the hard wing cover but have no wings underneath.

For the most part, troglobites depend on food entering their world from the surface. One "delivery service" is a flood that carries leaves, twigs, or even logs into the cave. Bacteria and other organisms are also washed in by floods, blown in by the wind, or carried in by animals.

Another major source of food in many cave systems is delivered by bats in the form of guano. When thousands of migrating bats return to a cave each year, insect communities quickly spring to life in the accumulating droppings. Large deposits of guano support an array of spiders, mites, and millipedes, along with fungi. The dung of large trogloxenic species, such as pack rats and raccoons, also brings food energy inside the cave. A succession of insect and microbe populations can live on the dung as it decomposes. As one insect species thrives, another goes into decline, and a third begins to increase.

Still, food is a scarce resource in the dark zone, and troglobitic species have evolved to make the best of their spartan circumstances. According to preliminary research, many troglobites burn calories more slowly than their surface relatives, a characteristic that enables the cave dwellers to save energy. Troglobitic species also live longer and reproduce at a lower rate. Troglobitic crayfishes and shrimps, for example, produce fewer eggs than do related species living aboveground. And when the eggs hatch, the offspring mature more slowly than surface species.

Myriad connections to the surface

Cave ecosystems are often compared to islands. Both have well-defined borders. But speleologists now realize that a cave is a small part of a whole subterranean environment. And the cave is connected to the surface through shafts, sinkholes, even tiny fissures and cracks.

Unfortunately, this connection makes cave environments—known or unknown—susceptible to human activities aboveground. When people contaminate ground water supplies in karst landscapes, for example, life in any underlying cave is threatened. The contamination may come from many sources. In cities, residential sewage disposal systems, the collection and treatment of municipal wastewater, and the disposal of liquid and solid wastes in landfills can allow pollutants to seep into cave systems. Some industries can produce chemical by-products with potential for destroying cave habitats, such as the brine produced during petroleum processing. In rural areas, runoff from croplands treated with fertilizers and pesticides can contaminate ground water and disrupt cave life. People sometimes use sinkholes as dumping sites, a practice that can bring pollutants into direct contact with cave systems.

Other activities that affect cave ecology include mining operations, improper well construction, and accidental spills of petroleum products. Damming streams in karst areas can flood caves upstream from the dam and limit water from entering caves downstream. And because limestone is valuable for construction projects, karst areas are often quarried. That activity literally slices cave ecosystems out of the Earth.

Tourists, cavers, and speleologists cause damage as well. Careless visitors, not to mention vandals, can destroy in a few seconds the delicate speleothems that have taken thousands of years to form. Even breathing and sweating change the chemistry of the air, disturbing the ecological balance.

All these problems pose a serious threat to cave species. Most troglobites have low rates of reproduction and require many years, perhaps decades, to attain sexual maturity. Such species cannot evolve quickly to adapt to changing circumstances. Ironically, the longevity of troglobites may be the death of them. Many highly specialized aquatic species may become extinct not from one huge dose of pollutants, but from smaller amounts that accumulate over the creatures' long lives.

Evidence of cave water pollution is accumulating at alarming rates worldwide. And when underground waters are extracted for human use in karst areas—an action that has created sinkholes in Alabama, Florida, and in many other parts of the globe—the caves below as well as the surface are altered. To speleologists, caves are fragile windows through which we can glimpse ecosystems very different from those on the surface. But the view may be lost unless humanity manages our activities aboveground in order to protect the wilderness below.

For further reading:

Chapman, Philip. *Caves and Cave Life*. HarperCollins, 1993.

Culver, David C. *Cave Life: Evolution and Ecology*. Harvard University Press, 1982.

Larson, Lane and Peggy. *Caving. The Sierra Club Guide to Spelunking*. Sierra Club Books, 1982.

Rea, Tom, ed. *Caving Basics. A Comprehensive Manual for Beginning Cavers*. National Speleological Society, 1987.

Silver, Donald M. *One Small Square. Cave*. W. H. Freeman, 1993.

Jane Goodall's Challenge

After decades of ground-breaking studies of wild chimpanzees, Jane Goodall has a new mission— to change public attitudes about conservation and the humane treatment of animals.

AN INTERVIEW WITH JANE GOODALL
BY JINGER HOOP

T *he figure of Jane Goodall—a slender, khaki-clad woman with a blond ponytail—is known to millions of people from National Geographic television specials documenting her research on wild chimpanzees in the east African nation of Tanzania. Under the guidance of the famous anthropologist Louis S. B. Leakey, Goodall began her research on chimpanzees in 1960. She was the first person to undertake an in-depth study of chimpanzees in the wild, and her discoveries showed that chimps are capable of behaviors scientists once believed distinctively human. At 61, Goodall is still scientific director of the international research station she founded at Tanzania's Gombe National Park, but field work is no longer the major focus of her life. Today, she spends only a few weeks of the year at the research station, devoting most of her time to giving speeches about the chimps, conservation, and the treatment of animals.*

Science Year: The books and documentaries about your work at Gombe make it seem a little like conducting research in the Garden of Eden. One widely published picture shows you sitting on a Tanzanian mountainside, watching the sun set and sipping coffee. Other photos show chimps reaching out to touch your hand and play with your hair. Was your life in Gombe really as idyllic as those images make it seem?

Goodall: Actually, the research can be very frustrating. Sometimes it's just so difficult to keep up with the chimps, crawling through thickets, getting stuck in the thorns. You'll be watching the chimps do something fantastic, and then off they go, and you've lost them completely. Or rain suddenly comes down in a deluge. Fatigue is also a problem. Sometimes you get so physically tired, you just can't keep up. That's very frustrating.

"*I* feel very real affection and respect toward the chimps, and they show me respect to some extent and trust and tolerance."

But the joys of the work come every day. There's triumph in struggling through the horrible, beastly undergrowth, getting scratched and sweaty and torn and near tears—and then suddenly catching up with a group of chimps and seeing them do something amazing. I always feel great excitement at Gombe, because I never know what each day is going to bring. After 35 years there, we're still learning new things.

SY: How do you describe your relationship with the chimps you've studied?

Goodall: That's difficult to do. They're not like family. And it's a different relationship from that with a pet, because I'm not responsible for the chimps and they're not dependent on me in any way. I think the best way to describe the relationship is to say that I feel very real affection and respect toward the chimps, and they show me respect to some extent and trust and tolerance. And from me to them, there's something else I guess we can describe as love. I believe that captive chimps will show love for a human, but not wild chimps.

SY: What do you miss most about the chimps when you are away from Gombe?

Goodall: One of my favorite things is being with a mother chimp and her infant, watching the development of the mother-child bond and watching the youngster grow up. There's hardly a time when I've been out with a mother and child that I don't see something that I've never seen before—the way the infant plays with the objects around him, some gesture from the mother to the child that I hadn't noticed, or something the mother has begun doing differently with this child than with her other children.

SY: Your observations over the years showed that chimpanzees are capable of humanlike behaviors.

Goodall: There are so many similarities! The long period of childhood, important for chimps as for us because they have a lot to learn, which they do by observing and imitating others. The enduring, supportive bonds between family members. The nonverbal communication, including kissing, embracing, and holding hands. Chimps are capable of compassion and true altruism. Intellectually, they show abilities once thought uniquely human. And, like people, the chimps show bad sides as well as good ones.

SY: One of the most startling behaviors you observed was a female chimp and her daughter stealing baby chimps from their mothers, and then killing and eating the babies.

Goodall: Yes. We try not to intervene in interactions between the

"*O*ne of my favorite things is being with a mother chimp and her infant, watching the development of the mother-child bond and watching the youngster grow up."

Jane Goodall

When Jane Goodall walked into the African bush to study chimpanzees in 1960, she lacked the usual credentials of a university-trained biologist. But in her own way, she had spent two decades preparing herself for the work to come. Her groundbreaking career was no doubt shaped by her unusual preparation for it.

Goodall was born on April 3, 1934, in London. Almost from infancy, she loved animals. One of her earliest memories is of crying inconsolably after a man killed a dragonfly that had been hovering over her baby carriage. When she was only two, she piled her bed with earthworms from the garden so that she could lie next to them and learn how they "walked" without legs.

At the start of World War II (1939-1945), Goodall's father joined the British army, and Jane, her younger sister, Judy, and her mother moved to a farm near the English channel. In that setting, Goodall became an amateur naturalist. She remembers crouching one long afternoon in a hen house, waiting to see a chicken lay an egg. The wait lasted five hours, and Goodall today says the experience provided her with her first lesson in observing animals—patience.

Goodall was a good student, but she preferred being outdoors to doing her schoolwork. Reading *The Story of Doctor Doolittle,* by Hugh Lofting, made her yearn to travel to Africa and "talk to the animals" as Dr. Doolittle did. She also read Tarzan stories and admits to feeling jealous of Tarzan's wife, Jane, whom Goodall considered "a bit of a wimp. I thought I'd have made a much better mate for Tarzan myself," she remembers today.

By age 9, Goodall knew what she wanted to do with her life—live among the animals of Africa and write books about them. Unable to afford a university education, Goodall went to secretarial school on the advice of her mother, who said that secretaries could get jobs anywhere in the world. But she was 23 before the chance to go to Africa came with the invitation to visit a friend whose family had purchased a farm in the eastern African nation of Kenya.

After three weeks in Kenya, Goodall knew she wanted to stay. She found a secretarial job in Nairobi, the capital. While working there, Goodall one day visited the city's natural history museum and met its director, Louis S. B. Leakey, an anthropologist who later became famous for his discoveries of African fossils of early human beings. As Leakey gave Goodall a tour of the museum, he quizzed her on her knowledge of the animal world. Impressed with her answers, he offered her a job as an assistant secretary on the spot.

A young Jane Goodall embraces a favorite stuffed animal—a toy chimpanzee.

Goodall worked for Leakey for nearly a year, on occasion accompanying the anthropologist and his scientist wife Mary on expeditions to search for fossils. Although Leakey was primarily interested in studying fossils of early human beings and their ancestors, he also wanted to find a window onto their behavior. He theorized that wild chimpanzees might provide that view, since chimps are the animal most closely related to human beings.

When Leakey decided to send a researcher to observe chimp behavior at the Gombe Stream Chimpanzee Reserve (now called Gombe National Park) in a remote, mountainous region of Tanzania, Goodall asked to take charge of the project. Leakey agreed, saying that Goodall's lack of academic training would make her a good observer, because her mind would be "uncluttered by theories." (Leakey would try the same formula again in 1966, when he chose Dian Fossey, an American occupational therapist, to begin the first major study of gorillas in the wild. Fossey, whose work was chronicled in the book and motion picture *Gorillas in the Mist,* was murdered at her research camp in Rwanda in 1985.)

By 1960, Leakey had raised enough money to finance Goodall's research. Tanzanian authorities balked at the idea of the 26-year-old Goodall setting up camp alone in the bush, however, so Goodall's mother offered to accompany her. The older woman transformed their primitive camp into a first-aid clinic and befriended the villagers who lived nearby.

Goodall left camp early every morning to search for signs of some of the 10,000 or so chimpanzees that lived on the reserve. The intervals between sightings were frustratingly long, and whenever the chimps saw her, they ran away. It was more than a year before the chimps allowed

Goodall to observe them up close. After that, she tried to track the chimps wherever they went, crawling under the thorny undergrowth, climbing treacherous slopes, sleeping on the floor of the jungle.

In the years that followed, Goodall glimpsed a surprising view of chimpanzees' life in the wild. One of her most important observations was that the chimps can fashion primitive tools—for example, by stripping a vine of its leaves and then using it to draw insects out of a termite mound. That single discovery revolutionized our views not only of chimps but also of people. Previously, human beings were thought to be the only animal that made tools. "Now we must redefine *man*, redefine *tool*, or accept chimpanzees as humans," Leakey said when Goodall reported her finding.

A Gombe chimpanzee eats insects she has drawn out of a stump using a stripped twig. The discovery that chimps make such tools was one of Goodall's most important.

Another important discovery was that chimps are not the peaceful creatures scientists had thought. Goodall found that chimpanzees kill and eat baby baboons, monkeys, and wild pigs, and on rare occasions, even other chimpanzees. And neighboring groups of chimps sometimes attack each other in a warlike fashion.

Goodall took breaks from field work to attend Cambridge University in England. She received the Ph.D. degree in *ethology* (the study of the behavior of animals) in 1965. The previous year, Goodall married Hugo van Lawick, a Dutch baron and photographer with the National Geographic Society. Goodall had met van Lawick when he came to Gombe to make a film about her work.

In 1967, the couple had a son, Hugo Eric Louis, nicknamed Grub. For the first three years of Grub's life, Goodall stopped personally tracking the chimps so that she could stay close to her child—the chimpanzee style of mothering. Because chimpanzees had been known to attack the babies of villagers, Goodall and her husband fashioned a cagelike playpen and a caged-in veranda to protect their son. Until age nine, when Grub went to live in England with Goodall's mother and go to school, the boy lived at Gombe.

In 1974, Goodall and her husband divorced. She married again in 1975. Her second husband, Derek Bryceson, director of Tanzania National Parks, died in 1980.

Today, Goodall spends 10 months out of the year traveling and giving lectures on behalf of the Jane Goodall Institute for Wildlife Research, Education, and Conservation, which she founded in 1975. Between tours, Goodall sometimes stops for a few weeks in England at the house where she grew up or at her son's home in Dar es Salaam, Tanzania. She spends the remainder of her time at Gombe, where she lives in a small house on the beach at Lake Tanganyika.   [J. H.]

Goodall relaxes at her home near the Gombe research station. On the wall hangs a picture of the chimpanzee she named David Greybeard. He was the first chimp to approach her, and she believes his fearlessness encouraged the other chimps to accept her presence among them as well.

> "*A*fter more than 30 years living with and learning from the chimpanzees, the time has come for me to try to give something back to the species that's given so much to me."

chimps, but this was so bizarre. We thought the mother, named Passion, might well kill off all the newborn chimps, and we wouldn't have any left to observe! But she was so dead set on what she was doing that she paid no attention to us, even when one of the field staff threw a rock at her. In the end, Passion and her daughter Pom probably killed as many as 10 infants. Cannibalism among chimps is rare, however, though violence between neighboring social groups is not uncommon.

SY: You decided not to intervene when rival groups attacked each other.

Goodall: We couldn't. Grown chimpanzees are probably six times stronger than human beings, and the chimps were like people with battle lust—there was no way we could stop these fights. They were absolutely violent.

SY: Has that violence ever been directed at you?

Goodall: Lately, yes. After all these years at Gombe, we now have one rogue male chimp. He likes a sense of power, I think, and is very dangerous. He has always bullied younger chimps and females, and then he turned his attention toward human observers. He directs his aggression at me in particular. Why me, I don't know.

SY: Does he see you as the "dominant" researcher at the station, perhaps?

Goodall: I don't think so. Perhaps it's that he has never, ever had the tiniest bit of fear of me. I've known him since he was a baby. When he was very small, he wanted to play with us, but we didn't play with any of the infant chimps because that would be interfering in their normal behavior. Maybe this frustrated him. But I don't think it was that, because right from the beginning he was bullying the other chimps.

He is the biggest, strongest chimp we've ever had, probably 10 times stronger than I am, and he will charge at me like a tank. He is trying to intimidate me, not kill me, but the terrain is so rugged that he could easily tip me over a precipice. Then it'll be "Good-bye, Jane."

SY: So that's why you've taken to the lecture circuit!

Goodall: Actually, the real reason is that I consider this my pay-back time. After more than 30 years living with and learning from the chimpanzees, the time has come for me to try to give something back to the species that's given so much to me. And it's time to share with other people what I've been fortunate enough to learn about chimps.

I'm also traveling and making speeches because I've seen such horrible mistreatment of chimpanzees. Once you find out the extent to which the chimpanzees are becoming endangered in the wild, once you see the chimps for sale at the side of the road in Africa or squeezed into tiny cages in America, then if you care about the species, you have to try to do something about it.

SY: What's happening to the chimps in Africa?

Goodall: The four African countries of Gabon, Cameroon, Congo, and Zaire have the only significant populations of chimpanzees, but even in those strongholds, the numbers are being depleted rapidly. In some countries, the main problem is that the chimpanzee's forest habitat is being destroyed due to logging and mining. In other areas, the chimpanzees are killed by hunters, because chimp meat is a delicacy in many parts of west and central Africa. The hunting is illegal, so the hunters smoke the meat to make it impossible for anyone to know for sure what type of animal it came from.

Poachers may also shoot mother chimps in order to steal the babies and sell them to people who want them as circus animals or pets or lab animals. It's not only cruel to obtain chimps this way, it's also very wasteful. We estimate that for every baby chimp that survives long enough to be sold, many others die from being wounded, traumatized, dehydrated, or malnourished. And other adult chimps are shot and killed when they rush in and try to protect the screaming female and her infant. So we estimate that for every one baby chimp that survives to be sold, about 10 other chimps have to die.

SY: How are chimps treated in captivity, by and large?

Goodall: Although zoos are improving as more people understand the special needs of primates, there are hundreds of chimps living in terrible conditions in zoos around the globe, especially in the developing world. This is not surprising because often the

> **"Although zoos are improving as more people understand the special needs of primates, there are hundreds of chimps living in terrible conditions in zoos around the globe, especially in the developing world."**

> **"If** you watch a chimpanzee child and a human child, you find that their faces and bodies express joy and fear and despair in very much the same way."

humans there are also suffering due to poverty. And chimpanzees can still be bought as pets. They may be treated well for a few years, but as they outgrow the "cute" stage, grow strong, begin to resent discipline, and become potentially dangerous, their owners can no longer cope. In the United States, such chimps often end up in medical research laboratories. In many labs, the chimps languish, each one alone in a small cage: bars above, bars below, bars all round. The cages are bleak, barren, sterile, and boring, and the chimps live there for life. Some labs, however, are improving, trying to provide more space, to keep the inmates in pairs, and to give them things to do to stimulate their minds. Finally, the chimps used in entertainment are typically trained by being beaten with iron bars to instill instant obedience. When they get big, they too often end up in labs.

SY: This brings up the very controversial issue of animal rights. Do you consider yourself an animal rights activist?

Goodall: I've always desperately tried to avoid putting up red flags, and a label like "animal rights activist" can be a red flag. You immediately think of somebody who is going to throw bombs, break into buildings, destroy equipment—somebody who acts aggressively and destructively.

What I'm interested in doing is changing attitudes, not destroying things. I want to help change the attitudes of human beings toward nonhuman beings. Very often, people still think about nonhuman beings as "mere animals." People believe that animal pain is somehow very different from our pain, and that what looks like suffering in animals somehow isn't really suffering.

I want to help people see that human beings are not the only creatures who have personalities. We aren't the only species capable of rational thought and problem solving. We aren't the only ones who have emotions and can experience psychological suffering.

SY: How are these ideas related to your research with chimpanzees?

Goodall: The chimpanzee has taught us what animals are capable of, because chimps are so like us. The anatomy of the human brain is very similar to that of the chimpanzee brain. The genetic material in chimps and human beings is 98.4 percent the same. And we now know that chimps are capable of intellectual performances we used to think unique to ourselves, from reasoned problem solving, such as tool using and making, to understanding the needs of others, and to using abstract symbols in communication.

Because of all these similarities, we have every reason to believe that chimps' emotional feelings are very much the same as ours. Certainly if you watch a chimpanzee child and a human child, you find that their faces and bodies express joy and fear and despair in very much the same way.

SY: Many of your scientific colleagues would disagree with the premise that animals have personalities, however.

Goodall: That's changing fast. Thirty years ago, when I wrote my first paper for the scientific journal *Nature*, I referred to the chimpanzees at Gombe as *he* and *she*. The editor crossed out the words and substituted *it*. In those days, scientists describing animal behavior were not allowed to use the words *personality* or *motivation* or *adolescence* or *childhood* or *excitement*. But today animal experts use them all the time.

I was fortunate in that Louis Leakey arranged for me to go out into the field to study chimps without my having had any scientific training. I didn't know that animals weren't supposed to have personalities. I could see things as they were.

SY: At the time, you were criticized for being too emotionally attached to the chimps. After you gave names to the chimps, critics said that was a sign that you were not observing chimp behavior in the cold light of scientific inquiry. But today some scientists have proposed that your methods could be considered a "female" approach to the study of animals in the wild. Is that how you characterize your techniques?

Goodall: I've had many, many discussions on this subject. To be honest, I don't think my techniques had anything to do with being a woman. It was just that I didn't have any training in the usual way of doing things, and so I didn't know what the rules were. When you have animals as childhood pets, you automatically give them names. You automatically assume that they're happy or sad, and you develop intuitive feelings towards them.

I do believe that scientists can be emotionally involved in what they are watching and at the same time be objective in what they're noting down on paper. It does require self discipline. But while you mustn't let your emotions interfere with what you're seeing, that doesn't mean you shouldn't experience those feelings. I think that if you don't feel empathy with the animals you're observing, you can miss a lot of cues that eventually lead to understanding. Once you've begun to understand intuitively, you can become strictly objective in testing the hypotheses you've formed and categorizing what you see.

SY: Could you give an example of an observation that was made sharper by your empathetic relationship with the chimps?

Goodall: Yes—the relationships between a mother chimp and her infant. The interactions between the two are very subtle, but I found it very easy to sense what a chimpanzee mother was feeling, particularly after I had a child of my own.

SY: Earlier you said that you try not to interfere with the lives of the chimps. Does that become harder if you feel sympathy for them? For example, when a polio epidemic swept the chimp community in 1966, you made the decision to give them vaccine.

Goodall: I see no problem with intervening if it's a question of life or death. The only reason not to intervene would be if you wanted to learn whether the animal could survive its illness or wounds. That's not a question I want to answer. I'm interested in animal personalities and life histories, so I want them to live.

Besides, with the chimp population dwindling so rapidly, every individual in the chimpanzee community is important for the long-term survival of the species. And we humans are responsible for inflicting so much pain and suffering on the chimps that we owe it to them to help them if they're ill.

If you were an anthropologist observing a primitive culture of human beings, you'd help them if they got sick. Otherwise, what sort of person would you be? To me it's exactly the same situation if you're studying chimpanzees, hyenas, or any other kind of animal.

SY: You're often described as sort of a super "Earth Mother," unfailingly patient, gentle, and full of compassion for children and animals. Is that ladylike image the real you?

Goodall: I doubt that I'm often very ladylike, but I suppose the other characteristics do fit. Most of those qualities—in fact, most of the success I've had in my life—I lay at my mother's door. When I was a girl dreaming of going to Africa to "talk to the animals" as Dr. Doolittle did, my mother encouraged me without question. That was remarkable, because 50 years ago when I was a girl, my family had no money—none. Africa in those days seemed to be a whole other world, the "dark continent." It was a mysterious land, full of jungles that seemed to go on forever, the land of Tarzan and the apes. Moreover, there was absolutely no precedent for a young person—male or female—tramping off into the wilds. It hadn't been done.

So my mother's friends would say, "Why don't you tell Jane to dream about something she can actually achieve?" But Mum never listened to them. She used to say to me, " Jane, if you really want to do something and you work hard and take advantage of every opportunity and *never give up*, you'll find a way." Today, when young people ask how they can follow in my footsteps, I tell them just what my mother said to me.

SY: What other advice do you have for young people?

Goodall: That these days it's much harder to do field work without getting college degrees in science. The profession is much more competitive than when I was getting started. Moreover, when you're going out to do research in the developing world, you very often must get clearance from the government, and officials aren't going to give it to someone without the proper academic qualifications. So it's much harder to break in by the back door as I did. I paid my dues, and I got my Ph.D. in the end, so I don't mind telling young people they must stay in school. I just did it backwards.

SY: Do you encourage would-be biologists to focus on creatures other than chimps—perhaps insects or microbes—that have not been so thoroughly studied?

Goodall: No, no, no. There is still much to be learned about chimps! We don't yet know why some females move from one community to another during adolescence. We have no idea why Passion and Pom became cannibals. We don't truly understand relationships between neighboring groups of chimps. We have huge amounts to learn about the differences in behavior among chimps living in different parts of Africa—and that research is becoming urgent because the chimpanzees are vanishing in more and more areas. And we have so much to learn about what one chimpanzee can communicate to another who is out of sight. Surely their calls communicate more than we are giving them credit for. But we don't know yet.

"Most of the success I've had in my life I lay at my mother's door."

SY: All those projects require field work in Africa, of course.

Goodall: Yes, but young people may find something fascinating to learn about right on their doorstep. What a wonderful study it would be for students all over the world to collect information on a creature like the sparrow, which lives just about everywhere, from the inner city to the country. Young people could study the birds and then pool their findings by submitting photographs, videos, drawings, paintings, poems, and essays. What a lot we would learn about the sparrow.

You could conduct a wonderful study if you just went into a zoo and observed sparrow behavior in the cages of the different animals. Would sparrows behave differently in the different cages? I don't know, but it's great question to ask. How about observing the behavior of sparrows in airports and outdoor restaurants?

I've founded a program for young people in 30 nations to encourage just that sort of thing. The program, called Roots & Shoots, emphasizes hands-on activities, preferably organized by at least two schools working together, one advantaged and one disadvantaged. Students preschool- to college-age plan activities that benefit the environment, nonhuman beings—and each other, because we're animals, too.

SY: What made you decide to start the program?

Goodall: I was reacting to environmentalists who say that there is no hope of saving the planet, that we have gone too far in destroying the environment. They say that the hole in the ozone layer, the destruction of forests, the possible change in global climate are all so bad that even if everyone changes their behavior now it's still too late. We're all as though on a train going very fast downhill in a dark tunnel with no headlights and no brakes.

SY: You don't see it that way?

Goodall: Not at all. I think there is hope for solving our environmental problems, precisely because we are a problem-solving species. If we hadn't been so, we never would have come into existence at all.

"I think there is hope for solving our environmental problems, precisely because we are a problem-solving species."

Our early ancestors were surrounded by fearsome beasts with sharp claws and teeth. The beasts could run faster than us and climb up trees after us—and yet we survived by using our intelligence.

We have only just begun to realize the environmental damage we're doing. Now that we understand the nature of the problems, I believe that we can find solutions and come up with healing technologies. After all, look at what we have accomplished without our backs to the wall, just in the name of progress. We sent people to the moon and built airplanes that fly faster than sound and created fax machines and computers—all out of scientific curiosity.

SY: Are you saying that children will be the ones to create solutions to our environmental problems?

Goodall: Yes. Now that our backs are to the wall, I'm placing my hope in children. Children are more flexible than adults, so they can more easily change the way they think. They also find it easier to change their personal behavior, something we have to do to clean up the environment. We have to be less wasteful. We have to be less destructive. We have to be less greedily materialistic. It's much easier for kids to do that. Many are teaching their parents, telling them not to leave the water running while they clean their teeth, to recycle the family refuse, and so on.

Encouraging young people is one of the main reasons I give some speeches each year. And the most important message I give to any audience is that every single individual matters. The chimps have taught us that individual *non*human beings as well as human beings matter. Each one of us has a role to play in this strange life of ours, and each one of us can make a difference. But we humans get a choice—do we want to use the gift of our lives to try to make the world a better place? Or don't we care?

For further reading:

Goodall, Jane. *The Chimpanzee Family Book: Jane Goodall—With Love.* The Jane Goodall Institute, 1994.

Goodall, Jane. *The Chimpanzees of Gombe: Patterns of Behavior.* Belknap, 1986.

Goodall, Jane. *In the Shadow of Man.* Houghton Mifflin, 1971.

Goodall, Jane. *My Life with the Chimpanzees.* Pocket Books, 1988.

Goodall, Jane. *Through a Window: My Thirty Years with the Chimpanzees of the Gombe.* Houghton Mifflin, 1990.

Peterson, Dale and Goodall, Jane. *Visions of Caliban: On Chimpanzees and People.* Houghton Mifflin, 1993.

For more information:

Information about the Jane Goodall Institute, chimpanzees, and Roots & Shoots clubs can be obtained from The Jane Goodall Institute, P.O. Box 599, Ridgefield, CT 06877.

Physicists have finally confirmed the existence of a subatomic particle that may be the last remaining fundamental building block of the universe.

Found—The Top Quark

BY ROBERT H. MARCH

March 2, 1995, was a red-letter day for researchers at the Fermi National Accelerator Laboratory near Batavia, Ill., and for their colleagues around the world. At a dramatic press conference, two teams of Fermilab investigators jubilantly announced that there was no longer any serious doubt that they had discovered what may be nature's last missing building block of matter, a subatomic particle known as the top quark. The announcement, however, hardly came as a surprise. At an earlier press conference, in April 1994, one of the research teams had reported suggestive, though not convincing, evidence that it had found the top quark. What had changed in the intervening months was the degree of certainty regarding the existence of the elusive particle. By March 1995, three times as much data had been collected to strengthen the case, and a second team had compiled similar experimental results.

Fermilab particle physicists—investigators of matter at the smallest levels—emphasized that the finding, though significant, didn't point to anything new or unexpected. Researchers in the field had been convinced for years that the top quark had to exist—they simply hadn't been able to find it. Moreover, the discovery of the top quark did not signal the opening of an exciting new era of research, but rather the conclusion of what might be the last chapter in the age-old quest for the basic building blocks of matter.

That chapter deals with the so-called Standard Model, a theoretical picture of the basic units of matter that had guided research in particle physics for more than 20 years. Failure to find the top quark would have cast doubt on the Standard Model and forced physicists to re-

Opposite page:
A researcher at the Fermi National Accelerator Laboratory (Fermilab) in Batavia, Ill., checks electronic images of particle collisions in search of patterns indicating the presence of the top quark. The background image is a collision pattern containing a rare "signature" of the top quark.

think their ideas of how the universe is constructed at the most fundamental levels. With the top quark in hand, physicists could begin turning their attention to other questions in their search for the ultimate nature of matter.

It is a search that goes back to the dawn of scientific thinking in ancient Greece. It has been above all a quest for simplicity, motivated by the belief that underlying the complexity and unruliness of the everyday world, there exists a much simpler order. In that realm, far too small for the human eye to see, all matter—whether in the stars above our heads or the dirt beneath our feet—would reveal itself to be made of just a few elementary building blocks.

One of the first thinkers to theorize about matter at the smallest scales was the Greek philosopher Democritus, who lived from about 460 to 370 B.C. Democritus said matter could be reduced to tiny particles that he called *atoms*, meaning "uncuttable." He chose that name because he envisioned the particles as being the most basic bits into which anything could be divided. We still use the word atom for the smallest complete unit of an element, such as iron or gold. But in the past 100 years, scientists have learned that atoms, far from being uncuttable, can be split apart into a number of even smaller pieces.

Deeper into the atom

The discovery of the atom's true nature began in 1897 when the British physicist Joseph John Thompson discovered that atoms contain lightweight, negatively charged particles. Thompson theorized that these particles—electrons—were embedded in a positively charged sphere containing most of an atom's *mass* (quantity of matter).

In 1911, the work of another British physicist, Ernest Rutherford, led to a better view of the atom. Rutherford fired *alpha particles* (helium atoms stripped of their electrons) at thin sheets of gold foil and found that most of the particles passed through the foil while some were deflected. From this discovery, Rutherford concluded that the massive positive portion of an atom is concentrated in a very small central nucleus. The electrons, he said, circle the nucleus at enormous speed, leaving a great deal of empty space around the nucleus.

Physicists continued to develop their view of the atom. In 1913, the Danish theorist Niels Bohr theorized that an atom's electrons are confined to certain shells, or orbits, around the nucleus, an idea that was later confirmed and refined. The following year, Rutherford proposed that the proton, a massive, positively charged particle that had been discovered in 1902, must be a part of the nucleus. And in 1932, another British researcher, James Chadwick, found that the nucleus also contains other particles with a mass close to that of the proton but with no electric charge. These neutral particles were dubbed neutrons.

For a while the subatomic world looked simple enough, with just three basic parts—electrons, protons, and neutrons—required to make an atom. But as physicists soon learned, they had only begun to understand how matter is constructed. Further experiments with machines

Terms and concepts

Antimatter: Matter that is opposite in electric charge and certain other properties to regular matter.

Boson: A "messenger" particle that transmits a force between other kinds of particles.

Electron: A low-mass, negatively charged particle that is a fundamental component of atoms. Electrons belong to the lepton family of particles.

Electronvolt: A unit used to express the energy of subatomic particles. One electronvolt is the energy acquired by an electron passing through a 1-volt battery.

Leptons: A family of particles that includes the electron and several other particles.

Mass: The property that allows matter to resist being accelerated and gives it weight in a gravitational field. More generally, the amount of matter something contains.

Neutron: A relatively massive, uncharged particle in the nucleus of an atom.

Proton: A relatively massive, positively charged particle in the atomic nucleus.

Quarks: Fundamental particles, from which many other particles, including protons and neutrons, are constructed.

Standard Model: The accepted picture of fundamental particles and forces.

The author:
Robert H. March is professor of physics at the University of Wisconsin at Madison.

called particle accelerators, which slam beams of particles together or into stationary nuclei, showed that atoms were quite complex.

Particle accelerators, which can be thought of as giant microscopes able to peer deep into the atom, use electrical forces to boost protons or other charged particles to very high speeds. The faster the particles go, the more energy they possess. The earliest particle accelerators could fit on a tabletop, but they grew progressively larger as physicists sought to achieve higher and higher energies. Fermilab, the world's most powerful accelerator, which began operation in 1972, has an accelerating ring 6.4 kilometers (4 miles) around. And the Superconducting Super Collider (SSC), a huge accelerator that was being constructed in Texas until the United States Congress ended its funding in late 1993, would have been 87 kilometers (54 miles) in circumference.

The energy imparted to a speeding particle in an accelerator is expressed in units called *electronvolts*. An electronvolt (eV) is a tiny energy unit, the energy gained by a single electron passing through a 1-volt battery. (A standard flashlight battery is 1.5 volts.) But particles can be accelerated to enormous energies. The first generation of particle accelerators, developed in the early 1930's, accelerated beams of particles to energies of about 1 million electronvolts (MeV), and by the early 1950's machines had been developed that produced energies in the billions of electronvolts (GeV, from *giga*, the prefix for billion).

The early particle accelerators were often called "atom smashers," because they were used to break atomic nuclei apart for study. Over a period of 25 years, these machines unlocked most of the secrets of the nucleus. And with larger machines in the GeV range, physicists discovered that the proton and neutron were not simple objects but had complicated internal structures.

Imposing order on a profusion of particles

The GeV accelerators of the 1950's and 1960's created a dizzying number of previously unknown nuclear particles rarely found in nature. They could do this because, as the famous German-American physicist Albert Einstein demonstrated in his equation $E = mc^2$, matter and energy are equivalent. Under the right conditions, matter can be converted into energy, and energy turned into matter. When two particles are accelerated in opposite directions to an energy of many GeV and then crashed together, the combined energy of the collision condenses into a swarm of particles that flash into momentary existence and then decay into other kinds of particles. The only visible remnant of a collision is an array of swirling lines captured with a camera or other recording device, tracing the myriad paths of the various particles.

By the 1960's, the number of particles created by the collisions was becoming bewildering. Surely, in their number and variety, the particles could not all be fundamental building blocks of matter. Physicists were desperate for a theory that would impose order on the apparent chaos of the subatomic world.

In 1964, two American physicists, Murray Gell-Mann and George

Smaller and smaller units of matter

Atoms, once thought to be the smallest units of matter, are now known to be made of many smaller parts, including the fundamental particles known as quarks.

The name *atom*, meaning *uncuttable*, was coined by the ancient Greek philosopher Democritus, who theorized that all matter is composed of these tiny and—so he thought—indivisible units.

Atoms

The true nature of atoms began to be understood in the 1800's. In 1897, the British physicist Joseph John Thompson discovered the electron, a negatively charged particle in the atom. Another British physicist, Ernest Rutherford, theorized in 1911 that nearly all of an atom's *mass* (quantity of matter) is concentrated in a central, positively charged nucleus, with the electrons whizzing around it at tremendous speeds.

Rutherford's conception of the atom

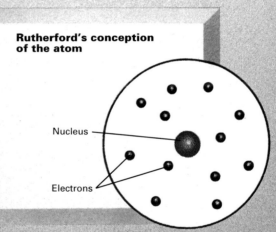

Nucleus

Electrons

In 1913, the Danish physicist Niels Bohr refined that view, suggesting that the electrons are confined to particular orbits around the nucleus.

The Bohr model of the atom

Electrons

Physicists learned in the 1920's that the nucleus' positive charge is derived from particles called protons. In the 1930's, British physicist James Chadwick discovered that the nucleus also contains particles with no electric charge, which he called neutrons.

In the 1960's, two American physicists, Murray Gell-Mann and George Zweig, theorized that neutrons and protons are composed of even smaller particles, which Gell-Mann named quarks. The quarks that make up matter in today's universe are called the up quark and down quark. A proton consists of two up quarks and one down quark, and a neutron is made of two down quarks and an up quark. Quarks carry fractional charges; an up quark has a positive charge of two-thirds, and a down quark carries a negative charge of one-third. Thus, a proton has a positive charge of one and a neutron has no charge at all.

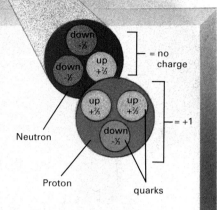

The Standard Model

Quarks fit into an overall theory of matter called the Standard Model. According to the Standard Model, there are two families of matter particles—quarks and leptons—with six members in each family. All matter in the everyday world is made of just four particles: the up quark, the down quark, and two leptons—the electron and the electron neutrino. The other particles are created in high-energy collisions in particle accelerators. The masses of the various particles are expressed in energy units called electronvolts (eV).

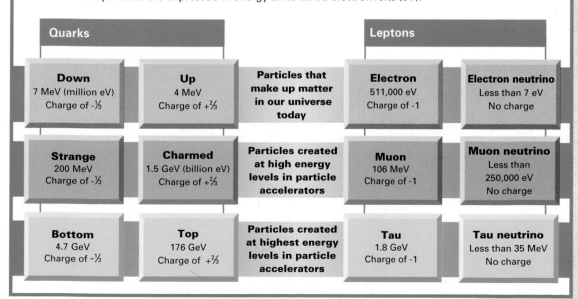

Quarks			Leptons	
Down 7 MeV (million eV) Charge of -⅓	**Up** 4 MeV Charge of +⅔	Particles that make up matter in our universe today	**Electron** 511,000 eV Charge of -1	**Electron neutrino** Less than 7 eV No charge
Strange 200 MeV Charge of -⅓	**Charmed** 1.5 GeV (billion eV) Charge of +⅔	Particles created at high energy levels in particle accelerators	**Muon** 106 MeV Charge of -1	**Muon neutrino** Less than 250,000 eV No charge
Bottom 4.7 GeV Charge of -⅓	**Top** 176 GeV Charge of +⅔	Particles created at highest energy levels in particle accelerators	**Tau** 1.8 GeV Charge of -1	**Tau neutrino** Less than 35 MeV No charge

Zweig, offered a theory that seemed to do just that. They proposed that protons, neutrons, and many of the new particles being created in particle accelerators were composed of combinations of truly fundamental particles that Gell-Mann called *quarks*.

Quarks, according to the theory, had one very unusual property: They were never seen alone, but only in combinations of two or three. Another peculiarity was that they carried electric charges that were a fraction—either $-\frac{1}{3}$ or $+\frac{2}{3}$—of the fundamental unit of electric charge carried by the proton. When quarks combined to make particles, these fractional charges added up to a single positive or negative charge or to no charge at all.

The theory predicted that only three kinds of quarks—called *up, down,* and *strange*—were required to make up all the known subatomic particles. Protons and neutrons were made of up and down quarks. A proton consisted of two up quarks and one down quark; a neutron contained two down quarks and one up quark. The strange quarks were found in several other kinds of heavy particles that are seldom seen in nature but which are often created during high-energy collisions in particle accelerators.

By 1978, high-energy research had created various new particles requiring the existence of a fourth and fifth quark, which were dubbed *charmed* and *bottom.* And the evolving quark theory suggested that quarks come in pairs, so physicists concluded that a sixth quark—the top quark—must also exist.

Fitting quarks into an overall view of matter

The quark theory fit into a larger scheme of matter, the Standard Model. According to the Standard Model, matter is made up of 12 fundamental particles divided equally into two major families, quarks and *leptons.* Leptons, which are thought to be fundamental particles with no smaller parts, include the electron, two heavier versions of the electron, and three uncharged particles called neutrinos. Neutrinos were long thought to be massless, but recent research has indicated that they may possess a tiny amount of mass.

Only the two lightest members of each family—the up and down quarks, and the electron and electron neutrino—play any major role in the universe today. All the heavier quarks and heavier charged leptons have only a momentary existence, because they are highly unstable. These particles can be created in particle accelerators, but they existed in nature in abundance only in the first few moments after the *big bang,* the colossal explosion of matter and energy that astronomers believe gave birth to the universe billions of years ago. When physicists push particle accelerators to higher and higher energies, they are in effect duplicating the conditions of the big bang.

Another kind of matter, known as *antimatter,* is also rarely seen in our world, though it plays a large role in the subatomic realm and is created in profusion in particle accelerators. Antimatter is like regular matter but opposite in electric charge and certain other properties.

Thus, for example, the antimatter equivalent of the proton is the negatively charged antiproton, which is made of three antiquarks. It is a rule of nature that for every particle of matter that comes into existence, an antiparticle must also be created at the same time. It is fortunate for us that antimatter is not found in the everyday world, because when regular matter and antimatter come into contact, they annihilate each other in a burst of pure energy.

In addition to the fundamental building blocks of matter and their antimatter opposites, there are particles called *bosons* that act as "messengers," transmitting the three basic forces that operate in the microworld. One of these messenger particles is the massless photon, or particle of light, which transmits electric and magnetic forces. Another is the gluon, also without mass, which conveys the strong force that binds quarks together in protons and neutrons. And finally, there are three heavy particles—the W^+, W^-, and Z°—that transmit a much weaker force that is responsible for some forms of radioactivity.

The force-carrying messenger particles are emitted by one particle and quickly absorbed by another. Thus, they have only a temporary, fleeting existence. But without them, our world would not be possible. Bosons are the "mortar" that holds together the "bricks," the fundamental building blocks, to form atoms and molecules—and people.

The Standard Model, while bringing order to the subatomic world, is hardly the elegantly simple picture of reality that physicists had been hoping for—not with 12 kinds of bricks and several kinds of mortar. This complexity causes many scientists to believe that the Standard Model is not the ultimate picture of nature we have been seeking. Perhaps, they say, quarks and leptons are not fundamental particles after all but rather are constructed from an even simpler set of building blocks. Other scientists, however, think that quarks and leptons may be as basic as things are going to get. They contend that nature has no obligation to conform to our ideas of how it should be constructed and that its essence may be complexity, not simplicity.

The elusive top quark

For years, the validity of the Standard Model was open to question because the reality of quarks could not be verified. Quarks produced in particle accelerators leave only indirect evidence of their vanishingly brief existence, so it took nearly a decade of experimentation before most physicists accepted quarks as real particles. But by the 1980's, the quark theory was firmly established, and researchers had found convincing evidence for the up, down, charmed, strange, and bottom quarks. The top quark, however, continued to elude them.

What made the top quark so hard to find was its enormous mass, now estimated at 176 GeV. (Because of the equivalence of mass and energy, the mass of a particle is usually expressed as the number of electronvolts needed to create it.) Since the top quark could be produced only in a pair with an antitop quark, more than 350 GeV of energy was required for its creation. Until 1985, no accelerator in the

Success at Fermilab

The discovery of the top quark at Fermilab capped years of hard work in search of the particle. The quest involved hundreds of physicists using some of the largest and most complex scientific equipment in the world.

Finding the top quark

Fermilab researchers discovered the top quark by smashing beams of protons and antiprotons together and examining the collision debris with the aid of the huge electronic detectors.

Collider Detector at Fermilab

Path of antiprotons

Point of proton-antiproton collisions

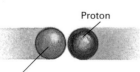

Proton

Antiproton

A proton and antiproton collide after being accelerated in opposite directions to nearly the speed of light (300,000 kilometers [186,000 miles] a second).

The particles annihilate each other, producing a burst of pure energy.

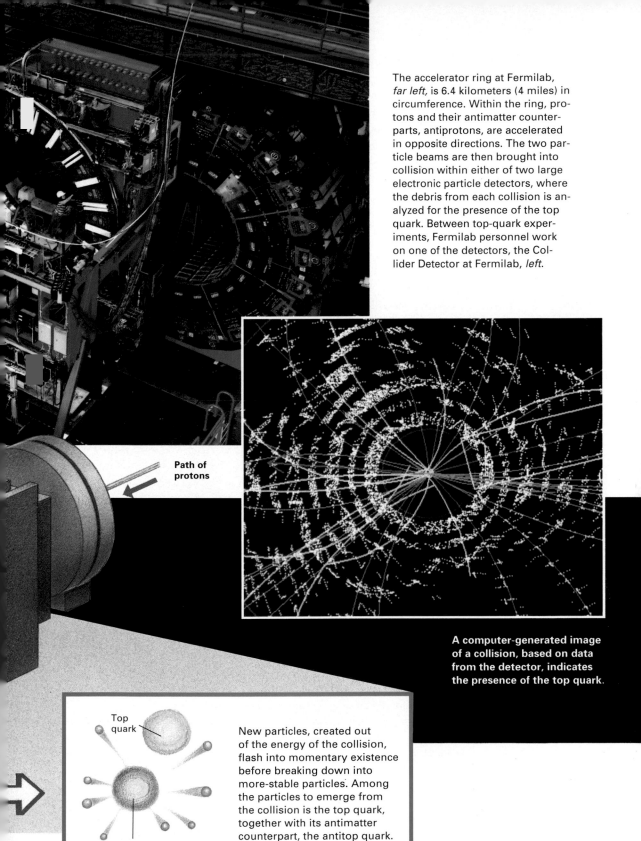

The accelerator ring at Fermilab, *far left*, is 6.4 kilometers (4 miles) in circumference. Within the ring, protons and their antimatter counterparts, antiprotons, are accelerated in opposite directions. The two particle beams are then brought into collision within either of two large electronic particle detectors, where the debris from each collision is analyzed for the presence of the top quark. Between top-quark experiments, Fermilab personnel work on one of the detectors, the Collider Detector at Fermilab, *left*.

Path of protons

A computer-generated image of a collision, based on data from the detector, indicates the presence of the top quark.

Top quark

New particles, created out of the energy of the collision, flash into momentary existence before breaking down into more-stable particles. Among the particles to emerge from the collision is the top quark, together with its antimatter counterpart, the antitop quark.

Antitop quark

world, including the one at Fermilab, was powerful enough to produce such energies. In that year, Fermilab completed modifications to its accelerator ring that changed it from a single-beam accelerator to one that uses two beams of particles—one of protons, the other of antiprotons. The beams are accelerated in opposite directions to just a shade under the speed of light (about 300,000 kilometers [186,000 miles] a second) and then brought to a sharp focus. There, many of the protons and antiprotons collide and disappear in violent flashes of energy.

With 2 trillion electronvolts, the search is on

The alterations enabled Fermilab to achieve an energy of nearly 1 trillion electron volts (TeV, from *tera*, the prefix for trillion) per beam. When the beams collide, their total combined energy—close to 2 TeV—is available for particle creation. With the upgraded machine, named the Tevatron, the search for the top quark could begin.

The production of top quarks was expected to be a very rare event, happening in fewer than 1 collision in a billion. Identifying that 1-in-a-billion occurrence would be no easy task. The Fermilab researchers would have to examine the particle tracks left by countless individual collisions. The track left by a top quark itself would not be visible because the particle (and its antimatter counterpart) would survive for less than a trillionth of a quadrillionth of a second before decaying into other particles, far too short a time for it to emerge from the collision site. Moreover, the particles the top quark breaks up into are themselves highly unstable and short-lived. Only after two more particle decays would particles stable enough to be observed be created. By the end of this complicated chain of events, 20 or so particles would have been generated. Physicists would be looking for particular patterns, or signatures, of particle creation in which the production of a top quark was the most likely initial event.

They would be aided in that task by an impressive array of electronic particle detectors. In modern accelerators, the point where the particle beams collide is surrounded by layers of detectors that produce an electronic signal whenever an electrically charged particle passes through them. These signals go to computers that decide instantaneously whether something noteworthy has happened, and, if so, record all the signals on magnetic tape. Other computers then use the recorded data to reconstruct the paths of the particles and create a detailed image of the debris emerging from the collision.

The Tevatron has two such detector systems. One of them, called the Collider Detector at Fermilab (CDF), was responsible for the data presented in April 1994. The other is known simply as "D-Zero," a code name designating its location along the Tevatron ring. The detectors are huge and expensive devices. The CDF, for example, is the size of a three-story building and contains more than 100,000 individual particle detectors arranged in more than 100 layers.

By the 1990's, scores of Fermilab investigators were occupied with studying the images being generated by the CDF. Calculations showed

The Next Challenge—the Higgs Boson

Imagine holding a large rock in your hand. It would be heavy, and if you dropped it, it would fall to the ground in response to the Earth's gravity. These properties of a rock are due to its mass, and they seem so obvious that we give them no thought. But why matter has mass has long been a mystery to physicists.

Mass is often defined as the quantity of matter in an object, but physicists also think of it as the property that gives things inertia—resistance to being accelerated. Consider that same rock far out in space, away from all gravitational influences. If the rock was at rest, its mass would oppose any force trying to push it into motion. If the rock was already in motion, its mass would cause it to keep moving at the same speed in a straight line and to resist any effort to stop it or change its direction.

In 1905, the noted physicist Albert Einstein discovered that an object without mass must always move at the speed of light (about 300,000 kilometers [186,000 miles] a second), the ultimate velocity in the universe. The massless photon—the transmitter of light and other forms of electromagnetic radiation—moves endlessly at that speed unless absorbed. So do several other massless particles.

Without mass, the universe would be a very boring place. There would be no stars or planets. In fact, there would be no matter at all as we know it because no stable atoms could form. The universe would be nothing but empty space filled with massless particles zipping about at the speed of light.

Mass, as Einstein also discovered, is a form of "frozen" energy. Today, we know that ordinary matter exists because energy was bundled into particles—quarks and electrons—that joined to form atoms. The question is, how was the energy packaged into those particles to give them mass?

Particle physicists now think they know the answer to that question. In the first fiery moments of creation, they theorize, one special kind of particle pulled off the seemingly miraculous feat of collecting and concentrating energy and then fusing with other particles to give them mass.

This hypothetical miracle particle is called the Higgs boson. It is named for the theorist who proposed it, Peter Higgs of Edinburgh University in Scotland. Higgs demonstrated mathematically in 1964 that such a particle could exist. He did not say that its existence was required for the universe to have its present form, but other theorists began to consider that possibility. Today, the Higgs boson plays such an essential role in explaining how forces operate in the microworld that most particle physicists are convinced it must be real.

The vacuum from which the Higgs particle supposedly drew energy to create mass is not the familiar vacuum of outer space that we know today but a much different sort of vacuum that existed when the universe was a tiny fraction of a second old. That vacuum was seething with energy and newly created particles, including Higgs bosons. In a twinkling, with the help of the bosons, swarms of particles with mass came into being.

Although the universe is now cold and no longer filled with high-energy particles, physicists can search for Higgs bosons by approximating the conditions of the early universe. They do that with the aid of particle accelerators, the huge machines they use to smash speeding particles into one another to create new particles. If enough energy could be generated, an occasional Higgs boson might be created. The boson would break apart almost immediately into more-stable particles, but its disintegration would provide an identifiable pattern, or signature, marking its brief existence.

Physicists are not sure just how much energy is needed to create Higgs particles. They think, though, that the now abandoned Superconducting Super Collider (SSC) would have been more than adequate for the job. Without the SSC, searchers for the Higgs boson will have to settle for the Large Hadron Collider (LHC), a less powerful machine slated for construction near Geneva, Switz-

Without the Higgs boson, physicists theorize, our universe of stars and galaxies would not exist, because no atoms could ever have formed.

erland. But few theorists are optimistic about the prospect of producing the Higgs particle in detectable numbers with the LHC.

The Higgs boson is the last remaining undiscovered piece of the Standard Model, the accepted picture of fundamental particles and forces. It is a particle that physicists would dearly love to find. For the present, however, it appears that the Higgs boson will remain on the "hypothetical" list for many years to come. [R. H. M.]

that during one eight-month period, from August 1992 to May 1993, the Tevatron had probably created nearly 100 top quarks. But finding the telltale signatures for that handful of events among the tens of millions of collisions that the CDF had recorded was a difficult task.

Nobody could look at all of the events recorded by the computers—there were simply too many of them. The hunt for top-quark signatures thus began by ordering the computers to sort through the mass of data looking for events with certain desired characteristics. The researchers continued to narrow the sample of possible signatures until they arrived at a few "gold-plated" candidates for the top-quark.

Actually, the hardest part of the search was not identifying the best signatures but showing that those signatures were indeed caused by the top quark. Some sequences of particle decay initiated by other kinds of particles produce signatures very similar to those of the top quark. These "fake" patterns must be ruled out before an event can be accepted as a true top-quark signature.

Separating the fakes from the genuine article is based on probabilities. Physicists might determine, for example, that a certain signature should occur no more than once in 10 million collisions if it is caused by a non top-quark event. If the pattern shows up several times that often, it is more likely to be a top-quark signature than a fake.

Tentative success, and then certainty

By October 1993, two Fermilab teams working with the CDF had found three different signatures that they felt were reasonably likely to have resulted from the top quark. However, there were too few examples of any one of the signatures for the results to be conclusive. Together, the two teams had found 12 possible top-quark events. Calculations showed that about four of those should be fakes, indicating that eight were true top-quark signatures. But because the probabilities of the fake-event rates were somewhat uncertain, the physicists could not say with complete confidence that the events were not all fake.

Under normal circumstances, the CDF researchers would have opted to wait for more convincing data before making an announcement. But in early 1994, it looked like it might take another year or two before a convincing case could be made for the top quark. In the meantime, news of the 12 top-quark candidates was spreading through computer networks to particle physicists around the world. The Fermilab experimenters therefore decided to combine the data compiled by the two CDF teams into a single report that was then subjected to an intensive review by all of those involved with the research. In the end, 399 members of the Fermilab group decided that the results were solid enough to risk putting their names on the report.

Despite the uncertainty, most physicists accepted the Fermilab findings as "probably real." And further data from the Tevatron supported the earlier evidence. By the end of 1994, CDF researchers and a team using the D-Zero detector were finding additional signatures that were most likely due to the top quark, and the D-Zero investigators had submitted their own paper confirming the CDF results. In early 1995, still more signatures were found with both detectors. In March, Fermilab held another press conference, this time to announce that the top quark had definitely been discovered.

The confirmation of the top quark was a triumph for particle physicists. But by filling in the final blank in the Standard Model's list of particles, they were left with little more to do. In a field that has been based on moving ever forward to new and deeper levels of understanding, coming to the end of the frontier was for particle physicists a frustrating situation.

The SSC, which would have accelerated two proton beams to energies of about 20 TeV, had been designed to break particle physics out of that impasse. For physicists who continued to dream of a few "ultimate" particles from which all others are made, the SSC provided the hope of finding evidence that both quarks and leptons are constructed of smaller, simpler parts. Aside from that quest, a primary mission of the SSC was to find one final piece of the Standard Model, a messenger particle called the Higgs boson that physicists think endows other particles with mass. (See THE NEXT CHALLENGE—THE HIGGS BOSON.)

With the demise of the SSC, the search for the Higgs boson and for ultimate building blocks will most likely shift to Europe. The European Laboratory for Particle Physics (CERN) near Geneva, Switzerland, is planning to build a particle accelerator called the Large Hadron Collider (LHC), a proton-proton collider that initially will generate beam energies of about 5 TeV and may eventually reach 7 TeV. (Hadrons include any particles made of quarks.) For a while, it appeared that the LHC, too, might be axed, because several of the 19 CERN member nations were balking at paying for the expensive facility. But in January 1995, the project got the go-ahead.

For physicists who were gearing up to work at the SSC, the LHC was a decided comedown. It may not generate enough energy to produce significant numbers of Higgs particles, and in any event it will not be ready before the year 2003. Particle physicists say that, given such prospects, it is getting harder and harder to attract promising young people to the field. Other areas of physics, such as astrophysics and laser optics, appear to be "where the action is." It is possible that after a highly productive 60-year reign on the forefront of physics, particle accelerators may finally be put to rest. Finding the top quark may prove to be one of their final triumphs.

For further reading:

Cashmore, Roger, and Sutton, Christine. "The Origin of Mass." *New Scientist*, April 18, 1992, pp. 35-39.

Close, Frank. *The Cosmic Onion: Quarks and the Nature of the Universe.* Heinemann Educational Books, 1983.

Lederman, Leon, and Teresi, Dick. *The God Particle.* Houghton Mifflin, 1992.

Weinberg, Steven. *The First Three Minutes: A Modern View of the Origin of the Universe.* Basic Books, 1988.

The Radiation Question

BY LEN ACKLAND

Scientists have learned a great deal about ionizing radiation since the beginning of the Atomic Age 50 years ago. But uncertainties remain about the health effects of low doses.

I n April 1945, four months before the Atomic Age began with the dropping of two atomic bombs on Japan, a group of American scientists began a secret government experiment to determine how nuclear radiation affects the human body. Over a two-year period, the scientists injected 18 patients who had life-threatening illnesses with small amounts of plutonium, one of the radioactive elements used to make the atomic bombs, and watched to see what effects this caused. The details of the study remained a secret until 1993, when this and other stories of government-sponsored radiation experiments—some of which are considered highly unethical—began to appear in the press. In early 1995, a special presidential committee reported that between 1945 and 1975, at least 9,000 people had been subjects in such experiments.

These radiation experiments and the bombs exploded over Hiroshima and Nagasaki 50 years ago illustrate two extremes of the dangers posed by radiation. One extreme is that certain radioactive material can be made into atomic bombs that cause tremendous destruction instantaneously. The other extreme involves long-term exposure to small amounts of radioactivity, such as that experienced by workers at a nuclear power plant.

The most obvious damage from a nuclear explosion comes from the initial blast and the resulting fire. But a more subtle danger comes

The author:
Len Ackland is director of the Center for Environmental Journalism at the University of Colorado at Boulder.

from the release of a particular kind of energy known as ionizing radiation. This form of energy gets its name from its ability to turn ordinary atoms into electrically charged particles called ions. Ions are highly reactive and capable of interfering with the natural chemical processes in living things. A large amount of ionizing radiation, such as that released by an atomic bomb, can kill people within a matter of days or weeks, depending on the size of the dose. In smaller quantities, such as those used in many of the radiation experiments, ionizing radiation may cause cancer and other health problems that appear years after people have been exposed.

In 1945, scientists knew relatively little about the effects of ionizing radiation on human beings, and the effort to better identify the risks led government researchers to conduct the radiation experiments. Since the 1940's, medical researchers have completed numerous reputable studies, some with animals and others examining the health of Japanese bomb survivors and workers in the nuclear industry. As a consequence, researchers have gained a good understanding of the health effects of large amounts of ionizing radiation, whether produced by atomic bombs or by nuclear accidents such as the one in 1986 at the Chernobyl nuclear power plant in the former Soviet Union's Ukrainian Republic.

But considerable uncertainty still exists about the effects of lower doses of ionizing radiation. This uncertainty has fueled public concerns over the safety of medical and dental X rays and the potential health risks of living near nuclear power stations or nuclear weapons plants. Unfortunately, experts say that the debate over the long-term health effects of low-level radiation may continue for years to come.

The release of ionizing radiation is intimately tied to the structure of the atom, a subject that scientists began to understand in the late 1800's. The first type of ionizing radiation was discovered in 1895, when German physicist Wilhelm C. Roentgen found that streams of electrons from a *cathode* (negatively charged electrode) in a vacuum tube produced mysterious, invisible rays when they struck the metal plate at the opposite end of the tube. He found that the rays could pass through such materials as paper and skin but could not penetrate bone, metal, or other dense substances. He also found that the rays could darken a photographic plate and could be used to photograph bone structure. Unable to explain these rays, Roentgen dubbed them *X rays*. Over the next decade evidence accumulated to show that X rays are electromagnetic radiation, like visible light or radio waves, but with a much shorter wavelength.

In 1896, just months after Roentgen's discovery, French physicist Henri A. Becquerel found that uranium ore also emitted invisible rays. By the end of 1898, French physicist Marie Curie had coined the term *radioactivity* to describe this spontaneously emitted radiation. She and her husband Pierre later discovered radium, an element much more radioactive than uranium.

While the Curies learned much about the properties of radioactivity, its precise origin remained a mystery until scientists learned more about the structure of the atom in the 1900's. Atoms are the basic building blocks of chemical elements. Every atom contains a *nucleus* (core) made of positively charged particles called protons and particles called neutrons, which have no charge. Surrounding the nucleus are negatively charged particles called electrons.

The Earth contains 92 naturally occurring elements—from hydrogen, with one proton and one electron, to uranium, with 92 protons and 92 electrons. All atoms of a single element have the same number of protons in the nucleus. Atoms with the same number of protons but different numbers of neutrons are called *isotopes* of the element. For example, one isotope of uranium, designated Uranium-238, has 92 protons and 146 neutrons in its nucleus, while the isotope Uranium-235 has 92 protons and 143 neutrons. The number of neutrons does not affect the atom's chemical properties, but it may make the nucleus unstable. The nuclei of unstable isotopes approach stability by spontaneously emitting radiation until a stable isotope is produced.

We now know that this so-called radioactive decay produces three major types of ionizing radiation with different degrees of penetrating power. The types of radiation given off are called alpha, beta, and gamma. Although these phenomena display properties of both particles and waves, alpha and beta radiation are typically described as particles and gamma radiation as waves.

An alpha particle consists of two protons and two neutrons. These relatively massive particles are too bulky to penetrate deeply into solid materials. A typical alpha particle travels less than 5 centimeters (2 inches) in the air and can be blocked by a barrier as thin as one or two sheets of paper.

Beta particles are electrons or their positively charged counterparts, positrons, emitted from the nucleus when a neutron or a proton undergoes a transformation. Beta particles can penetrate thicker barriers. For example, beta particles typically can penetrate almost 1.3 centimeters (0.5 inch) through wood.

Gamma rays are a high-energy form of electromagnetic radiation, which includes radio waves, visible light, and X rays. Gamma rays usually are emitted from a radioactive nucleus with the emission of alpha or beta particles, but they can also be emitted alone. Gamma rays have more penetrating power than any other kind of naturally occurring radiation. Some are so powerful that a 2.5-centimeter (1-inch) iron plate can stop only about half the gamma rays that strike it.

As scientists were gaining an understanding of the nature of radiation, its affect on living matter was becoming a subject of concern. Shortly after Roentgen discovered X rays, scientists recognized that the rays could cause severe burns, and by 1903, physicians knew that X rays could cause sterilization, cancer, and other damage to organs.

In the 1920's, the deaths of researchers and others heightened con-

Atoms, ions, and ionizing radiation

Ionizing radiation is the name given to high-speed subatomic particles or high-energy waves that can change atoms into electrically charged particles called *ions*. Three kinds of ionizing radiation—alpha particles, beta particles, and gamma rays—come from the nuclei of radioactive atoms. X rays, another type of ionizing radiation, are emitted when fast-moving electrons strike matter. Ionizing radiation has natural as well as artificial sources.

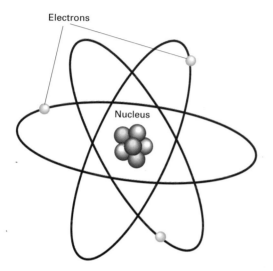

An atom consists of a nucleus surrounded by orbiting electrons. The nucleus contains two types of particles, positively charged protons and neutrons, which have no charge. Electrons carry a negative charge. If the number of orbiting electrons equals the number of positively charged protons in the nucleus, the atom is electrically neutral.

How ions are formed

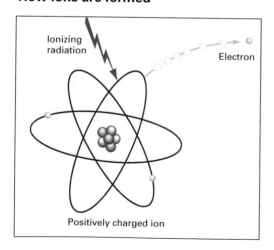

Positively charged ion

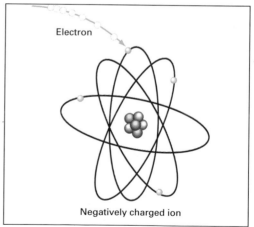

Negatively charged ion

When ionizing radiation strikes a neutral atom, one or more electrons may overcome their attraction to the nucleus and break away. When a negatively charged electron is lost, the atom becomes a positively charged ion.

A freed electron may join an electrically neutral atom. By accepting an additional negatively charged electron, the atom becomes a negative ion.

Types of ionizing radiation

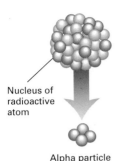

Nucleus of
radioactive
atom

Alpha particle

An alpha particle consists of two protons and two neutrons and is given off by a radioactive atom undergoing a nuclear transformation.

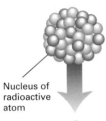

Nucleus of
radioactive
atom

Beta particle

A beta particle is an electron or its positively charged counterpart, the positron. Beta particles are given off by a radioactive atomic nucleus when it undergoes a nuclear transformation.

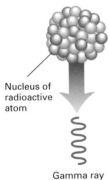

Nucleus of
radioactive
atom

Gamma ray

Gamma rays are high-energy electromagnetic waves, which are released from a radioactive atomic nucleus.

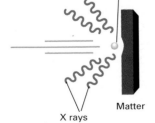

Electron

Matter

X rays

X rays are high-energy electromagnetic waves, which are produced when fast-moving electrons strike matter.

Natural sources of ionizing radiation can be found throughout the environment. One well known source is uranium, *above*, a radioactive metal in the Earth's crust. Other natural sources include radon, a radioactive gas produced by the radioactive decay of uranium, and cosmic rays, high-energy particles from space.

Artificial sources of ionizing radiation include X rays produced by X-ray machines for medical and industrial uses, *above*.

How ionizing radiation damages human cells

Ionizing radiation can cause health problems ranging from skin burns to cancer, and high doses of radiation are quickly fatal. Those effects occur because of the way radiation damages body cells—in particular, the component of cells called DNA (deoxyribonucleic acid), the molecule of which genes are made.

How DNA is damaged

DNA is a complex molecule consisting of two long strands of linked chemical subunits. Ionizing radiation that strikes a cell can damage a DNA molecule directly or indirectly.

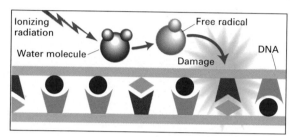

Water, the most abundant molecule in the cell, tends to absorb most of the radiation that strikes a cell. Ionized water molecules may form molecules called *free radicals*, which react readily with other biochemicals in the cell. If a free radical reacts with a DNA molecule, it can damage the DNA.

If ionizing radiation strikes a DNA molecule, it can ionize the molecule and damage it directly.

How the cell responds to DNA damage

In general, DNA can be damaged in three ways: one of the two DNA strands is broken, both strands are broken, or one of the DNA subunits is chemically changed. The cell attempts to repair the damage but is not always successful.

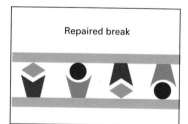

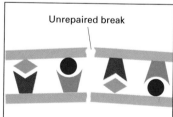

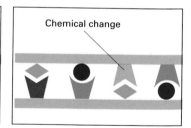

The cell can generally repair a single-strand break in the DNA molecule. Once the genetic material is repaired, the cell functions normally.

The cell usually cannot repair a double-strand break in the DNA molecule. Because the genetic material is severely damaged, the cell dies.

The cell may not repair a chemical change, or mutation, in the DNA. Such mutations may lead to cancer. If the mutation occurs in an egg or sperm cell, the changed genetic information can be passed along to offspring.

cerns about the dangers of exposure to radioactive elements such as radium. The first published report of a death associated with radium appeared in 1924 in New Jersey, involving a female factory worker who had used a radium mixture to paint luminous watch dials. An investigation found that the woman and her co-workers licked the tips of their brushes in order to make finer points for painting tiny numbers on the dials. In the process, they unwittingly swallowed some radium. Nine of the workers developed *radiation sickness*, a collection of symptoms that include nausea, diarrhea, and the destruction of bone marrow, infection-fighting white blood cells, and soft tissues. The nine workers died by the end of 1924. Many others contracted cancer.

At the time of this incident, physicians in Europe linked ionizing radiation to other fatalities. High cancer rates among European uranium miners were traced to radon, a radioactive gas.

Researchers soon learned that the deadly power of ionizing radiation lies in its ability to create ions that disrupt the normal chemical processes in the cell. Whether cells are exposed to ionizing radiation because radioactive atoms have been inhaled or swallowed, or because radiation is entering the body from external sources, such as cosmic rays or radioactive materials in the environment, the effect will be the same.

Cells are most severely injured if the radiation damages the cell's DNA (deoxyribonucleic acid), the complex molecule of which genes are made. Genes are the hereditary units that control the structure and function of the cell. Ionizing radiation, or the ions it creates, can seriously damage the cell's DNA by causing breaks in the molecule or changes in the molecule's chemical structure. The number of breaks increases with the size of the radiation dose.

When the DNA molecule is damaged, three things can happen. If the breakage is severe, the cell may die outright. If the damage is not so great, natural repair mechanisms in the cell may be able to patch up the DNA. The third possibility is that the damage will cause a small chemical change in the molecule, creating a *mutation* (change) in a gene. A mutation could eventually cause the cell to become cancerous. (See also HUNTING FOR CANCER GENES.) If the mutation occurs in the egg or sperm cells, a genetic defect could be passed on to the person's offspring.

The potential of radiation to kill cells, however, has also made ionizing radiation a useful medical treatment for cancer. In radiation therapy, technicians carefully aim a beam of ionizing radiation at the site of a tumor to kill cancer cells in the area. Physicians may also give cancer patients injections or oral doses of radioactive isotopes to kill tumor cells in a specific tissue. For example, a radioisotope of iodine, which accumulates in the thyroid, can be used to kill cancer cells in the thyroid gland.

The growing evidence of radiation's potential to harm cells led to a push for safety standards as early as the 1920's. Despite continuing uncertainty about what constitutes a safe dose, an international congress in 1928 set the first international standard for safe exposure to X rays at a monthly limit of ¹⁄₁₀₀ the amount of X rays that redden the skin.

Radiation doses are often measured in units called sievert or millisievert (thousandths of a sievert). These units measure the amount of radiation absorbed by various tissues and organs and take into account the different biological effects of various types of ionizing radiation. A chest X-ray delivers a dose of about 0.02 millisievert; a dental X ray, about 0.001 millisievert.

In 1931, the annual dose limit was set at what today would be 0.72 sievert. Over the years, the standards for safe exposure levels to radiation were tightened. Today, the International Commission on Radiological Protection, headquartered in Didcot, England, recommends that people receive no more than 1 millisievert annually from artificial sources, such as medical and dental X rays. That figure is 0.6 millisievert less than the average dose a person living in the United States receives annually from artificial sources, according to the National Council on Radiation Protection and Measurements (NCRP).

In addition to artificial sources, there are natural sources of ionizing radiation. On average, U.S. residents receive about 3 millisievert of ionizing radiation from natural sources each year, according to estimates by the NCRP. Radioactive elements are the major natural source of ionizing radiation. The largest single amount—55 percent of the average annual exposure, or 2 millisievert—results from radon in the environment. Some ionizing radiation also comes from cosmic rays.

Estimating safe dosages of radiation is not an easy task. In determining how a dose of radiation is likely to affect the human body, scientists have to take several factors into account. One variable is the *dose rate*,

Radiation doses and effects

Radiation doses are commonly measured in units called millisievert. Doses of 1,000 millisievert or more over the whole body at one time can cause radiation sickness and other serious health effects. Scientists remain uncertain about the long-term health effects of repeated doses of low-level radiation. But on average, a person living in the United States receives only tiny doses of ionizing radiation, less than 4 millisievert per year.

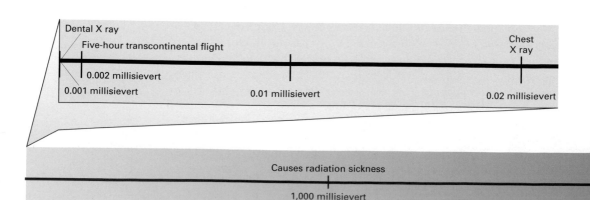

Dental X ray
Five-hour transcontinental flight
Chest X ray
0.002 millisievert
0.001 millisievert
0.01 millisievert
0.02 millisievert

Causes radiation sickness
1,000 millisievert

the rate at which a person receives a certain quantity of radiation. A large dose that would be fatal if delivered all at once could be survivable if spread out over a period of days or weeks, because the body would have an opportunity to repair the damage to vital cells.

A second factor is the part of the body that receives the radiation. Human cells are most susceptible to the deadly effects of radiation when they are replicating, because cells in the process of dividing have little time to repair any DNA damage. Cells that divide rapidly, such as the bone marrow and white blood cells, are thus more sensitive to radiation than the cells of muscle and nerve tissue. Radium, for example, is deadly in part because it is chemically akin to calcium and tends to accumulate in the bones. There, radium nuclei give off alpha particles that destroy the bone marrow, the vital blood-forming tissue.

A third variable is simply the natural biological differences between individuals, which depend upon such factors as a person's age, sex, and general health. Those differences mean that the same radiation dose can affect people in different ways.

Because of all these variables, no one can predict exactly how a person will respond to a certain dose, unless it is very large. And so, researchers describe health effects in terms of probabilities. For example, if a group of people were exposed to 4 sievert over the whole body within a 24-hour period, researchers estimate that without treatment, about 50 percent of the people would die within 30 days. Scientists could not, however, predict exactly which individuals would die.

Researchers also agree that high doses of ionizing radiation received by people during a short time period increase the risk of cancer. The health records of more than 41,000 Japanese survivors of the two atomic bomb attacks have been studied extensively in an effort to better understand the cancer effects.

Although researchers concur that high doses of ionizing radiation to

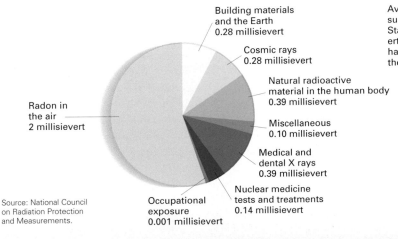

Building materials and the Earth
0.28 millisievert

Cosmic rays
0.28 millisievert

Natural radioactive material in the human body
0.39 millisievert

Miscellaneous
0.10 millisievert

Medical and dental X rays
0.39 millisievert

Nuclear medicine tests and treatments
0.14 millisievert

Occupational exposure
0.001 millisievert

Radon in the air
2 millisievert

Average annual radiation exposure for a resident of the United States totals about 3.6 millisievert from all sources. More than half of this amount comes from the radioactive gas radon.

Source: National Council on Radiation Protection and Measurements.

Causes sterility in females

Causes sterility in males

Average lethal dose without treatment

2,500 millisievert

3,500 millisievert

4,000 millisievert

Source: Hall, E. J. *Radiobiology for the Radiologist.* 4th ed. Lippencott, 1994.

an entire body can be deadly, scientists disagree about the effects of low doses. Many experts believe that a dose threshold exists, below which the effect of the radiation is insignificant. They also believe that the higher the radiation dose, the higher the risk of cancer—a result evident among the Japanese survivors who received high or medium doses of radiation.

But a growing number of other researchers argue that any dose of ionizing radiation is potentially harmful, and a few propose that low doses over long time periods actually produce more cancer than a single high dose. According to this theory, high—but survivable—doses of radiation will quickly kill cells, which are then expelled from the body. But low doses over time can lead to genetic mutations that may eventually cause cancer. And as the length of time the person is exposed to the low doses increases, so will the risk that one or more cells will develop a cancer-causing mutation.

The latest comprehensive scientific overviews of this issue have been a 1990 report by the U.S. National Research Council's Committee on the Biological Effects of Ionizing Radiations (BEIR) and the 1993 report by the United Nations Scientific Committee on the Effects of Atomic Radiation. Both studies note that in many countries, including the United States, the lifetime probability of dying of cancer is about 20 percent, or about 1 chance in 5. The BEIR report also estimated the additional risk of cancer for people exposed to a moderate dose of radiation and concluded that people exposed to an instantaneous, whole-body dose of 0.1 sievert of ionizing radiation have a 1 in 125 chance of developing cancer from the dose.

In arriving at that estimate, the BEIR report stressed the uncertainty in the calculations, noting that the causes and development of radiation-induced cancer are complex and not well understood. To make the data even murkier, radiation-induced cancers cannot be distinguished from cancers caused by other factors.

The BEIR and the UN reports, like many others, used calculations based on the health records of Japanese atomic bomb survivors to estimate the effects of much smaller doses spread out over a much longer period of time. A potential flaw of that approach was pointed out in an October 1992 report by scientists at Lawrence Livermore National Laboratory in New Mexico. The New Mexico scientists argued that studies of atomic-bomb survivors had underestimated the amount of radiation the people had received, and, as a result, the cancers among the survivors were caused by higher doses than previously calculated. This report suggests that current safety standards based on the Japanese survivor data are overly stringent.

The opposite view is represented by British researcher Alice Stewart of the University of Birmingham, who studied death records of 7,342 people who worked at the Hanford nuclear weapons plant in Washington state between 1944 and 1978. Those workers had received radiation exposures below the occupational safety standard, which was 150 millisievert per year until 1956 and 50 millisievert per year thereafter. Of the total, 1,732 of the workers died of cancer by 1987. Stewart's statistical analysis indicated that about 3 percent of those cancer deaths resulted from occupational radiation exposure. Her results, which were published in March 1993, suggest that safety standards for low-dose radiation are not stringent enough. Some scientists have disputed Stewart's statistical method, however.

These two studies illustrate the contradictory conclusions that have been drawn for decades in studies of the health effects of low-level ionizing radiation. Better answers may come as scientists in western Russia gather data on the health of people living near the Mayak plutonium production plant in the southern Ural Mountains. A series of radiation releases in the 1950's and 1960's contaminated the surrounding area, where more than 400,000 people lived. Russian researchers hope to determine whether and how the residents' chronic exposure has affected their health.

Such studies may help solve the central mystery about the biological effects of ionizing radiation: Is there a dose limit below which the risk to the human body is acceptable? Until a definitive answer is found, many experts believe that the exposure safety standards for radiation workers and the general public will contain a high degree of guesswork.

For further reading:

Caufield, Catherine. *Multiple Exposures: Chronicles of the Radiation Age.* University of Chicago Press, 1990.

Milne, Lorus J., and Margery Milne. *Understanding Radioactivity.* Macmillan Children's Book Group, 1989.

Pochin, Edward Eric. *Nuclear Radiation: Risks and Benefits.* Oxford University Press, 1983.

Welsome, Eileen. "The Plutonium Experiment," *Albuquerque Tribune* series, Nov. 15-17, 1993.

ADD
TREES HERE

FERTILIZE
THE OCEAN

ADD CLOUDS HERE

PLUG
OZONE HOLE

Engineering the Globe: A Fix for the Environment?

Scientists have proposed huge "geoengineering" projects to battle ozone depletion and global warming. But ecologists warn that the schemes carry dangerous risks.

BY YVONNE BASKIN

In October 1993, a group of marine biologists and other scientists tried to make the surface of the Pacific Ocean bloom. In an unprecedented experiment about 500 kilometers (310 miles) south of the Galápagos Islands, the research ship *Columbus Iselin* zigzagged across a square plot of ocean 8 kilometers (5 miles) on each side, dripping a dilute iron solution into the ship's wake. Within hours, algae in the patch began to grow faster. The 40 scientists aboard appeared to have solved a long-standing puzzle: Why do algae grow so poorly in these sunny, nutrient-rich waters? The answer seemed to be that the plants lacked enough iron, a mineral important for cell growth.

But these early results worried some of the scientists. The experiment carried uncomfortable implications for the future of a concept known as *geoengineering*—purposefully changing the global environment. Fertilizing the oceans with iron was one of a growing list of dramatic geoengineering proposals gaining serious scientific attention in the 1980's and early 1990's to cancel out the unintended effects of human pollution.

The *Columbus Iselin* experiment was launched as a test after scientists proposed adding iron to millions of square kilometers of the ocean in order to create giant algal blooms. The experts believed that through the process of *photosynthesis*—in which plants use sunlight, water, and carbon dioxide to make food—the algal blooms would take in some of the millions of tons of carbon dioxide that spew into the atmosphere during the combustion of *fossil fuels* (coal, oil, and natural gas). Be-

The author:
Yvonne Baskin is a free-lance science writer.

cause carbon dioxide is a heat-trapping greenhouse gas, many scientists believe that carbon dioxide pollution will eventually lead to *global warming*, a rise in Earth's average surface temperature that could adversely affect people around the world.

Other geoengineering schemes to combat global warming are more fanciful—placing giant mirrors in orbit, shading the atmosphere with an umbrella of dust, or creating artificial clouds. And some projects would attempt to destroy chlorofluorocarbons (CFC's), the gaseous compounds that are destroying part of the protective ozone layer in the upper atmosphere.

Troubling ecological questions

Yet most scientists and policymakers remain greatly troubled by the notion of tinkering with the environment on such a grand scale, especially when the results are largely unpredictable. Many scientists feel that tampering with the environment without fully understanding the possible consequences is dangerous and scientifically unsound. To those experts, the *Columbus Iselin* cruise raised deeply troubling questions. If the test was successful, would it lead to a rush to try a much larger experiment, one that might have unpredicted consequences? For example, would a large-scale algae bloom cause havoc in the ocean ecosystem by allowing some organisms to thrive at the expense of others? And as the growing algae took in vast amounts of carbon dioxide, would the loss of heat-trapping gases in the atmosphere change Earth's climate, creating unforeseen environmental problems?

Thus, many scientists aboard the *Columbus Iselin* sighed with relief when the algal bloom stopped growing only three days after the iron was added to the water, capturing a mere 10 percent of the extra carbon dioxide they had initially predicted it might. It is unlikely that there will be pressure to try this as a geoengineering project on a large scale anytime soon.

Nevertheless, an increasing number of scientists in the mid-1990's say they feel uneasily obligated to explore the feasibility of other geoengineering projects, because our pollution problems may otherwise continue unchecked. An obvious way to lessen the threat of global warming is to cut back on the use of fossil fuels. But doing that quickly requires changing lifestyles and industrial practices. Such changes may be costly and disruptive, and thus far, policymakers in most nations have resisted asking citizens to make economic sacrifices to head off what they perceive as a distant threat. In developing nations, the situation is different, but the effect is the same. Many people resent being told to slow their economic development to help fix environmental problems caused largely by the heavy use of fossil fuels in industrial nations. Finally, some scientists believe that even if some nations cut fossil fuel use, Earth's rapidly growing population will make it impossible for the overall use of fossil fuels to decline.

Bold proposals for deliberately modifying Earth's climate are nothing new. Around 1960, Russian geographer Nikolai Rusin, in a pam-

Chlorofluorocarbons (CFC's): Synthetic gases that contain chlorine, fluorine, and carbon atoms. The gases are used in refrigerating and air conditioning systems, as cleaning solutions in electronics plants, and to make plastic foams. Chemical reactions with CFC's in the stratosphere destroy ozone molecules.

Global warming: A predicted rise in Earth's average surface temperature due to a buildup of heat-trapping gases in the atmosphere.

Geoengineering: Large-scale engineering projects designed to counter the global effects of pollution.

The greenhouse effect: Warming of Earth's atmosphere as a result of gases that trap heat energy radiating from the Earth's surface. Most greenhouse warming comes from gases with natural sources—water vapor, carbon dioxide, methane, and clouds. But burning coal, oil, and natural gas also releases carbon dioxide, and chlorofluorocarbons (CFC's) also trap heat. An enhanced greenhouse effect is predicted to lead to global warming.

Ozone: A molecule made up of three oxygen atoms. In the stratosphere, ozone molecules protect life on Earth by absorbing much of the sun's damaging ultraviolet radiation.

Photosynthesis: The process by which plants create food. During photosynthesis, plants combine carbon dioxide, water, and sunlight to form sugar. In the process, they release oxygen.

Phytoplankton. Microscopic marine organisms and photosynthetic bacteria that form the base for much of the oceans' food chain.

The global warming problem

Most geoengineering projects were designed to combat *global warming,* a projected rise in Earth's average surface temperature. Global warming may occur because human activities are increasing the amount of heat-trapping gases in the atmosphere.

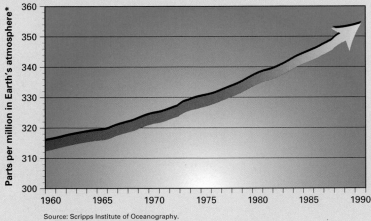

Source: Scripps Institute of Oceanography.
*One part per million equals 0.0001 percent.

Levels of the heat-trapping gas carbon dioxide have been increasing steadily since 1960. The increase is due largely to the combustion of *fossil fuels* (coal, oil, and natural gas).

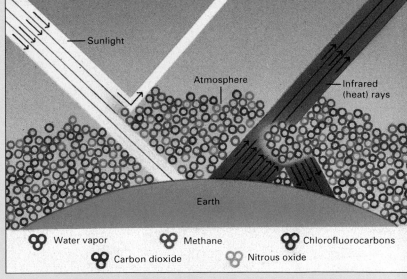

A lake bed lies exposed as the result of a severe drought, *above.* Such droughts may become more common in some parts of the world if global warming occurs. Other areas may become wetter, scientists say, as the warming changes worldwide climate patterns.

Rising carbon dioxide levels are a concern because of the *greenhouse effect,* the process by which heat-trapping gases allow most of the sunlight that reaches Earth to enter the atmosphere and trap some of the *infrared* (heat) rays coming from Earth's surface. The heat-trapping gases include carbon dioxide, methane, water vapor, nitrous oxide, and chlorofluorocarbons (CFC's), which are better known for their role in ozone destruction. The greenhouse effect makes Earth warm enough to support life, but excess heat-trapping gases from human activities may lead to global warming.

Searching for solutions to global warming

Scientists have proposed several schemes to counter global warming, ranging from planting vast tree farms to dumping iron into the oceans. The proposals are highly controversial, because experts fear they may have un-known—possibly disastrous—ecological effects. Another concern is that the possibility of a "quick fix" may divert attention from efforts to avoid global warming by reducing carbon dioxide pollution.

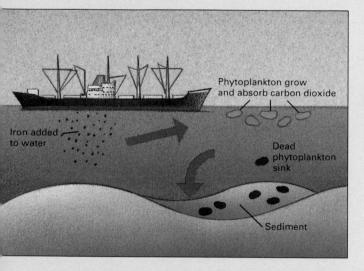

Phytoplankton grow and absorb carbon dioxide

Iron added to water

Dead phytoplankton sink

Sediment

One geoengineering proposal involves stimulating the growth of marine plants by dumping large amounts of iron—a plant nutrient—into the ocean. Marine organisms, such as phytoplankton and seaweed, absorb carbon dioxide during *photosynthesis,* the process in which green plants harness the energy of sunlight to make food. According to one scientific theory, the added iron would boost phytoplankton growth, and the marine organisms would pull more carbon dioxide from the atmosphere. As the plants died, they would sink to the bottom and eventually harden into limestone sediments.

A scientist aboard the research vessel *Columbus Iselin* prepares iron sulfate, *top,* to be added to the Pacific Ocean in a 1993 attempt to test the ocean fertilization theory. Scientists on the ship prepare a device to measure iron concentrations in the water, *above.* The researchers found that most of the iron clumped up and sank before causing much phytoplankton growth.

A worker tends to a sapling in a tree farm in Nepal. Such farms could be planted on a global scale to reduce carbon dioxide levels, according to a relatively uncomplicated geoengineering proposal. The millions of new trees would absorb carbon dioxide from the atmosphere during photosynthesis. The excess carbon would remain in their tissues so long as the trees were not allowed to burn or decay.

Releasing soot, dust, or other particles into the atmosphere could reduce global warming by creating sunlight-blocking haze or clouds, according to some scientists. Burning sulfur in shipboard incinerators would produce airborne particles that water vapor would condense around to form clouds. Another proposal is to tune jet engines to burn less efficiently in order to release soot into the atmosphere.

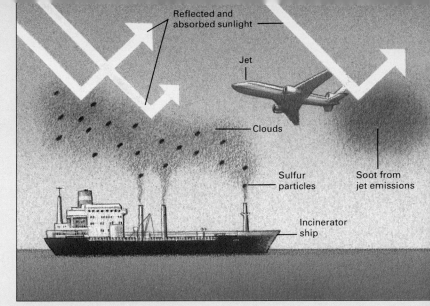

Reflected and absorbed sunlight

Jet

Clouds

Sulfur particles

Soot from jet emissions

Incinerator ship

Benefits and drawbacks of geoengineering proposals to counter global warming

Proposal	Benefits	Drawbacks
Planting trees.	Trees farms could help slow global warming by absorbing carbon dioxide from Earth's atmosphere. Once grown, the trees could provide fuel for electric power plants that would otherwise use coal.	Massive amounts of land would be required to plant enough trees to be effective. Many tree farms would need irrigation and fertilization, which might deplete scarce water supplies and increase pollution. Importing fast-growing but nonnative tree species may also attract nonnative insects or other life that could disrupt the native ecosystem.
Stimulating phytoplankton growth by dumping iron into the oceans.	More phytoplankton could help slow global warming as some carbon dioxide from Earth's atmosphere is absorbed by plants that eventually sink to the sea floor.	The plan would require fertilizing a huge area of ocean, and the effect would probably not last long. Excess phytoplankton growth would likely disrupt the ocean food chain or cause other harmful effects. Bacteria feeding on dead phytoplankton might remove large amounts of oxygen from the water.
Adding soot or dust to the atmosphere.	The soot or dust could help slow global warming by blocking some sunlight.	The effect would not last long and the dust would require constant resupply. Dust particles in the atmosphere might provide additional surfaces for ozone-destroying chemical reactions, leading to greater ozone depletion. The effect would not be uniform around the globe.
Launching sun shields into the atmosphere.	The shields could help slow global warming by blocking some sunlight.	To be effective, the shields would be so large that they would be very expensive, difficult to launch, and difficult or impossible to control.
Adding sulfur particles to the air above the oceans to increase cloud formation there.	The particles could help slow global warming as the new clouds block and reflect some sunlight.	The sulfur particles might wash back to Earth in the form of acid rain, killing marine life and harming plants. The effect would not be uniform around the globe.

phlet called *Man vs. Climate,* discussed the possibility of suspending a ring of tiny white particles around the Earth to direct more sunlight toward the poles, melting the frozen tundras of Siberia and Canada in order to allow more human development there. In the late 1970's, after scientists had begun to worry about carbon dioxide buildup, Russian climatologist Mikhail Budyko suggested creating a planetary sun screen made of aerosols that could reflect enough sunlight back into space to avoid a large greenhouse effect.

Geoengineering proposals received little serious attention until the late 1980's, when policymakers began to take a hard look at ways to halt the threat of global warming. By 1992, the U.S. National Academy of Sciences (NAS) convened a group of top scientists to advise the federal government on science issues. They released a report entitled *Policy Implications of Greenhouse Warming.* In the view of these scientists, geoengineering could not be automatically dismissed as an option for preventing a global warming.

Planting trees to counter global warming?

The proposed engineering fixes for greenhouse warming involve one of two basic strategies. The first is to capture carbon emissions and lock them away in long-term storage, thus preventing a potentially dangerous carbon dioxide buildup in the atmosphere. Almost all proposals in this category rely on the unique ability of green plants to take carbon dioxide from the air and, through the process of photosynthesis, store the carbon in leaves, roots, and stems. The storage is only temporary, however, because when plant matter decays, carbon dioxide returns to the atmosphere. Grasses, flowers, and tree leaves die and fall in a short time, quickly cycling their stored carbon back to the air. But the trunks, limbs, and roots of trees can hold carbon for decades or even centuries—until the trees die and decompose or until people cut them down and burn them.

Thus, the least controversial geoengineering scheme is simply to plant more trees. As a group, plants already contain three times more carbon than the atmosphere, and 90 percent of that carbon is locked up in trees. Although the United States has lost one-fourth of its tree cover since European colonists arrived, enough trees remain and enough new ones are planted each year that U.S. forests annually absorb more carbon dioxide than they release. But studies show they could capture more.

In 1990, U.S. Forest Service researchers released a detailed analysis of how much U.S. land could support additional trees. They concluded that if the nation made a massive commitment to plant forests on marginally productive farmland, the resulting tree cover could absorb more than 56 percent of the nation's carbon emissions. Two years later, the NAS took a more conservative approach, estimating that reforesting could help absorb about 10 percent of U.S. carbon emissions. Even that would require 28 million hectares of trees, about 3.6 percent of the land area of the contiguous states.

Geochemist Gregg Marland of Oak Ridge National Laboratory in Oak Ridge, Tenn., who served on the NAS panel, notes that many scientists now regard tree farming, coupled with reducing the destruction of existing forests, as possibly one of the most effective geoengineering proposals. In tree farming, also called tree harvesting, growers plant trees, which are eventually cut down and burned as fuel in electric power plants that would otherwise burn coal. Although the trees give off carbon dioxide when they burn, the trees planted as replacements can absorb much of that carbon as they grow. Electric utilities and other energy users would harvest, burn, and replant trees in a continuous cycle, leaving coal and its fossil carbon stored underground forever.

Fertilizing the ocean and other schemes

Fertilizing the ocean was a much more controversial proposal for removing carbon dioxide from the atmosphere, though based on the same logic. Algae do not live for decades as trees do, but when algae die, they sink and dissolve in deeper water or are eaten by other microscopic organisms. Some dead algae may reach the sea floor to become buried in layers of sediment. In any case, some of the carbon-containing plant matter never releases its carbon back into the air. Interestingly, about 20 percent of the world's oceans, especially the far North Pacific and the Antarctic seas, lack the expected amount of plant life. In 1984, three different groups of scientists concluded that if algae in these ocean regions were to bloom lushly enough to use up the available nutrients, the algae would cause atmospheric carbon dioxide levels to fall to those seen during the last Ice Age, when glaciers covered much of the Northern Hemisphere. Other scientists found the idea far-fetched.

In 1988, marine biologist John H. Martin of Moss Landing Marine Laboratories in Moss Landing, Calif., proposed a way to make the algae bloom. He hypothesized that the sluggish growth was due to lack of iron. When Martin added iron to algae growing in large bottles in the laboratory, the amount of algae increased by 10-fold. Martin theorized that during the ice ages, dust blowing from the dry, windswept continents had sprinkled the oceans with trace amounts of iron, which triggered the growth of algae and in turn reduced atmospheric carbon dioxide levels. In 1988, Martin half-joked: "Give me half a tanker of iron, and I'll give you an ice age." The statement triggered an uproar, yet the iron hypothesis itself was intriguing enough to make oceanographers push for the open-ocean test that took place in 1993.

Martin died five months before the ship sailed, but marine biologist Richard T. Barber, chief scientist on the *Columbus Iselin* cruise, said that most of those aboard regarded the results as a victory for Martin's iron hypothesis but evidence that ocean fertilization is not likely to be a quick fix for global warming. Two things happened that Martin's laboratory experiments could not predict: one, the iron clumped up and sank to a depth of about 30 meters (100 feet); and two, tiny grazing marine animals feasted on the algae and kept their bloom in check.

Thus it was mostly iron, not carbon, that sank below the surface.

More advanced ideas for using plants to cleanse the air of carbon dioxide appeared in Japan in the early 1990's. In 1995, scientists at Japan's Ministry of International Trade and Industry were involved in a $48-million research effort to investigate ways to increase the air-cleaning abilities of plants. One project aims to create drought-resistant plants by altering the plants' genes, the hereditary material that controls an organism's structure and function. Japanese genetic engineers believe that if drought-resistant plants could thrive in desertlike environments, they would provide an additional carbon dioxide reservoir in regions of sparse plant life. Another Japanese project aims to insert modified genes into plants to increase their carbon dioxide use.

A different approach: Blocking sunlight

The second major group of geoengineering proposals to counteract global warming would adopt a different strategy: shading Earth from incoming sunlight so there will be less heat for greenhouse gases to trap. The NAS committee estimated that blocking out only 1 percent of incoming sunlight could cancel the climate warming caused by doubling the carbon dioxide concentrations in the atmosphere.

Perhaps the simplest way to block sunlight is to bounce it back into space by increasing the *albedo* (reflectivity) of the Earth. That could be accomplished by painting roofs and other structures white. But only a fraction of incoming solar radiation actually reaches the surface, so an increase in albedo would have much more impact if it could be done high in the atmosphere.

Engineers have proposed two schemes for creating reflective sunshades above the Earth. Both plans would place shades in Earth orbit. One shade would use giant mirrors; the other, dust particles. Scientists have already dismissed the idea of a single huge orbiting mirror, because it would have to be thousands of kilometers in area to be effective and would prove impossible to launch and control. A single orbiting mirror would also cast a huge shadow across some regions as it moved around the Earth. Instead, experts say, to counteract the warming caused by a doubling of carbon dioxide emissions, 55,000 smaller reflective screens could be sent into orbit in the high atmosphere. But even these smaller screens would have to be huge—roughly 10 kilometers (6 miles) across—and the NAS panel concluded that launch costs alone would also make this scheme impractical.

Fine dust particles launched into the *stratosphere* (upper atmosphere) could also reflect enough sunlight to cool the Earth by an amount that would offset global warming. By directly reflecting sunlight, the dust would enhance some important but little-understood cooling properties of clouds and haze, which already reflect some incoming sunlight back into space. Indeed, scientists now believe that clouds and haze may account for a puzzling discrepancy between the 0.5 Celsius degree (0.9 Fahrenheit degree) warming Earth has experienced during the 1900's and what most computer climate models predict should have

The ozone depletion problem

Another group of geoengineering proposals address the loss of ozone, a form of oxygen, in Earth's upper atmosphere. The ozone layer helps protect life by absorbing much of the sun's damaging ultraviolet radiation. Ozone loss could increase the incidence of skin cancer and cause other health problems in living things.

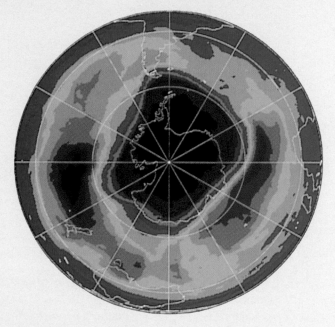

Measurements of ozone above Antarctica show that in 1994, a thinning or hole in the ozone layer had enlarged to a record size. (Dark purple, purple, and blue areas represent the lowest ozone concentrations). CFC's, a class of manufactured chemicals used mainly in refrigerators and air conditioners, are responsible for the ozone destruction. Although most CFC's have been banned, the chemicals remain in the atmosphere for 50 to 100 years, and ozone depletion is expected to continue well into the 2000's.

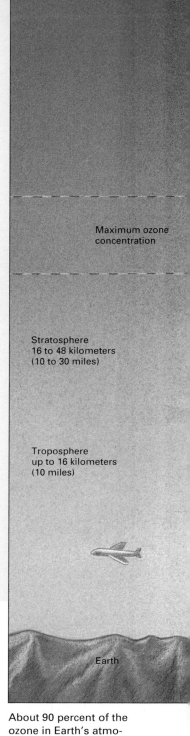

Maximum ozone
concentration

Stratosphere
16 to 48 kilometers
(10 to 30 miles)

Troposphere
up to 16 kilometers
(10 miles)

Earth

About 90 percent of the ozone in Earth's atmosphere is concentrated in a region known as the stratosphere, about 16 to 48 kilometers (10 to 30 miles) above Earth's surface.

happened. Most models, which do not take into account the reflective properties of clouds and haze, calculate that the temperature increase should have been about twice as large.

Volcanic eruptions and certain types of algae in the ocean create natural haze by releasing *sulfate aerosols* (tiny droplets of sulfuric acid) into the atmosphere. Sulfate aerosols cool the Earth in two ways: directly, by creating haze that shades the lower atmosphere, and indirectly, by serving as "seeds" around which water droplets condense to form clouds. More sulfate compounds increase the number of small droplets and help create brighter clouds, causing more incoming sunlight to bounce back into space.

Searching for solutions for ozone depletion

Scientists have proposed few geoengineering schemes to combat the loss of ozone in Earth's upper atmosphere. Most of the ideas have been criticized as unworkable or farfetched.

A project suggested by physicist Alfred Wong of the University of California, Los Angeles involves sending giant, electrified metal screens into the stratosphere. The screens would release electrons that prevent chlorofluorocarbon molecules from destroying ozone. Helium-filled containers would keep the screens aloft, and solar panels would provide the needed electricity.

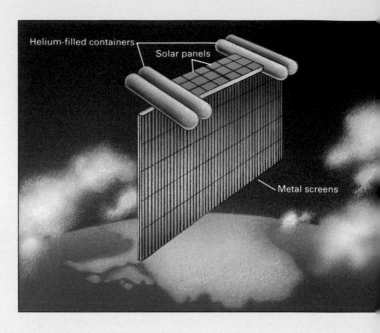

Helium-filled containers

Solar panels

Metal screens

The massive eruption of Mount Pinatubo in the Philippines in 1991 demonstrated how dramatically natural sulfate aerosols can cool Earth. Pinatubo sent up a layer of debris and sulfur-containing gases that formed a cloud in the stratosphere. As the cloud spread around the globe, average world temperatures dropped up to 0.5 Celsius degree —far more than the normal yearly variation of about 0.2 Celsius degree (0.4 Fahrenheit degree). If global warming is truly underway, and if volcanic haze is temporarily masking its effect, then Earth's climate should return to the record-breaking warmth of the 1980's when Pinatubo's dust settles, many scientists believe. Indeed, atmospheric scientists reported in January 1995 that Pinatubo's cooling effect appeared to have ended in 1994. And according to the National Aeronautics and Space Administration's Goddard Institute for Space Studies in New York City, 1994 tied 1987 as the fourth warmest year on record.

But what if human beings replaced some of Pinatubo's debris by spewing dust or sulfate aerosols into the stratosphere on purpose? Scientists calculate that the amount of additional dust needed would be about 1 percent of the amount already being swept into the atmosphere by natural sources. There are numerous proposals for lofting such material: using helium or hydrogen-filled balloons; launching it aboard surplus rockets; or firing dust-filled artillery shells into the stratosphere. Another possibility is simply to dump more soot into the atmosphere by tuning the engines of commercial jets to burn fuel inefficiently at high altitudes, or hiring planes to deliberately foul the sky.

With many cautions attached, the NAS concluded that such schemes

Benefits and drawbacks of geoengineering proposals to counter ozone depletion

Proposal	Benefits	Drawbacks
Sending large electrified metal screens into the upper atmosphere above Antarctica.	Electrons released from the screens would combine with chlorine atoms from CFC's to prevent the atoms from destroying ozone.	The screens might not release enough electrons to be effective.
Adding propane gas to the upper atmosphere above Antarctica.	Propane would react chemically with chlorine atoms and prevent ozone destruction.	Byproducts of the chlorine-propane reactions might produce other molecules that free even more chlorine atoms.
Destroying CFC's in the atmosphere by blasting them with beams from high-powered lasers mounted on mountaintops.	The lasers could eliminate CFC's before the molecules begin to destroy ozone.	Laser technology to shoot CFC molecules out of the sky does not exist yet and will probably require vast amounts of energy.

"appear feasible, economical, and capable of mitigating [reducing] the effect of as much carbon dioxide equivalent per year as we care to pay for." Yet because of the uncertainties surrounding this scheme, the scientists said that the projects should not be attempted.

Clouds reflect sunlight back into space much as dust particles do, and experts estimate that a 4 percent increase in ocean cloud reflectivity could offset the predicted warming caused by a doubling of atmospheric carbon dioxide levels. Scientists believe that the release of sulfate aerosols above the oceans would increase cloud reflectivity there. To artificially engineer this effect would require a fleet of 200 ships equipped with incinerators that would cruise the subtropical seas year-round burning sulfur, the NAS panel found.

Can we plug the ozone hole?

Geoengineering approaches to CFC pollution attempt to attack what some scientists believe is an even more urgent problem—the destruction of Earth's protective ozone layer high above the planet. The protective layer contains a high concentration of ozone molecules, each made of three linked oxygen atoms. By absorbing much of the sun's most damaging ultraviolet radiation, these molecules protect life on Earth. Scientists first discovered evidence of rapid ozone destruction above Antarctica in 1985. CFC's, used mainly in refrigeration and air conditioning systems, cause ozone destruction through a series of reactions in which chlorine atoms freed from the CFC's bind with oxygen. Most industrial nations signed an agreement in 1987 to phase out the manufacture and use of CFC's, and revisions to that agreement banned the manufacture of most CFC's after the end of 1995. However, these gases can persist for as long as 100 years in the atmosphere, which means that ozone levels will be threatened into the late 2000's.

In 1991, atmospheric scientists Ralph Cicerone of the University of California in Irvine and Richard Turco of the University of California in Los Angeles (UCLA) suggested an ozone-saving plan to dump about 45,000 metric tons (50,000 short tons) of propane gas into the atmosphere above Antarctica each spring. The researchers theorized that the propane would react with CFC molecules in such a way that the chlorine would no longer be able to react with ozone. But the two scientists later said that their proposal would harm ozone even more. By-products of the chlorine-propane reactions would produce other molecules that liberated even more chlorine atoms, they said.

Other ideas for reducing CFC's abound, however. Physicist Thomas Stix of Princeton University in Princeton, N.J., has proposed constructing an array of infrared lasers on high mountain passes to blast away at the air, selectively destroying CFC molecules before they reach the stratosphere. Today's lasers are not powerful enough for such a task, however. In May 1994, another UCLA scientist, plasma physicist Alfred Wong, proposed using a fleet of blimps dangling 20 or so gigantic zinc or aluminum screens above the Antarctic. Solar panels would charge the screens with electricity, so that electrons would be released from the metal. The electrons would then combine with the destructive chlorine atoms, turning them into ions that no longer react easily with oxygen. Other physicists have claimed that the screens could not generate enough electrons to be effective, however.

A solution worse than the problem?

The most immediate obstacle to fixing the atmosphere through any geoengineering scheme is that virtually all of the proposals involve "significant missing pieces of scientific understanding," according to the NAS panel. Researchers simply do not understand the workings of the environment well enough to predict the full consequences of any of the plans. For instance, atmospheric scientists cannot say for certain whether schemes to remove carbon dioxide from the atmosphere would harmlessly slow global warming or would instead cause an unintended overcorrection that could plunge Earth into another ice age. Scientists still know so little about clouds and haze, for instance, that precise estimates of the likely extent of a global warming are currently impossible. Estimating how much extra haze and clouds would be necessary to prevent the warming requires making a doubly unreliable calculation. Climate researcher Stephen H. Schneider of Stanford University in Palo Alto, Calif., also points out that a global warming will change the temperature unevenly across the globe and throughout the seasons. So even if a haze screen works, it is likely to leave a spotty pattern of cool and warm patches and climate extremes that in some places might make the solution worse than the problem.

Some geoengineering schemes may also work against each other. The chemical reactions that destroy ozone occur largely on the surface of ice crystals, for instance, and many atmospheric chemists strongly suspect that shooting more dust and sulfate aerosols into the stratosphere will worsen ozone depletion by creating seeds around which ice crystals may form. And emitting more sulfate particles into the clouds most likely means getting them back a week or two later as the sulfuric acid-containing precipitation known as acid rain.

At a more basic level, many people feel that geoengineering violates the belief that deliberate pollution, even to counter unintentional pollution, is wrong. Others fear that politicians and other policymakers will be tempted to do nothing about carbon dioxide emissions if they believe that the problem can eventually be "fixed" by technology.

Policymakers who see geoengineering as an easy way to reverse pollution will nonetheless confront a multitude of political and legal questions. Does a single nation have the right to try altering the global climate? Should an international body like the United Nations set an international geoengineering policy? Could a governing body make the policy last long enough to work? Would dissenting nations have the right to veto a project? And what happens if a geoengineering project goes awry? Would geoengineers be liable for damages caused by any unwanted climate changes, droughts, or floods?

Even with all these issues unresolved, a growing number of scientists say they feel it would be irresponsible not to explore geoengineering options and gather data on their feasibility. Indeed, the NAS panel called for more research to learn about the "likely advantages and disadvantages" of climate engineering. Schneider, who served on the NAS panel, agrees that although geoengineering is not the optimal solution, "as a risk hedger, it would be immoral and unethical not to try to come up with a back door in case the worst happens and we can't get people to wise up in time." If today's climate modelers are correct, it's possible that in 50 years or so, human beings may be grateful for a few well-studied geoengineering fixes.

■ ■ ■

Questions for thought and discussion

Suppose that scientists determine that global warming is occurring and that droughts and storms from climate changes in the next decade will likely devastate farmland throughout Africa, Asia, and the United States. The experts predict, however, that some areas, such as Russia, Scandinavia, and Canada, may benefit from global warming as crop-growing regions shift farther north.

Questions: Under these circumstances, would you favor attempting a geoengineering project? If so, which one? What group or individual should have the authority to decide whether to go forward with the project? How should disagreements on the issue between nations be handled?

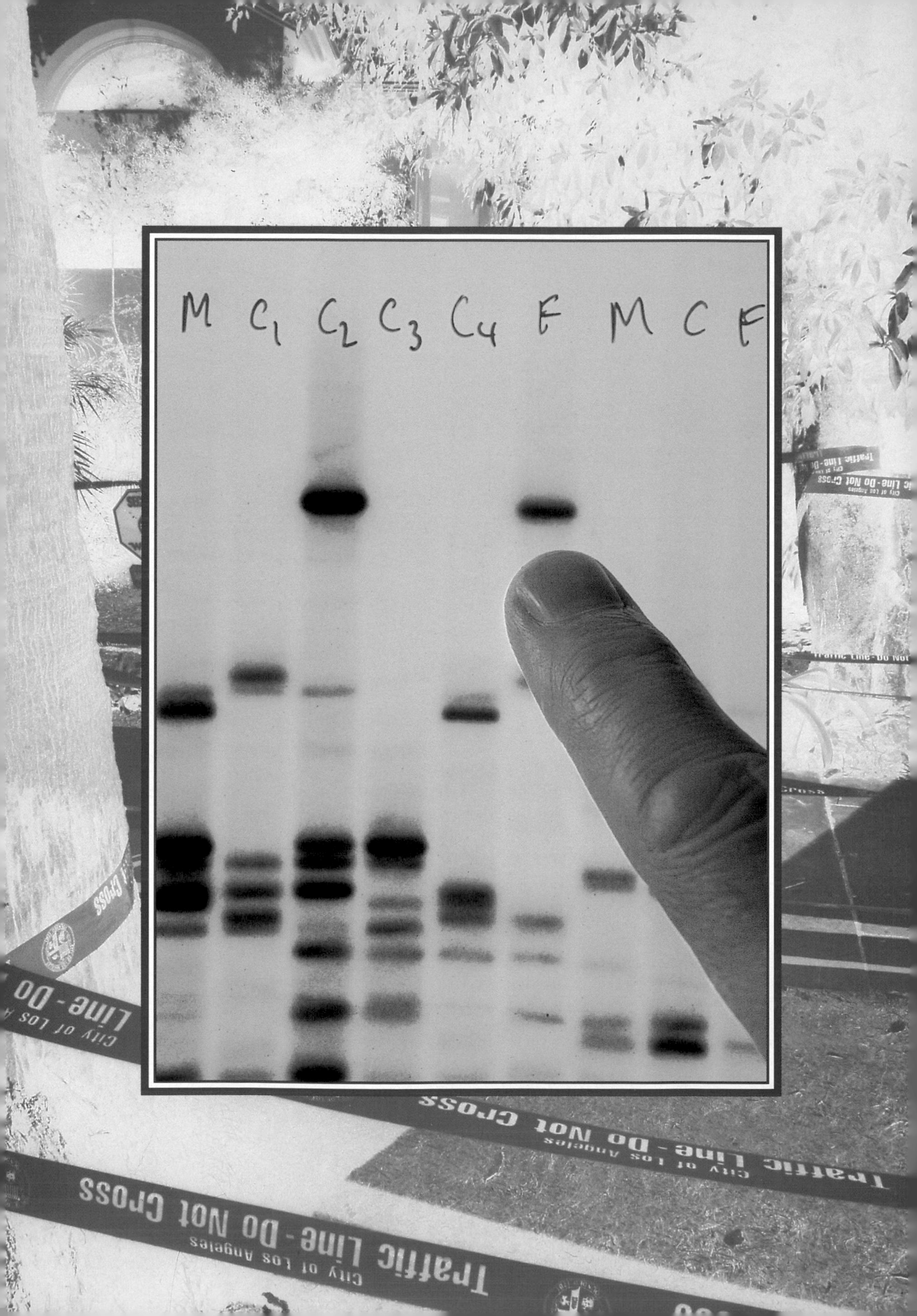
M C1 C2 C3 C4 F M C F
Traffic Line - Do Not Cross
City of Los Angeles

New Tools of the Forensic Scientist

BY JOHN I. THORNTON

Seeking obscure traces of evidence and linking them to criminal suspects is the work of the forensic scientist. As technology has advanced, so have the tools of forensics.

One drop of blood, a single hair, some carpet fibers, a trace of gunpowder—these tiny clues can help send a criminal to prison or set an accused man or woman free. Some cells in the blood droplet and hair contain DNA, which, like a fingerprint, can be used to identify its owner. Carpet fibers, tiny and unremarkable to the naked eye, show traceable features when examined with a sophisticated microscope. A hand that has fired a gun bears vanishingly small spheres of antimony, lead, and barium, even if it appears clean.

The techniques by which investigators find and interpret such clues make up the field of forensic science. The workshop of the forensic scientist, or *criminalist*, is the crime laboratory, where evidence collected by police officers, lab technicians, or the criminalists themselves is sent. In the first United States crime laboratories, established in the 1920's, the techniques of forensic science were quite limited. Throughout the mid-1900's, research advances in many fields of science produced small but steady additions to the forensic toolbox.

Then, in 1987, forensics made a quantum leap when it adopted a two-year-old procedure developed by geneticists. The ability to analyze differences in human genetic material yielded "DNA fingerprinting," a technique that many experts call the most important step forward ever in forensic science. DNA fingerprinting took center stage in 1995 during the highly publicized murder trial of former football star O. J. Simpson.

Although less well known, advances in traditional fingerprinting techniques, microscopy, and computing have also begun to play key roles in criminal trials. Together, these developments are revolutionizing the way forensic scientists do their job of gathering evidence against the guilty and removing suspicion from the innocent.

Finding the offender: From body parts to blood

The history of forensic science is a relatively recent one, with the field's first scientific method dating only to 1879. This technique, called the Bertillon system, enabled police to identify suspects and criminals based on the person's body shape. The identification required measurements of 11 parts of the human body that did not change significantly after a person had grown to adult height.

The system was soon supplanted by a much better way of identifying people, fingerprint analysis. By 1910, law enforcement agents in the United States were routinely taking the fingerprints of suspects and filing them according to the major pattern in the print—loop, whorl, arch, or a combination of the three. When fingerprints were discovered at a crime scene, police could then take the prints of any known suspects to see if the patterns matched. If there were no suspects in the case, agents could search the fingerprint files to look for a match. Statisticians calculate the probability of two randomly selected people having identical fingerprints at approximately 1 in 10 billion. Because there are only 5.7 billion people on Earth, it is safe to say that no two people have the same fingerprints.

Forensic scientists began to use blood typing to help identify criminals in the 1910's. This technique allowed police to determine whether blood on a suspect's clothing might have come from the crime victim, for example, or whether any blood found at the scene of the crime might have been shed by the suspect. The most common system for blood typing classifies human blood as type A, B, AB, or O. The four types contain different proteins on the surface of red blood cells, which cause the cells to clump together when certain types are mixed.

Blood typing is no match for fingerprinting as a means of pinpointing a guilty person, however, because all four types of blood are relatively common. If investigators found that a criminal shed type O blood at a crime scene, they could rule out 55 percent of the population as suspects, but could not say which of the remaining 45 percent committed the crime.

The ultimate tool: Testing a suspect's DNA

The development of DNA testing in the late 1980's gave forensic scientists a far more precise method of classifying blood—or any other biological sample that contains genetic material, such as semen, bone, or

The author:

John I. Thornton is professor of forensic science at the University of California in Berkeley.

Terms and concepts

DNA: Deoxyribonucleic acid, the molecule of which genes are made. DNA carries the coded information for inherited characteristics.

Forensic science: The technique of using scientific methods in solving crimes.

Forensic scientist: A person who examines evidence in a crime laboratory. Also known as criminalists, they may collect evidence and often testify in court cases.

Genes: The basic units of heredity. They are located in most human cells, on threadlike structures called chromosomes.

PCR: Polymerase chain reaction, a method used to produce millions of copies of certain genes. Forensic scientists use PCR to examine the DNA of crime suspects.

RFLP: Restriction fragment length polymorphism, a method used to compare DNA fragments based on their lengths. Also called *DNA fingerprinting* or *DNA profiling.*

Trace evidence: Microscopic evidence such as hairs, fiber, pollen, sand, soil, or tiny fragments of glass or paint.

hair. If criminalists cannot find any fingerprints at a crime scene, the discovery of biological material can provide enough evidence to pinpoint a suspect. Even if the biological evidence is damaged or otherwise unsuitable for extensive DNA testing, criminalists may still be able to use it to rule out suspects.

The two types of testing involve taking apart molecules of DNA (deoxyribonucleic acid) to make comparisons among them. When intact, a DNA molecule is shaped like a twisted ladder. Each "rung" of the ladder is made up of a pair of linked compounds called bases. The bases consist of only four compounds—adenosine, thymine, cytosine, and guanine—with adenosine always paired with thymine and cytosine always paired with guanine.

The DNA in a single human cell contains about 3 billion base pairs. In all people, many of the rungs of the DNA ladder are exactly the same, but each person's DNA also contains some stretches in which the sequence of bases is unique. (Only identical siblings have exactly the same DNA.) DNA testing targets the regions of DNA known to differ among people. By doing so, scientists can determine whether two biological samples—one from a suspect, the second linked to a crime—are likely to have come from the same person.

The RFLP test—DNA "fingerprinting"

There are two major types of DNA analysis, one based on a technique called restriction fragment length polymorphism (RFLP) and the other based on polymerase chain reaction (PCR). The RFLP test was developed in 1985 by British geneticist Alec Jeffreys of Leicester University in England. In a forensic investigation, this method takes several weeks to complete.

A technician begins the test by isolating DNA from the cells of biological material found at the scene of a crime. At the same time, DNA is isolated from blood samples collected from one or more persons considered to be suspects. A special protein called a *restriction enzyme* is added to each sample to chop the DNA into pieces. The enzyme cuts the DNA at certain series of base pairs. Because each person's sequences of bases differ in some places, the samples of chopped up DNA will contain uniquely sized pieces.

A process called electrophoresis allows the DNA fragments to be sorted by size. The fragments from each sample are placed together in a gelatinlike substance, and an electric current is passed through the gel. The current forces the pieces of DNA to move through the gel, the smaller pieces moving farther than the longer ones. When the process is over, the fragments are lined up according to size.

The pieces are too small to be seen, however, so technicians use another process to create a visible image. First, the DNA is treated with a chemical that causes the two chains of the double helix to split apart, like a zipper being unzipped. The separated chains are transferred to a solid material such as a sheet of nylon, and pieces of DNA called probes are added. The probes are designed to attach to the areas of

Using DNA to finger a suspect—or to clear one

The analysis of DNA (deoxyribonucleic acid, the molecule genes are made of) is one of the most important forensic tools used to identify people linked to a crime. There are two types of DNA tests, both of which compare DNA from the cells of a suspect with genetic material from samples of hair, skin cells, blood, or other biological material found at the crime scene.

DNA fingerprinting: The RFLP test

The most accurate DNA test is the restriction fragment length polymorphism (RFLP) test. The RFLP test requires a crime-scene sample that is relatively fresh and large—consisting of several strands of hair or a dime-sized drop of blood, for example.

First, technicians extract DNA from the two samples. DNA molecules have the shape of twisted ladders and consist of two strands of compounds joined together at the "rungs."

Next, technicians add an enzyme that chops the DNA into pieces. The lengths of some of the fragments vary from person to person.

The fragments are placed in a gel, and an electric current is passed through it. The current forces the fragments to move through the gel, and the shorter bits of DNA move farther than longer ones. At the end of this step, the fragments are sorted by size but are too small to be seen.

A chemical is added to the gel that causes the two strands of DNA in each fragment to unlink, like a zipper unzipping. The fragments, still sorted by size, are transferred to a piece of nylon.

Technicians now add radioactive strands of DNA called *probes*. The probes are designed to link up with some, but not all, of the fragments. Any excess probes are washed off.

The nylon is placed under photographic film, which the radioactive probes expose. The film is developed to create a greatly magnified image of the radioactive probes bound to the spread-out DNA fragments.

The pattern of dark bands from the suspect's blood is compared with the pattern made using DNA from the crime scene. If the two patterns match exactly, odds can be millions to one that the two samples are from the same person.

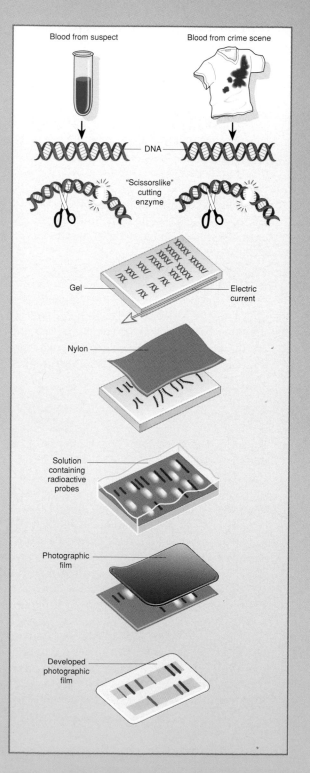

Blood from suspect — Blood from crime scene

DNA

"Scissorslike" cutting enzyme

Gel — Electric current

Nylon

Solution containing radioactive probes

Photographic film

Developed photographic film

Comparing a few genes: The PCR test

A less precise DNA test uses a technique called polymerase chain reaction (PCR). This test is useful when only a small number of cells from the crime scene are available or when the cells are old and the DNA is damaged. The PCR test is not sensitive enough to prove that a particular individual was involved in a crime, but it can conclusively rule out a suspect.

First, technicians extract DNA molecules from each sample.

Next, technicians treat the sample to unzip the strands of DNA. Segments of DNA called primers are added to mark off the gene or genes of interest.

An enzyme and nucleotide subunits are added to make new DNA strands between the primers. One of the nucleotide subunits includes a tag that can be identified later.

The double-stranded DNA segments are again unzipped, and the primers, enzyme, and nucleotide subunits repeat the process of making new strands of DNA. A machine repeats this cycle over and over again, doubling the number of DNA segments with each cycle.

The tagged copies are treated one last time to unzip their strands of DNA, and these are placed on a membrane that has single strand versions of DNA stuck to it. These are genes that are known to vary greatly among people. If the tagged copies of the gene match any of the different versions stuck to the membrane, they zip together. Unzipped copies are washed away.

A chemical is added that causes a colored spot to appear wherever the tagged copies are. The colored spots are visible to the naked eye, and they tell the technician which versions of the gene are present in the sample.

Technicians compare the versions of the genes found in the two samples of DNA. If the suspect's DNA and the crime scene DNA contain the same versions, then both samples may be from the same person. If the genes do not match, then the person can be ruled out as a suspect.

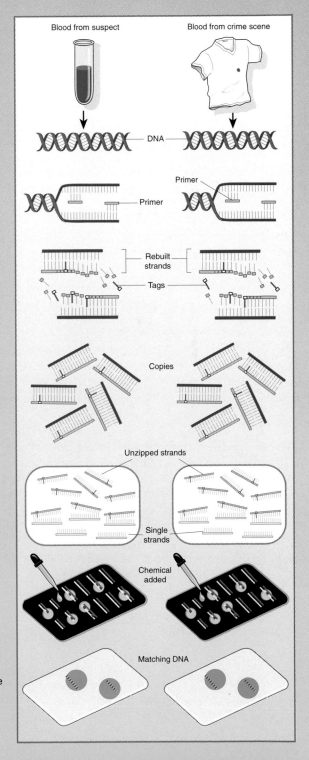

DNA known to differ from person to person. Each probe is also "tagged" with a radioactive element to make it visible. When the probes find these pieces of DNA on the nylon sheet, they attach to them—zipping the zipper.

Technicians then place a piece of X-ray film over the nylon sheet, and the radioactive probes expose the film. The resulting X-ray image contains a complex pattern of bands that looks something like a supermarket bar code. This pattern is the DNA "fingerprint." Experts compare the pattern on the DNA fingerprint from the cells at the crime scene with the DNA fingerprint belonging to the suspect. If the test is done carefully, the odds of a random match are extremely low—1 in several billion.

The PCR test

The second method of comparing DNA is PCR. Rather than looking at many parts of the DNA in a sample, the PCR test zeroes in on specific *genes,* stretches of DNA that control the production of various proteins. The gene most often examined in forensic PCR is called HLA DQ alpha. This gene controls production of a protein in the immune system, and geneticists have discovered that there are many different versions of it in the population.

To perform the PCR test, a technician isolates DNA from the sample. Then the isolated DNA is placed along with other compounds that are necessary to make copies of DNA in a machine called a thermal cycler. By raising the temperature of the mixture, the machine causes the two strands of the DNA molecule to unzip. Then the machine lowers the temperature, and the other compounds in the mixture form new complementary strands of DNA out of the chemical subunits. The process repeats many times, and with each repetition, the number of copies doubles. Millions of identical copies of the original DNA can be made overnight.

To determine which version of a gene is present in the sample, the copies are chemically tagged and then placed on a membrane that contains copies of all the known versions of the HLA DQ alpha gene. Each tagged copy attaches to its matching version on the membrane. Finally, technicians add a chemical that causes the tag to show up as a colored dot on the membrane. The location of the colored dot indicates which version or versions of the HLA DQ gene were in the sample.

As a tool for forensic science, PCR is not as powerful as the RFLP test. Like blood typing based on the ABO system, PCR can only narrow down the possible list of suspects. It is not unusual, for example, for 1 out of 100 people to carry the same versions of the HLA DQ alpha gene.

Because PCR can be performed quickly, however, criminalists often use it to rule out suspects before undertaking the more time-consuming RFLP test. According to statistics collected by the FBI, about 1 out of 7 cases submitted to their laboratory result in no evidence to link a

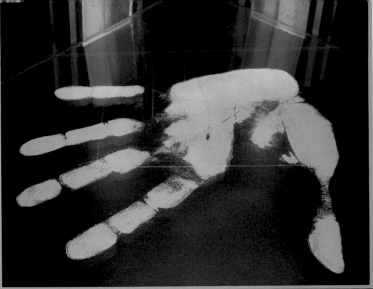

High-tech fingerprinting

New techniques allow criminalists to make hidden fingerprints visible and then to quickly search for a match. An invisible handprint, consisting of perspiration and oils from the skin, *left,* becomes visible under light from small, portable lasers. A beam of blue-green light causes perspiration in some prints to *fluoresce* (give off light).

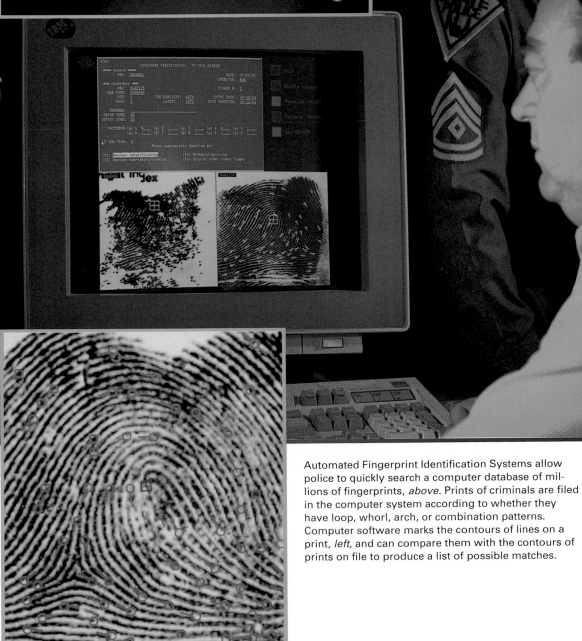

Automated Fingerprint Identification Systems allow police to quickly search a computer database of millions of fingerprints, *above.* Prints of criminals are filed in the computer system according to whether they have loop, whorl, arch, or combination patterns. Computer software marks the contours of lines on a print, *left,* and can compare them with the contours of prints on file to produce a list of possible matches.

suspect to a crime. But the main advantage of PCR is that it does not require as much biological material as is necessary for RFLP. PCR is thus useful in cases in which less than a dime-sized drop of blood is found or when the biological evidence is old and only small parts of it are usable. Since its first use in a criminal trial in 1987, PCR has assisted in the convictions of hundreds of people suspected of having committed crimes, but also has led to dozens of overturned convictions for people who had been wrongly imprisoned for crimes.

By far the most famous case to hinge on DNA evidence was the trial of O. J. Simpson, charged with the murder of his former wife Nicole Brown Simpson and her friend Ronald Goldman. During the trial, the prosecution argued that the crime scene contained droplets of blood that the RFLP test showed were genetically identical to O. J. Simpson's blood, and that smears of blood in O. J. Simpson's car and droplets on his socks were genetically identical to the blood of the victims.

Lawyers for Simpson sought to plant doubt in the jurors' minds that DNA testing was reliable, and proposed the theory that the biological evidence had been compromised before testing. To support their case, they sought the advice of the inventor of the PCR technique, Nobel-Prize winner Kary Mullis, who offered the opinion that forensic samples that had been scraped up from a sidewalk or might have been otherwise contaminated would not be sufficient to determine guilt or innocence in a criminal case.

Computer systems for catching criminals

The Goldman-Simpson murder scene contained a great deal of biological evidence, but such evidence is not always recovered at crime scenes. For this reason, advances in traditional fingerprint technology have had almost as much impact on forensic science as DNA testing. Highest on the list of important new technologies is the introduction of computer-aided identification of fingerprints. Automated Fingerprint Identification Systems (AFIS), as they are known, were first introduced in the United States in 1976 and have been used extensively since the mid-1980's.

Until the introduction of AFIS, local police agencies, state criminal investigation bureaus, and the FBI had to conduct "cold searches" of their fingerprint files to find matches by visually examining every fingerprint card within the appropriate classification categories. Such a search could take many hours, enough time for the criminal to flee the area. With the AFIS system, a search of about 2 million prints requires only about five minutes of computer time.

The heart of an AFIS system is a large computer database of fingerprints. An examiner enters a digital image of a fingerprint discovered at a crime scene, and the computer calculates positions, directions, and relationships among the fingerprint's loops, whorls, and arches. The computer then compares those data with the characteristics of the fingerprints on file and produces the names of possible suspects, listed

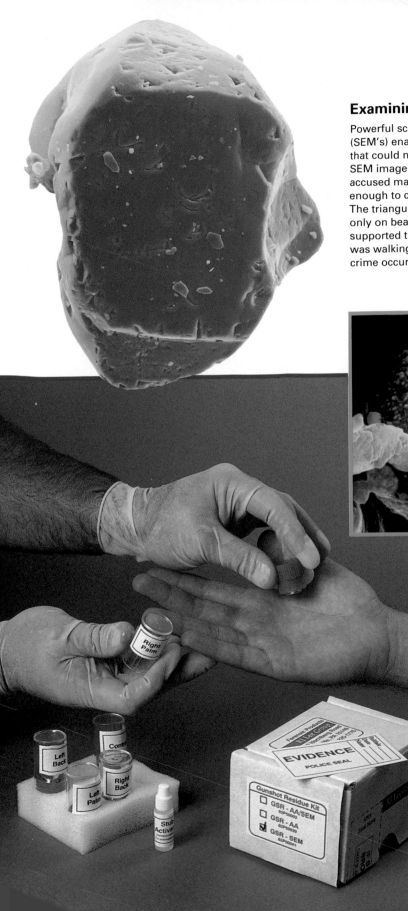

Examining microscopic clues

Powerful scanning electron microscopes (SEM's) enable investigators to see clues that could not otherwise be detected. An SEM image of a grain of sand found on an accused man's shoe, *left,* was evidence enough to clear him of a robbery charge. The triangular pits on the grain are found only on beach sand, and their discovery supported the accused man's alibi that he was walking on the beach at the time the crime occurred.

To determine whether a suspect recently fired a gun, investigators use a special adhesive to lift particle samples from the suspect's hands, *left.* The samples are examined with an SEM to look for the presence of telltale spherical particles, *above.* Using other lab techniques, criminalists can determine if the spheres contain the chemicals produced when a gun is fired—lead, barium, and antimony.

in order of the probability of a match. A fingerprint expert then makes a thorough visual comparison of the fingerprints to see if any fit the profile.

Finding hidden fingerprints

The computer system is helpful only if fingerprints can be recovered from the crime scene, however, and forensic researchers have also developed new methods to make even the faintest print visible. Prints that contain blood or dirt are easily seen, but a crime scene may also contain invisible fingerprints that consist only of the perspiration and oils that accumulate naturally on the fingers. To make these *latent* (hidden) fingerprints visible, criminalists have for decades dusted surfaces at crime scenes with powder that sticks to the oils and perspiration. They photograph the print, then lift it from the surface with clear adhesive tape. The tape transfers the print to a piece of paper, which forms a permanent record.

In the early 1980's, forensic researchers developed new methods of making latent prints visible that can be more efficient in some cases than dusting. Today, crime scene investigators typically use a small, portable laser to shine a beam of blue-green light over surfaces at the scene. The beam causes the perspiration in some latent fingerprints to *fluoresce* (give off light). Fresh fingerprints have greenish-yellow fluorescence, and older fingerprints tend to glow orange. Investigators can then photograph the glowing fingerprints to make a permanent record.

Not all fingerprints have natural fluorescence, because some people do not secrete the fluorescent components in their perspiration. Also, the passage of time causes latent prints to fade. About 99 percent of a fingerprint is water, which evaporates quickly, leaving behind only a small amount of solid material—salts and other compounds. In order to adequately visualize these prints, technicians may treat the crime scene with a chemical that makes it fluoresce when exposed to the laser beam.

For example, the fumes of a chemical called *cyanoacrylate*, the main ingredient in Krazy Glue, causes latent prints to become visible and white. To "develop" a print in the crime lab, a technician places a piece of evidence in an enclosed container, fills it with the fumes, and waits overnight for prints on the object to become visible. If the surface of the piece of evidence is white, it can be treated with a fluorescent dye to make any prints visible.

Because cyanoacrylate works especially well for visualizing fingerprints on certain plastics, criminalists can use it to find prints on such items as plastic bags in which drugs have been transported. Cyanoacrylate also provided the key to solving a famous serial murder case in 1985. That year, Los Angeles police found an automobile they believed had been used by a serial murderer known as the Night Stalker. Investigators built a structure around the car and filled the structure with cyanoacrylate gas. The process exposed a lone fingerprint. Using

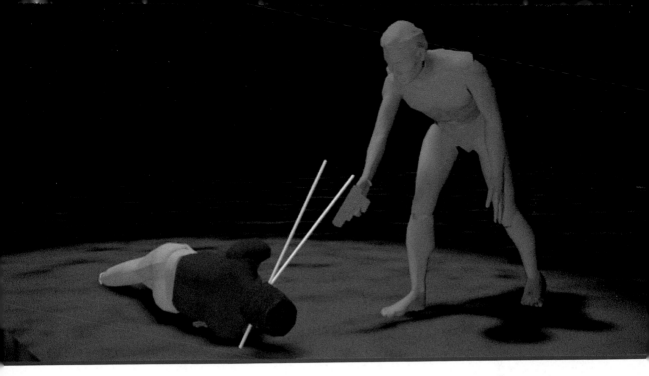

A computer re-creation of a murder is based on the known angles at which bullets struck a victim. Advances in computer technology enable investigators to manipulate three-dimensional figures on a computer screen and "reenact" a crime.

AFIS, agents were then able to quickly identify the print as that of Richard Ramirez, who was eventually convicted of 13 murders committed throughout southern California.

Who fired the gun?

Tying a suspect to a shooting has become easier since the development in the 1980's of a technique called energy dispersive X-ray analysis. The technique analyzes the particles from a suspect's hands to look for characteristic microscopic gunshot residue. The residue is formed when a firearm discharges, as solid material from the *primer,* the substance that ignites the cartridge, is liquefied by the high temperatures and pressures created by the igniting gunpowder. Extremely tiny globules of the chemical elements lead, barium, and antimony form while in the liquid state, then they immediately cool to become solid spheres.

To determine whether a suspect has recently fired a gun, agents press a piece of tape onto the skin of the suspect to remove any particles. In the crime lab, technicians examine the tape using a device called a scanning electron microscope. The microscope sends a focused beam of electrons across the surface of the particles on the tape. As the electrons strike the particles, they give off X rays whose energy level depends on the chemical composition of the particles. By analyzing the energy of the X rays coming from a particular particle, an analyst can determine which elements it contains. In this way, the characteristic mix of lead, barium, and antimony in gunshot residue can be distinguished from similar residue, such as lead particles from automobile exhaust or iron particles from welding processes.

In 1990, energy dispersive X-ray analysis helped determine the fate of Christian Brando, son of actor Marlon Brando. Police had charged Christian Brando with murder for shooting and killing Dag Drollet, the boyfriend of his half-sister. Police believed that he had simply walked up to and shot the victim as Drollet lay on a couch watching television. Brando insisted, however, that the shot had been fired accidentally as the two men struggled over the gun. Gunshot residue on the hands of Drollet—indicating that the victim's hands were on or near the gun when it fired—helped Brando receive the lesser charge of manslaughter.

Forensic experts have used energy dispersive X-ray analysis to help determine whether a shooting death is a murder or a suicide. The test was also useful in the aftermath of a chaotic shootout on a Toronto street in July 1993 in which the identities of the shooters were unknown. Two men were arrested but later set free when the X-ray analysis found no gunshot residue on their hands.

Linking a bullet to a gun

Another technique for tracking down a shooter links the bullet at a crime scene to the gun that fired it. As a bullet is fired from a gun, the barrel of the gun scratches the surface of the bullet very finely. These scratches, called *striae*, form a distinctive pattern by which each firearm can be known. For nearly 75 years, forensic scientists have used microscopes to compare bullets. In 1993, however, they began examining bullet surfaces using a new technology called *surface profile analysis*. The technique was originally developed for use in engineering and manufacturing.

A surface profile analyzer is a computerized instrument that scans a bullet and provides a three-dimensional map of the bullet surface. To make the map, the analyzer focuses a laser beam on the bullet to scan the entire surface. As the light reflects off the projections and depressions made by scratches on the bullet, a device graphs the peaks and valleys. When the entire surface has been scanned, the computer creates a composite three-dimensional representation of the bullet, showing all the scratches in fine detail. The bullet profiles can be entered into a database and searched using a computer, allowing criminalists to make quick comparisons among a pattern of scratches on the bullet found at a crime scene and among the patterns of scratches made by various guns.

Trace evidence: Guilty by a hair

Forensic scientists have found that scanning electron microscopes are well suited for the examination of many other types of evidence as well. Although the microscopes are not new to science, most forensic laboratories did not begin acquiring them until the 1980's, when their usefulness in the analysis of gunshot residue became apparent. Since then, many labs have begun using the microscopes to examine *trace ev-*

idence, microscopic evidence such as hairs, fibers, pollen, sand, soil, or minute fragments of paint or glass. A scanning electron microscope can magnify an image thousands of times while at the same time maintaining a significant depth of field, the area of sharpness surrounding the subject. The result is that criminalists can visualize and compare bits of evidence that could not be seen using a conventional light microscope.

All these tools show that forensic science has become vastly more sophisticated since the the field was established in the late 1800's. Even the famous fictional detective Sherlock Holmes, though possessing keen powers of observation, had to rely on the limited science of his day. "The more featureless and commonplace the crime is," wrote Sir Arthur Conan Doyle in *The Adventures of Sherlock Holmes,* "the more difficult it is to bring it home." But an old Malay proverb states, "Crime leaves a trail like a water beetle; like a snail it leaves its shine." Modern forensic science allows criminalists to find those trails, no matter how apparently featureless the crime.

For further reading:

Handbook of Forensic Science: The Official F.B.I. Guide. Diane Publishing Company, 1994.

Lee, Henry C., and Gaensslen, Robert E. *Advanced Fingerprint Technology.* Franklin Book Company, 1991.

Maples, William R., and Browning, Michael. *Dead Men Do Tell Tales: The Strange and Fascinating Cases of a Forensic Anthropologist.* Doubleday, 1994.

National Research Council. *DNA Technology in Forensic Science.* National Academy Press, 1992.

Saferstein, Richard. *Criminalistics: An Introduction to Forensic Science.* 4th ed. Prentice-Hall, 1990.

Wecht, Cyril. *Cause of Death.* Onyx, 1995.

Science Studies

Saving the Earth's Species

Species of plants and animals face extinction in all parts of the world. Ecologists blame human activities for creating the problem but believe that dedicated human efforts can solve it.

Introduction

During the past 200 years, several familiar animal species have disappeared from the face of the Earth. The last known passenger pigeon, once numbering in the billions, died at the Cincinnati Zoological Gardens in 1914. Other animals that have been wiped out include the dodo, the great auk, and the Tasmanian tiger.

If current trends continue, the list of well-known extinct animals will soon grow far longer. Conservation scientists say it is very likely that children born in the next decade will never have the chance to see a Siberian tiger, a mountain gorilla, a black rhinoceros, a blue whale, or scores of other remarkable creatures that once lived on the Earth in vast numbers.

Biologists have concluded that Earth is in the early stages of a *mass extinction*, a period in which the planet loses hundreds of thousands—perhaps millions—of animals, plants, fungi, and microorganisms. Mass extinctions have occurred before, but this age of extinction has an entirely different primary cause—the skyrocketing growth of the human population and the impact of human activities. As people chop down forests, dam rivers, expand cities, and pollute the environment, survival becomes increasingly difficult for other living things.

On a global scale, human activities risk destroying Earth's *biological diversity,* or *biodiversity,* the collective variety of its life forms. Scientists believe that this variety is essential to the survival of all species, including ours. Yet saving even one species can prove to be very difficult, in part because we know little about the complex ways creatures interact with their environment. And protecting wildlife is often controversial, because it requires limiting the freedom of human beings to use the environment for economic gain. On the pages that follow, five leading ecologists describe these and other complex issues surrounding the struggle to save the world's species.

Threatened Species Around the World

BY STUART L. PIMM

The mass extinction we face today is an enormous problem. It involves issues that are extremely complicated and, in many cases, relatively new to science. Moreover, the effects of this mass extinction span the globe. A complete catalog of species threatened with extinction would include every type of organism—microorganisms, fungi, plants, and animals alike. A tour of threatened environments would cover rivers, lakes, and marshes; land environments from deserts to rain forests; even whole continents.

One method scientists use to better understand—and explain—mass extinction is to focus their investigation on an isolated region or particular variety of organism. Using information gathered from such specific studies, scientists hope to piece together a picture of extinction patterns worldwide.

A case history: Extinctions in Hawaii

The islands in the Pacific Ocean—particularly Hawaii—have been a prime subject of such investigation. To the millions of tourists who visit each year, the Hawaiian islands are a tropical paradise, rich with exotic wildlife. But to ecologists, they illustrate on a small scale the process that is occurring in all parts of the globe. The chain of events is simple: Populations of plants, animals, fungi, and microorganisms in an environment remain fairly stable for thousands of years. Then the human population rises, and other species begin to die out.

In Hawaii, this process began when people first found the islands about 2,000 years ago. Since then, hundreds of Hawaiian species of plants and animals that lived nowhere else in the world have vanished.

How do we know that Hawaiian species have vanished? Skeletal remains of one type of animal—birds—provide firm evidence of the losses. Ornithologists who collect and catalog bird remains have found that Hawaii was once home to more than 100 species never seen today. Historical records show that those birds, like most Hawaiian birds, were unique—such as the honey eaters, which early settlers easily identified by their beautiful songs and specialized beaks and tongues.

The process of extinction in Hawaii was repeated throughout the Pacific islands. Ornithologists who have examined bird remains across this broad area estimate that as many as 2,000 species of birds have died out since people settled the Pacific Islands.

The author:

Stuart L. Pimm is professor of ecology at the University of Tennessee at Knoxville.

Human activities have been almost entirely responsible for the extinctions. Originally, Polynesians and, since the late 1700's, Europeans posed threats to birds in the Pacific Islands by hunting and by accidentally introducing foreign predatory species such as rats, which often infested the boats of explorers. These settlers also cleared forestland the birds needed for food and shelter.

Extinctions in other areas

Clearly, the small size and isolation of islands makes them vulnerable to human impact. But island creatures are by no means the only obvious victims. Ecologists can point to many other examples of recent species loss among many types of living things and in virtually all parts of the globe:

■ More than 40 kinds of freshwater fish in North America have become extinct in the past century, according to the United Nation's International Union for the Conservation of Nature and Natural Resources (IUCN). Rivers that once teemed with prized sportfish such as salmon have been depleted as people built dams, widened channels, and constructed irrigation networks. Some fish species have been killed off because people released foreign fish species into the waterways, and other animals that competed with the native species for food.

■ Australia has long been known as a land of fascinating mammals—particularly the marsupials, such as kangaroos and koalas. But of the 60 species of the world's mammals that are known to have become extinct during the last two centuries, 18 were native to Australia. More than 40 other mammal species in Australia have vanished from more than half of their former range or survive only in protected habitats. Scientists say the impact of agriculture on natural habitats and the release of foxes and other foreign species have contributed to the continent's struggle with extinction.

■ The southern tip of Africa is home to a unique ecological community called the *fynbos*, which supports an extraordinary variety of plants—about 8,500 species. Many of these species are shrublike plants that bear tiny flowers of many colors. In the past century, 36 species have become extinct and more than 600 others are at risk of extinction, primarily because people have brought in foreign plants that compete with the fynbos for space and sunlight.

■ In the Mississippi and St. Lawrence river basins of North America, naturalists once identified nearly 300 native species of freshwater clams and mussels. Of these, 21 have become extinct since the late 1800's, and another 120 are at risk of extinction.

Scientists say the construction of dams and canals and the pollution of waterways by fertilizer and sewage brought about this rapid decline in shellfish populations.

■ At first glance, amphibians appear to be a bright spot in the global picture. Only 5 out of more than 4,000 species of frogs, toads, and other varieties are known to have vanished in the past century. But ecologists have recorded massive declines in the populations of amphibians worldwide since the 1970's. Many declines occurred in areas that appear to be undisturbed by human activity. The global nature of these declines is particularly troubling because it suggests that there is a global cause, such as widespread pollution of the atmosphere. Populations may be declining because pollution damages amphibian eggs before the young can hatch.

How many species have been lost?

Examples such as these provide a clearer picture of the scope of mass extinction, but much more detailed information is necessary to accurately describe the problem's magnitude. Scientists have not yet had the time or resources to compile such data, so they are forced to rely on other methods.

Just as it is difficult to imagine the wide range of the extinction problem, it is also hard to determine exactly how many species have already died off. For one thing, taxonomists, the scientists who describe new species, have identified just a small fraction—perhaps 5 percent—of the world's species so far. So few species have been described that experts cannot say with certainty how many species, named and unnamed, exist in the world. Estimates range from 5 million to 100 million, most of them tiny creatures, such as the scores of insect species that live in tropical rain forests. Because we know so little about the variety of life

on Earth, it's likely that many species have died out without our knowing.

One way to estimate the scope of mass extinction is by basing our estimates on known losses among well-studied animals. For example, scientists believe that we have lost on average one species of bird in the Pacific Islands each year during the last 100 years. Most experts believe there are about 10,000 species of birds in the world today. So if the extinctions in the Pacific were the only bird extinctions—which, of course, they are not—we would have lost 1 percent

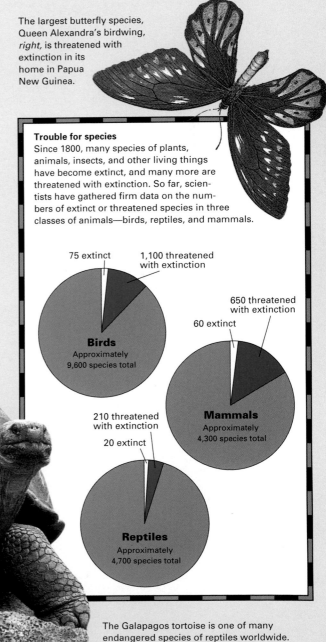

The largest butterfly species, Queen Alexandra's birdwing, *right,* is threatened with extinction in its home in Papua New Guinea.

Trouble for species
Since 1800, many species of plants, animals, insects, and other living things have become extinct, and many more are threatened with extinction. So far, scientists have gathered firm data on the numbers of extinct or threatened species in three classes of animals—birds, reptiles, and mammals.

75 extinct

1,100 threatened with extinction

Birds
Approximately 9,600 species total

650 threatened with extinction

60 extinct

Mammals
Approximately 4,300 species total

210 threatened with extinction

20 extinct

Reptiles
Approximately 4,700 species total

The Galapagos tortoise is one of many endangered species of reptiles worldwide.

of all bird species in the last 100 years.

Studies recording the populations of certain plants, mammals, and other groups of organisms lead us to believe that their rate of extinction was similar to that of birds. After all, the factors that caused the extinction of Pacific birds—habitat destruction and the introduction of foreign species—may have been equally damaging to most of the plants, insects, and other species on the islands.

So we can deduce that at the very least, 1 percent of all other species have been lost in the last century. What does the loss of 1 percent of all species in 100 years mean? If we presume there are 10 million total species—an estimate many scientists consider reasonable—then at the very least, 100,000 species have died out in the last 100 years. That is 1,000 species per year, or about 3 per day.

Disturbing predictions

Scientific estimates based on several types of data suggest that the pace of extinction may quicken in the future. Data on bird populations, for example, indicate that about 1,100 bird species are likely to become extinct in the next few decades—10 times more than the number that died out in the last century, and 10 percent of all birds. If 10 percent of all species were to die off in the next century, we would lose at least 10,000 species per year, or 30 species per day.

Even that estimate is likely to be too low, however, because extinctions inevitably grow more rapid as the loss of one species directly brings about the demise of others. A bird that feeds on the nectar of a specific plant, for example, may carry pollen from flower to flower, thus helping that plant reproduce. If the bird species dies off, the plant is likely to perish soon after. Considering factors such as these, ecologists estimate that, if current conditions persist, we will lose many more than 10,000 species per year.

A different method of predicting the number of species likely to die off in the future is based on studies of the outcome of habitat destruction. This rule of thumb, called the *species-area relationship,* indicates how many species are likely to survive in an area of a certain size. Through decades of research, naturalists have found that if a wilderness area is cut in half, about 15 percent of species in the original area will die out. If the remaining area is halved

Human activities have disturbed natural environments over much of the globe, causing a worldwide loss of species. Ecosystems in Europe, North America, and Asia are among the regions that have suffered the greatest damage. At least 18 key regions, dubbed ecological "hot spots," harbor an exceptionally large number of species but face a particularly serious threat of habitat destruction.

again, another 15 percent of the species will be lost.

By using the species-area relationship along with calculations based on other types of data, scientists have arrived at some startling predictions for the future pace of extinctions. Many ecologists predict that unless human activities change dramatically, we are likely to lose one-half of the world's species during the next 100 years. Such estimates may appear extreme, but scientists point out that archaeological records show that rapid species extinction followed the spread of human beings across the globe. And we already know of thousands of plant and animal species for which only specimens in museums remain.

Small numbers of settlers unintentionally exterminated many of the Pacific Island birds. Today's massive—and rapidly growing—human population is capable of much greater damage. The greatest loss of species, ecologists fear, is yet to come. 🍎

Europe

A s i a

Arctic Circle

Eastern
Himalaya

Tropic of Cancer

Western
Ghats
of India

Philippines

Africa

Sri Lanka

Northern Borneo

Ivory
Coast

Equator

Peninsular
Malaysia

Tanzania

New
Caledonia

Madagascar

Australia

Tropic of
Capricorn

Southwestern
Australia

Cape Floristic Province
of South Africa

Status of the environment

Hot spot area   Heavily disturbed area   Partially disturbed area   Mostly natural area

Sources: Conservation International; Norman Myers.

Antarctic Circle

Antarctica

The fynbos, a unique ecological community on the southern
tip of Africa, includes a variety of flowering plants. More
than 600 species of these plants face extinction.

The Iiwi, *above*, whose
beak is specially adapted
for feeding on nectar, is
one of several endangered
species of Hawaiian honey
creepers.

Extinctions Past and Present

BY NORMAN MYERS

You need only to marvel at the skeleton of an *Apatosaurus* or *Tyrannosaurus rex* in a museum to be reminded that extinction is not a new process. The last dinosaur species died out 65 million years ago, long before human beings walked the Earth.

By examining fossils of extinct creatures preserved in layers of rock, researchers have found that species have been dying off since life began almost 4 billion years ago. *Paleontologists* (scientists who study fossils) estimate that up to 98 percent of the species that once lived are now extinct.

Paleontologists and other scientists point out that most of those species vanished in the natural course of evolution, as creatures changed over thousands of millions of generations into more complex forms. Others died off during mass extinctions, periods when an unusually large number of unrelated species perished in an unusually short period of time. Those species simply disappeared, leaving no descendants.

Scientists believe that we can shed light on the crisis of extinction our planet now faces by examining previous episodes of mass extinction. As extinction expert David Raup of the University of Chicago has pointed out, overlooking the lessons of past extinctions is like trying to treat a mysterious disease without scanning the patient's medical records.

Mass extinctions of the past

At least five major episodes of mass extinction have occurred since life developed on Earth. Each time, at least one-fourth, and on average one-half, of all species died out within a few million years—a mere moment in Earth's geological history.

The largest mass extinction took place about 240 million years ago, marking the end of the Paleozoic Era. Scientists estimate that during that extinction, from 80 to 96 percent of all species disappeared. Marine organisms, which made up the great majority of species during the Paleozoic, were the hardest hit. Many species that lived on the ocean floor, such as sea lilies, died out. Flat shellfish called trilobites and a group of fish called placoderms, both common during the early Paleozoic, also became extinct.

Two other mass extinctions occurred earlier during the Paleozoic Era. The first marked the end of the Ordovician Period, about 435 million years ago. The next occurred in the later part of the Devonian Period, which ended about 360 million years ago. Tens of thousands of species of marine organisms, particularly tiny creatures such as graptolites, died out during these two episodes of mass extinction.

Another mass extinction occurred about 205 million years ago, ending the Triassic Period. At this time, many species of amphibians and reptiles became extinct. The extinction set the stage for the rise of the dinosaurs, which for a time became the world's dominant animals.

The most recent and best-known mass extinction took place at the end of the Mesozoic Era, about 65 million years ago, when the last living dinosaur species vanished from the Earth. Many other terrestrial species and many marine species also became extinct during this time. The extinctions led to the rise of mammals and marked the beginning of the Cenozoic Era, in which we live today.

No one can say for sure what caused the past extinction episodes, though scientists can offer theories. Some suggest that the extinction of dinosaurs 65 million years ago occurred because a large asteroid hit the Earth, throwing billions of tons of dust into the air and changing the environment so much that large animals could not survive. Other experts argue that the extinction was caused by the effects of widespread volcanic eruptions. Still others believe that a combination of factors killed off the dinosaurs.

Gradual changes in Earth's climate are likely causes for the earlier mass extinctions. What prompted such changes, however, is a subject of vigorous debate. One widely accepted theory suggests that geological forces led to the expansion of glaciers. As seawater froze, the sea level fell, reducing the size of warm oceans, where most organisms lived.

Many scientists agree, however, that every mass extinction must have been linked to some drastic change in the environment, regardless of whether it was brought on by an asteroid impact, volcanic eruption, or other phenomenon. Today's extinctions are similar to previous episodes because they, too, are the result of drastic environmental change.

Why today's extinctions are different

Scientists have also identified a set of key factors suggesting that the current extinctions are crucially different from those in the past. Recognizing these factors, scientists believe, is essential to solving the problems we now face.

One of the most notable differences is the rapid pace of today's extinctions. Ecologists estimate that we have lost hundreds of thousands of species in the past 50 years. The experts predict that if pres-

The author:

Norman Myers is a consultant in environment and development and author of several books on conservation.

ent trends continue, we are likely to lose one-half of all living species within the next century.

In contrast, mass extinctions of the past took place over hundreds of thousands, and in some cases millions, of years. Even if the final extinction of the dinosaurs had been caused by an asteroid impact, its effects would have lasted a comparatively brief time. Fossil evidence shows that the population of dinosaurs had already been dwindling for many thousands of years.

Another factor distinguishing the current episode is that the number of species at risk today is far greater than in the past. The reason for this is simple: There are many more species living today than ever before. Before the last mass extinction 65 million years ago, for example, the world's flowering plants numbered about 100,000 species. Today, biologists estimate, there are 200,000. Among mammals, insects, and other organisms, there have been large increases in the total number of species.

Paleontologists say that after the dinosaurs became extinct, at least 5 million years went by before an equally advanced group of animals evolved. The

evolutionary challenge the world will face after today's episode will be much more daunting, according to ecologists. That is because the current extinction involves all major categories of species. This contrasts sharply with what happened 65 million years ago, when most mammals, birds, and amphibians, and many reptiles survived.

All this leads to a disturbing conclusion. Even if the current episode results in the same percentage of extinctions as in the past—say, one-half of all species—the total number of species to die off will be much higher than ever before.

As the number of species on Earth has increased, the variety of characteristics among the world's life forms has also grown. Never before have the world's plants and animals shown such an astonishing degree of diversity. Millions of years of evolution have produced such highly sophisticated features as the backbone, the jaw, lungs, warm-bloodedness, and—in the case of certain mammals—the large and complex brain.

The presence of this biodiversity, however, means that the current trend of extinction could bring

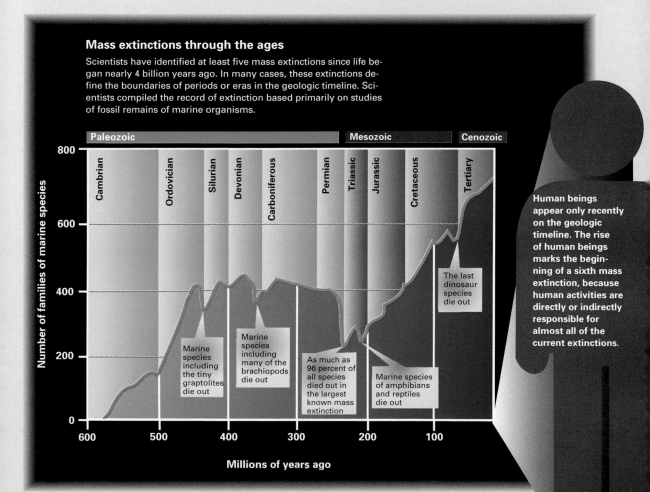

Mass extinctions through the ages

Scientists have identified at least five mass extinctions since life began nearly 4 billion years ago. In many cases, these extinctions define the boundaries of periods or eras in the geologic timeline. Scientists compiled the record of extinction based primarily on studies of fossil remains of marine organisms.

Paleozoic

Mesozoic

Cenozoic

Number of families of marine species

800

600

400

200

0

Cambrian

Ordovician

Silurian

Devonian

Carboniferous

Permian

Triassic

Jurassic

Cretaceous

Tertiary

Marine species including the tiny graptolites die out

Marine species including many of the brachiopods die out

As much as 96 percent of all species died out in the largest known mass extinction

Marine species of amphibians and reptiles die out

The last dinosaur species die out

Human beings appear only recently on the geologic timeline. The rise of human beings marks the beginning of a sixth mass extinction, because human activities are directly or indirectly responsible for almost all of the current extinctions.

600   500   400   300   200   100

Millions of years ago

about the world's greatest biological tragedy. The most critical factor in this tragedy may be the loss of key environments—particularly tropical forests and coral reefs—that are exceptionally rich in biodiversity and ecological complexity. Ecologists believe that over time these environments have served as the main "powerhouses" of evolution, generating the greatest number and variety of species. Virtually every major group of vertebrates and many other large categories of animals, along with flowering plants, originated in forests, coral reefs, and other regions of the tropics. But tropical environments today are among the most threatened regions.

Ecologists believe that the "bounce-back" period—the time it would take Earth to recover its present degree of biological diversity—could be as long as 25 million years. Furthermore, scientists say that many evolutionary processes that have persisted for millions of years could be suspended—if not completely ended—if vital habitats such as tropical forests are destroyed. In that case, the unique features of many extinct plants and animals may never have a chance to develop again.

"Death is one thing, an end to birth is something else," say biologists Michael Soule and Bruce Wilcox of Stanford University in California. Such experts predict that evolution may be likely to experience profound "hiccups," as life on Earth repeatedly attempts to recover its diversity but fails because of the environmental damage.

Human beings: The crucial factor

Ecologists say that the greatest difference between the present mass extinction and those of the past, however, is that today's extinctions are entirely due to the activities of a single species—*Homo sapiens,* or human beings. We are the sole species in the history of life to have the capacity to cause a mass extinction of many other species.

Human activities, including the clearing of forests, the spread of agriculture, the introduction of animals into new environments, and the pollution of air, water, and soil, account for almost all of the extinctions of the last several thousand years. Scientists predict that as the human population grows and human activities increase, the problem will become more serious. More people require more food and more space to live, and they create more waste.

Since 1950, the world's human population has grown from about 2.5 billion to about 5.7 billion people. In the next 50 years, the number of people is expected to double. Scientists warn that such a population explosion will have a devastating impact on the millions of other species with whom we share the planet. Furthermore, in most developed nations, where population growth is not as rapid, human activities such as agriculture and industry pose an equally serious threat to the world's species.

But in addition to acknowledging human beings' capacity to destroy, scientists say we should remember that we are also the sole species to ever have the capacity to save others. In this way, the current episode of extinction can be seen not so much as an insurmountable problem, but as a glorious challenge. ❦

Human population has exploded since the mid-1900's, and experts predict it will continue to grow at a tremendous rate. Ecologists say that the results of this growth will further endanger some other species.

Millions of people

Year	
2,000 B.C.	1,000 B.C.	A.D. 1	A.D. 1,000	A.D. 2,000

In Ontario, *above,* and other parts of central North America, agriculture and urban development have wiped out much of the original prairie. Such changes alter or destroy natural habitats, bring about the extinction of many species, and threaten many more with extinction.

Maps based on satellite photos of Brazil in 1978, *below,* and 1988, *bottom,* show the rapid rate of human encroachment in the Amazon rain forest. When people cut trails into the forest or chop down trees on plots of land, the natural habitat is fragmented, eventually leading to a loss of species.

Experts have developed a rule of thumb to roughly predict the number of species that have died off or are likely to do so in the near future. This rule, called the *species-area relationship,* says that if a wilderness area is cut in half, about 15 percent of the number of species in the original area will die out.

Original wilderness area

20 original species

Wilderness area cut in half

17 species remaining

3 species die out

Why Species Are Important

BY PETER H. RAVEN

When human beings first appeared on Earth about 2 million years ago, they lived in a biologically rich world, one that boasted millions of other species, including plants, animals, fungi, and microorganisms. Even those early people must have appreciated the natural beauty of living things around them, from individual species such as colorful birds to elegant combinations of species in the form of meadows, forests, and desert landscapes. Our ancestors drew pictures of the animals and plants around them, and evidence suggests that those prehistoric people used animals and plants in their rituals. The presence of nature must have played a significant role in shaping human cultures, and, perhaps, in determining the way in which modern human beings think.

Today, the beauty of living things remains an important part of our lives. We keep pets and house plants, enjoy paintings and photographs of beautiful natural scenes, and relish the beauty of parks and nature preserves. To our eyes, some places in the world are beautiful, and others are ordinary. The difference between them lies largely in the kinds of organisms that they include and the type of communities they form together.

It is easy to imagine how much less satisfying our lives would be if there were only a few species of birds, if all the world's coastlines were covered with buildings, or if forests were completely replaced by farm fields. But the aesthetic importance of nature is just one of several reasons to protect the varied and wonderful species of the Earth. Ecologists point out that living things are vital to the continued functioning of the planet's ecology, and that human beings rely on other species for many of our needs.

A practical view

The most obvious practical reason for preserving Earth's biodiversity is that it supports human life and society. We depend on other organisms, at least to some degree, for virtually every element of our lives. Our food, our medicines, many chemicals, a variety of building materials, and much of our clothing are all derived from living things. Even fossil fuels such as coal and oil, which supply most of the world's power, were formed from organisms that lived millions of years ago.

For example, the energy that sustains human life—and all other life on Earth—is produced entirely by plants. Through the process called *photosynthesis,* plants use the energy of sunlight to combine carbon dioxide with water to make food. When we eat plants or animals that consume plants, this food gives us energy to live.

It might seem obvious that we need plants to survive, but maintaining a *variety* of plants on Earth may be just as important. About 90 percent of all the calories that people consume are supplied by only about 100 kinds of plants, though there are tens of thousands of kinds of plants we might use as food. As the human population continues to grow, and as agricultural land becomes increasingly limited, the few species of plants that supply our food may no longer be sufficient. Soon people may need to look to other species to find food crops for the future.

Living organisms have also supplied almost all of our most important medicines. Many still come directly from plants, fungi, or bacteria. Others that are now made synthetically were originally discovered in nature. In many parts of the world, where manufactured drugs are not available, people use plants alone to treat illness. Since we have identified only a tiny fraction of all the organisms on Earth, we can be certain that many new sources of medicine remain to be discovered.

As scientists continue to make advancements in genetics—the study of heredity—preserving the Earth's biodiversity will become even more beneficial to society. The genes found in the cells of every organism determine the unique characteristics of each living thing. Through a process called genetic engineering, scientists have learned to transfer genes from one organism to another to produce different traits. Scientists used this process in the early 1990's, for example, to develop a variety of cotton that is naturally resistant to pests.

Genetic research has countless applications in agriculture as well as medicine and other fields. This research depends, however, on the continued existence of a variety of genetic material among living things. The loss of species also brings about the elimination of the valuable information found in their genes.

The potential of living things as a useful source of information is not limited to genetics. Every area of knowledge has benefited from the study of living things. Anthropologists have learned about prehistoric human beings by studying our closest living relatives, the apes. Engineers have learned about mechanics by studying the movement of animals.

These examples refer only to creatures that are well known, whereas most organisms have hardly

The author:

Peter H. Raven is director of the Missouri Botanical Garden in St. Louis.

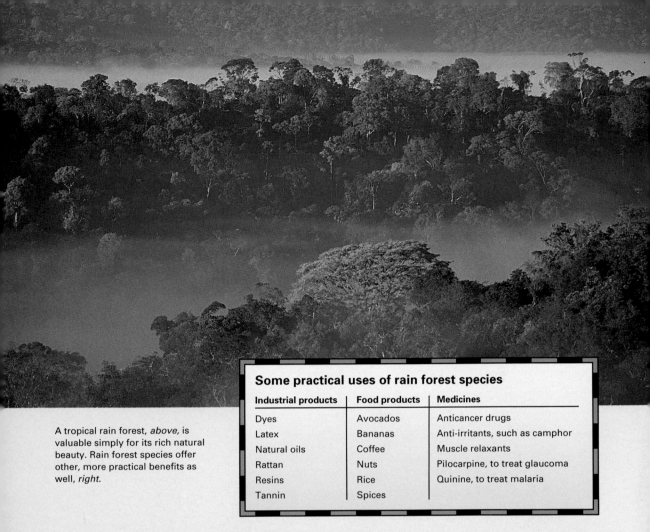

A tropical rain forest, *above,* is valuable simply for its rich natural beauty. Rain forest species offer other, more practical benefits as well, *right.*

Some practical uses of rain forest species

Industrial products	Food products	Medicines
Dyes	Avocados	Anticancer drugs
Latex	Bananas	Anti-irritants, such as camphor
Natural oils	Coffee	Muscle relaxants
Rattan	Nuts	Pilocarpine, to treat glaucoma
Resins	Rice	Quinine, to treat malaria
Tannin	Spices	

come under scientific study. Consider a group like the fungi, which have a huge economic importance. They are used to treat diseases of plants and animals, to preserve food and other products, to manufacture antibiotics, and to make a variety of baked goods and brewed beverages. But we know about only a very small proportion of the total species of fungi that exist. Every time an undiscovered species dies, society loses one more potential source for food, medicine, or knowledge, which we might have used to improve our own situation.

Ecological benefits

From a broader point of view, beyond the specific needs of human beings, preserving species is essential for ecological reasons. Living things provide what scientists call "ecosystem services." An ecosystem contains communities of plants, animals, and microbes along with the nonliving features of the environment such as soil and water. Certain species provide ecosystem services by protecting the soil from erosion, influencing the char-

acteristics of the atmosphere, transforming energy from the sun into food energy, shaping local and regional climates, and performing other functions. Because the species in prairies, rain forests, and other ecosystems do these things, Earth is a suitable place for us to live, and the planet operates as a self-perpetuating system. Killing off species, however, makes it more difficult for an ecosystem to operate successfully, and it may become more difficult for all living things to survive.

Forests, for example, provide a vital ecosystem service: removing massive amounts of carbon dioxide from the atmosphere as plants create food through photosynthesis. Increasing levels of this gas, which has been caused by the combustion of fossil fuels, have been linked with a potential warming of Earth's climate. Even a slight rise in the surface temperature of the Earth could alter the natural patterns of drought and flooding, and bring about widespread environmental damage. As forests are cleared and not replaced, the amount of carbon dioxide in the atmosphere rises to much greater levels.

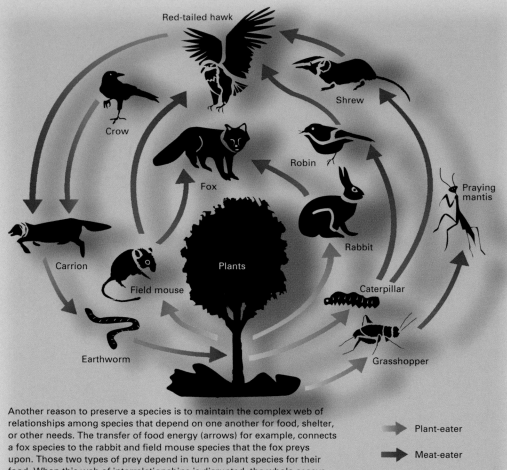

Another reason to preserve a species is to maintain the complex web of relationships among species that depend on one another for food, shelter, or other needs. The transfer of food energy (arrows) for example, connects a fox species to the rabbit and field mouse species that the fox preys upon. Those two types of prey depend in turn on plant species for their food. When this web of interrelationships is disrupted, the whole ecosystem may suffer. One extinction may bring about a series of other extinctions and may eventually disrupt the entire ecosystem.

Plant-eater

Meat-eater

Death and decomposition

People tend to take the ecosystem services for granted, despite evidence that the planet's ecology is under a tremendous strain. Since 1950, about one-fifth of all the world's topsoil has been lost to erosion, for example, largely because plants that naturally hold the soil in their roots were destroyed. The loss of fertile topsoil means fewer plants, less productive farms, and eventually less food for all animals.

The human obligation

Many ecologists say that understanding and maintaining natural communities is the key to sustaining life on Earth as we know it, and that every species is an important part of a whole system. But perhaps the most fundamental reason to protect species is an ethical one, rather than one based on ecology or economics. As far as we know, there are no microorganisms, no plants, no animals, and no fungi on any other planet. The living things that share the world with us are the only other known living things in the universe. Many people believe that we, as a single species, do not have the right to destroy a large proportion of our living companions.

The major destruction of other organisms by human beings began about 10,000 years ago, with the development of agriculture. At that time, our total world population was no more than several million people. As our population has exploded, so has our rate of consumption. Today human beings consume, waste, or change about 40 percent of the *net biological productivity* (everything living organisms produce) on land. It is easy to argue that we are already taking an unreasonable share of the Earth's bounty. Before we increase that share, ecologists believe, we should consider the substantial reasons to respect, value, and—most of all—preserve the organisms that support our lives on Earth. ❧

A History of Attempts to Save Species

BY ERIC G. BOLEN

People have contemplated their relationship with the natural world since ancient times. Some of the first written records of human attitudes toward other species appear in the Bible. One noteworthy passage, which appears in the book of Genesis, states that people "have dominion over the fish of the sea, and over the fowl of the air, and over every living thing that moveth upon the Earth." People have used this passage to justify two very different courses of action, however. Some say that human beings have the right to *exploit* (make unrestricted use of) animals and plants. Others believe that people have a duty to protect other species. This debate—over whether it is more important to exploit living things or to preserve them—continues even today.

During most of history, people exploited living things for food, clothing, shelter, or sport and made little effort to preserve them. Most people considered Earth's natural resources to be unlimited, and they worked hard to improve their methods of hunting and farming. But as the human population grew, there were many more people killing animals and many more farmers turning natural ecosystems into planted croplands. Human activities began to make a greater impact on the living world. As knowledge of this damage increased, some people—the first conservationists—began to call for more responsibility toward living things.

In North America, the first laws to protect any species of wildlife were passed during the 1600's and 1700's. Most of these laws, however, were intended to preserve stocks of game animals, such as deer and wild turkeys. Other animals received no legal protection, nor did any plants. At the same time, the North American colonists targeted some species, such as gray wolves, for elimination, offering people rewards for killing them.

Early conservationists

The notion that wildlife species should be preserved first became widespread in the late 1800's, particularly in the United States. Several American naturalists, including Henry David Thoreau and George Perkins Marsh, helped introduce the idea to the public. In his book *Walden* (1854), Thoreau suggested that people should live in harmony with nature rather than seek to dominate it. Marsh's book *Man and Nature* (1864), later retitled *The Earth as Modified by Human Nature*, was one of the first textbooks to discuss conservation.

The widespread killing of certain species during the 1800's also played a role in Americans' growing concern for wildlife. For example, commercial and sport hunting reduced the American bison population from about 60 million in 1860 to only about 550 animals in 1889. The tremendous population decline in such a short period demonstrated for the first time how easily and rapidly human activities could eliminate another species.

Many bird species also suffered from excessive hunting during the 1800's. Because plumes from herons and egrets were widely sought as decorations for women's hats, tens of thousands of these birds were slaughtered. Some of the first American wildlife conservation societies were formed in the late 1800's to protect birds. These local organizations were called Audubon Societies, in honor of the American naturalist John James Audubon.

Government gets involved

In 1872, the United States established the world's first national park, Yellowstone, in Wyoming, Montana, and Idaho. Soon after, the governments of Canada, Australia, and what is now South Africa created national parks within their borders.

The United States became the first nation to enact a major national conservation law when Congress passed the the Lacey Act in 1900. The Lacey Act made it a federal crime to transport illegally killed animals across state borders. The law also regulated the sale of bird feathers and other animal products and placed controls on the importation of animals.

U.S. President Theodore Roosevelt, a pioneer in the conservation movement, established the first national wildlife refuge at Pelican Island, Fla., in 1903. The island was set aside especially to protect egrets and herons, whose populations had been diminished by plume hunting. Through this action, Roosevelt formally endorsed federal protection of species. Pelican Island became the first unit of a national system of wildlife refuges that has grown to about 500 sites. Other federal refuges protect such imperiled species as whooping cranes, Atwater's prairie chickens, and trumpeter swans.

Another leader of the conservation movement was the American naturalist John Muir, who in 1892 founded the Sierra Club, which became an important conservation organization. Muir persuaded Congress to establish Yosemite National Park and Sequoia National Park and worked closely with President Roosevelt to promote wildlife conservation.

Measures to protect wildlife, however, were not always met with broad public approval. Controversy

The author:

Eric G. Bolen is professor of biology at the University of North Carolina at Wilmington.

Heads of American bison are displayed at a railway station in 1870. Massive bison hunts, often carried out from moving trains, brought the species to the brink of extinction.

arose in 1913, for example, when the city of San Francisco announced plans to build a dam across the Hetch Hetchy River in Yosemite National Park. Muir and other conservationists opposed the construction. But legislators eventually ruled that the water needs of San Francisco were more important than the need to preserve the river region, and the dam was built.

The modern environmental movement

The 1960's brought a new movement to clean up the environment and save plants and animals in the United States. The new generation of conservationists drew inspiration from the words of Aldo Leopold, an American naturalist who wrote *A Sand County Almanac* (1949) and many other books and articles on conservation. Leopold encouraged people to save all species, no matter how insignificant they may seem, because each is a working part of nature. "To keep every cog and wheel," he wrote, "is the first precaution of intelligent tinkering."

Silent Spring, a popular book written by marine biologist Rachel Carson in 1962, also influenced the movement to protect species. The book described how certain widely used pesticides such as DDT harmed wildlife, especially birds.

In response to mounting public concern, the U.S. Congress took a major step toward preserving species in 1966, when it passed the Endangered Species Protection Act. The act authorized the secretary of the Interior to identify and conduct re-

search on endangered species in the United States. The act also authorized the expansion of wildlife refuges to protect endangered species. In 1969, Congress passed the Endangered Species Conservation Act, which recognized endangered species outside of the United States and laid groundwork for more international cooperation in saving species.

Protection was extended to animals of the sea in 1972, when Congress passed the Marine Mammal Protection Act. This act suspended indefinitely the killing of all marine mammals—including whales, walruses, seals, manatees, and sea otters—so that

U.S. President Theodore Roosevelt, left, and naturalist John Muir, right, made important contributions to wildlife conservation during the late 1800's and early 1900's.

The controversy over the snail darter was among several issues leading to passage of the Endangered Species Amendments Act of 1978. This act established a federal review board to help resolve future conflicts between economic development and the survival of species.

Despite such revisions of the law, the struggle over the use of endangered species' habitats has continued. During the 1990's, for example, environmentalists and loggers in the Pacific Northwest were pitted against each other over the loggers' desire to cut trees in the region's old-growth forests, which are home to the endangered northern spotted owl. A similar conflict continues in the Southeastern United States, where logging threatens species such as the red-cockaded woodpecker. In other parts of the nation, developers have fought to build houses, shopping malls, and airports in regions occupied by endangered species. In nearly every case, those opposing the law have argued that economic benefits—such as the employment of local workers—outweigh the loss of species.

U.S. Secretary of the Interior Bruce Babbitt revised the federal government's approach toward protecting endangered species in 1993, when he established the National Biological Survey. This agency, renamed the National Biological Service in 1995, consists of research groups that were previously separated among divisions of the Department of the Interior. The new agency's chief function is to gather scientific data concerning the welfare of species and ecosystems in the United States.

International efforts

The protection of species is not an issue only in the United States, of course. Many nations struggle with the same environmental problems. And, because nature does not acknowledge national boundaries, international efforts are necessary to save some species.

The United States and Canada became pioneer nations in international protection of species in 1916, when they agreed to the Migratory Bird Treaty. The two nations pledged to prohibit the hunting and capture of most songbirds that migrate across their borders. The treaty also halted the hunting of waterfowl during nesting season and prohibited the sale or purchase of migratory birds and their nests, eggs, and feathers.

International attempts to protect species became more common after the United Nations (UN) was created in 1945. In 1948, UN officials formed the International Union for the Protection of Nature, which was renamed the International Union for the Conservation of Nature and Natural Resources

their dwindling populations could be examined.

In 1973, Congress passed the Endangered Species Act, an expanded version of the 1966 act. The new act extended protection to plants as well as animals, and prohibited any threat to endangered species, including hunting, collecting, or construction projects that would destroy the habitat of an endangered species. It also extended protection to wildlife subspecies, such as the Florida panther, a variety of mountain lion that would not otherwise have qualified for protection.

The National Forest Management Act, enacted in 1976, required the management of all species living in national forests. Before this law went into effect, the U.S. Forest Service often limited management to just a few species, particularly those valued for industry or sport.

These laws—particularly the Endangered Species Act of 1973—soon met with opposition from people who claimed the laws unfairly restricted economic development. By protecting the habitat of endangered species, they argued, the laws prevented landowners from making use of their land.

The first major controversy developed in 1978 over construction of the Tellico Dam on the Little Tennessee River. Ecologists discovered while the dam was being built that it was likely to ruin the habitat of the only known population of a small fish called the snail darter. By law, construction on the dam could not continue. But many citizens supported the dam project, because they believed it would bring economic benefits that were more important than the continued existence of a species of little fish. Congress eventually exempted Tellico Dam from the constraints of the Endangered Species Act, and the dam was completed. Small populations of snail darters were later discovered in other rivers, giving conservationists hope that the species will remain in existence.

Members of Greenpeace, an international group that uses direct, nonviolent confrontation to protest the killing of whales and other animals, raise their banner in 1989.

(IUCN) in 1956. The IUCN promotes worldwide conservation and gathers information on the endangered species of the world. The information is published in the *Red Data Book*. In 1961, the IUCN helped establish the World Wildlife Fund, which raises money for conservation programs.

International attempts to protect species took a major step forward in 1975, when the United States and nine other nations signed the Convention on International Trade in Endangered Species of Wild Fauna and Flora (CITES). This agreement regulates trade in wildlife and prohibits the international sale of endangered species or products derived from them, such as furs. By 1995, 128 nations had joined CITES.

Global conservation issues were at the forefront in June 1992, when delegates from 178 nations gathered in Rio de Janeiro, Brazil, for the UN Conference on Environment and Development, known as the Earth Summit. The conference was designed to seek international solutions for a variety of environmental problems, including the worldwide loss of species. Delegates forged the Convention on Biological Diversity, a treaty that acknowledged the importance of maintaining the variety of the world's plants and animals. By late 1994, the legislative bodies of 97 nations had ratified the treaty. The United States signed the treaty in June 1993, but as of mid-1995, Congress had not yet ratified it.

The need to save species is a particularly complicated issue for nonindustrial nations. A large percentage of the world's tropical rain forests and other areas of rich biodiversity lie within the borders of these nations. In many cases, however, most of the people live entirely by farming, and they must resort to cutting and burning the forest to make room for crops. In other cases, governments endorse the exploitation of forest resources in an attempt to boost the living standards of their impoverished citizens. Industrial nations have put pressure on these countries to preserve remaining habitats, while local farmers and businessmen have argued for the right to use the natural resources to climb out of poverty.

International experts say that it is possible, however, for a poor nation to protect its biodiversity and make money from it at the same time. They point to Costa Rica as an example. This small Central American nation has committed 12 percent of its land to national parks—more than any other country. Many nations have provided financial support for Costa Rica's conservation efforts, and today Costa Rica is able to derive millions of dollars per year from tourists who come to visit the nation's lush and unspoiled forests.

Scientists and officials from many nations express hope that international cooperation will help maintain the world's biologically rich and varied ecosystems. The Earth Summit and other efforts in the 1990's mark an unprecedented commitment to halt the loss of species. If such trends continue, experts say, we may eventually find a balance in the historic debate over the desire to exploit species and the responsibility to preserve them. ❦

A logger in Washington state protests environmental laws that may restrict logging and force layoffs in the forest industry.

The Science of Preventing Extinctions

BY THOMAS E. LOVEJOY

In the late 1800's, when the once-massive herds of American bison had dwindled to just a few hundred animals, zoologist William Hornaday led a campaign to reverse the animal's slide toward extinction. Hornaday and other members of the American Bison Society convinced the U.S. Congress to set aside land and contribute funds to save the species. In special reserves—including one in Washington, D.C.—bison grazed and bred in peace. Thanks to these efforts, the herd has grown to more than 15,000 animals.

Unfortunately, American bison represent one of only a few success stories among many attempts to save endangered species. In the context of today's extinction problem, the program to bring back bison seems remarkably simple. As time passes and threats to species worldwide become more serious, the challenge of protecting species grows more complicated. Ecologists believe that the problem calls for more drastic measures, a stronger public commitment, and greater knowledge about the working of ecosystems.

Protecting individual species

Since the conservation movement began in the late 1800's, most attempts at preserving wildlife have been directed toward saving individual species. Wild turkey and American alligator populations were restored simply by prohibiting hunting in their habitats. In other cases, a plant or animal species was saved by protecting or restoring its habitat. During the early 1900's, for example, conservationists helped wood ducks survive by furnishing nest boxes as a substitute for their natural homes— cavities in older trees—which were depleted with the clearing of forests. In the case of the small fish species called the Devil's Hole pupfish, the solution was to limit the volume of water extracted from groundwater supplies by local communities.

Conservationists have also attempted to save individual species through *captive breeding,* in which animals are bred and the offspring raised in captivity until they can be released into a protected wild area. During the 1980's, scientists successfully bred the peregrine falcon, whose population east of the Mississippi River was wiped out by the poisonous effects of DDT and other pesticides, which have since been banned in the United States. Several pairs of these falcons have been released in the wild and into large cities, where skyscrapers resemble the cliffs that are the falcon's natural nesting site.

Captive breeding, however, has suffered much criticism. During the early 1980's, controversy arose over the removal of California condors from the wild for captive breeding. Opponents of the move feared that once the few remaining condors were taken, there would no longer be support for protecting their southern California habitat. Condors were successfully bred at the San Diego Zoo, a leading institution for captive breeding. But efforts to reintroduce the birds by 1995 had largely failed because threats in their habitat, such as a contaminated food supply, still exist. Biologists have also had only partial success in returning some captive-bred animals, including the black-footed ferret and the golden lion tamarin, to the wild.

Nevertheless, captive breeding remains an important part of species conservation. Without such efforts, some animals would surely have become extinct. Although efforts to reintroduce California condors have failed, captive breeding has, at least, ensured that some of the birds are still living.

Today, biologists are developing new methods to breed animals while maintaining wild populations. For example, scientists have attempted to ensure that both captive-bred and wild Puerto Rican parrots are managed jointly. Management of these endangered birds has included placing eggs from captive nests into nests in the wild and other measures.

Scientists have become convinced, however, that Earth's biodiversity cannot be maintained solely through efforts to preserve individual species in isolation. Experts say that even in the United States—a nation with a comparatively strong set of environmental laws, many public and private conservation organizations, and a nature-oriented public—the single-species approach is not working well.

The centerpiece of this approach is the Endangered Species Act, which extends protection to any species on an endangered species list compiled by the Department of the Interior. Since the act was passed in 1973, many conservationists have expressed concern over its limitations and called for broader legislation. They point out that the process of creating the list requires so much time that many species become extinct before they can receive protection. And, too often, attempts to save a species are not begun until that species is officially declared endangered.

The author:

Thomas E. Lovejoy is Counselor to the Secretary on Biodiversity and Environmental Affairs at the Smithsonian Institution in Washington, D.C.

Protecting habitats

Today, many ecologists believe that conservation of wildlife would be more effective if efforts to protect a species began earlier. They believe efforts should start before the species reaches the brink of extinction, when its plight indicates that many other species in the ecosystem may soon become endangered. According to this view, the population decline among northern spotted owls in the Northwestern United States in the early 1990's could be seen as a signal that the entire region was facing environmental threats. Efforts to save the owl alone through limited measures such as captive breeding could not solve the problems the whole region faces. Many ecologists conclude that the main cause of the owl's endangerment—habitat destruction, primarily through logging—must be eliminated if the region's many species are to survive.

Many scientists thus argue that society should concentrate on conserving whole ecosystems, thereby saving the individual species that live within them. By focusing on managing whole ecosystems, along with all the species they include, biologists believe that they could drastically reduce the need for emergency measures to save individual species. Instead of attempting again and again to bring species back from the brink of extinction, scientists could devote their energies to finding ways for human activities to take place without causing so much environmental harm.

U.S. Secretary of the Interior Bruce Babbitt took strides toward this approach by establishing the National Biological Service in 1993. This science agency is charged with assessing the status of all U.S. ecosystems and the biodiversity within them. Officials hope that this type of "biological record-keeping" will make it possible to recognize and handle threats to species before they become serious problems.

Since its birth, however, the National Biological Service has suffered severe criticism from many legislators and citizens. Some argue that the agency's activities could threaten the rights of property owners. If the agency discovers an endangered species on private land, use of that property might ultimately be restricted to protect the species. Another common criticism is that the new agency costs too much to operate.

The whole-ecosystem approach has been applied to the California coastal sage scrub ecosystem, much of which has been eliminated since the mid-1900's by the urban development of five southern California counties. If development were allowed to continue, several species of plants and animals would likely vanish. But in 1993, conservation groups, industry leaders, and government officials began forging a plan to preserve enough of the sage scrub ecosystem to sustain the area's species.

Crucial areas of research

Although most ecologists agree that whole ecosystems and individual species should be considered in conserving biodiversity, many questions remain

about the best way to do that. Scores of scientists are busy conducting research to amass more data in those areas.

For example, one persistent ecological question is: how can we preserve wildlife when we know so little about it? The identity of millions of species, how they relate to their environment, and where they can be found are all unknown today. According to one approach, we could make progress by creating conservation pro-

Some attempts to save species since 1800	
Species	**Natural habitat**
Passenger pigeon	North America
Wood duck	Eastern United States
Kirtland's warbler	Central Michigan
California condor	Southern California
Whooping crane	North America
Bald eagle	North America
Atwater prairie chicken	Texas
American bison	Western United States
Gray whale	Pacific Ocean off North American coast
Black-footed ferret	North American Great Plains
Sea otter	Western coast of North America
Red wolf	Southeastern United States
Panda	China
Devil's Hole pupfish	Single desert sinkhole in Nevada
Snail darter	Central Tennessee
Paddlefish	Southern Mississippi River
Gila monster	Southwestern North America
American alligator	Southern United States
Sea turtle (includes 7 species)	World's oceans
Desert tortoise	Western United States
Giant sequoia	Sierra Nevada mountains, California
Venus flytrap	North and South Carolina

A researcher weighs a captive-bred golden lion tamarin. The brightly colored monkeys, native to eastern Brazil, are among several endangered animal species that scientists have bred in captivity and hope to reintroduce in the wild.

Management approach	Status of population
Protection from hunting	Extinct
Hunting restrictions; placement of nest boxes	Recovered from threat of extinction
Habitat protection; habitat maintenance through controlled forest fires	Increasing slowly
Captive breeding	Nearly extinct
Hunting ban; protection in refuges; captive breeding	Increasing slowly
Hunting ban; ban on certain pesticides	Increasing steadily
Hunting ban; protection in refuges; captive breeding	Nearly extinct
Protection in refuges	Recovered from threat of extinction
Hunting ban	Recovered from threat of extinction
Protection of individuals in zoos; captive breeding; disease control	Nearly extinct
Hunting ban; relocation	Increasing steadily
Hunting ban; protection in refuges; captive breeding	Increasing slowly
Hunting ban; captive breeding	Declining
Habitat protection and maintenance; captive breeding	Stable
Habitat protection; captive breeding	Stable
Habitat protection; captive breeding	Stable
Habitat protection	Stable
Hunting restrictions	Recovered from threat of extinction
Hunting ban; captive breeding; protective devices on fishing nets	Declining
Protection of individuals in zoos; habitat protection	Declining
Protection in parks	Stable
Habitat protection	Stable

grams based on the species we already know. Proponents of this view believe conservation practices based on known species are likely to save many that we have not yet identified.

Another important area of conservation research involves the design and size of wildlife refuges. Scientists have collected data about this subject by studying a trend called *habitat fragmentation*. Human activities, such as clearing forests or tilling fields, often leave behind only small tracts of the original ecosystem, known as habitat fragments. Scientists have found that over time, far fewer species are able to survive in these fragments than can survive in the original tract. These studies have caused scientists to question the long-term effectiveness of many of the world's wildlife refuges. Some experts argue that if the reserves are not expanded—or perhaps connected—the number of species within them will dwindle.

Other scientists are conducting critical research on the likely effect of global changes such as climate variations on biodiversity. During the history of life on Earth, periodic climate changes have caused natural communities to break apart and reassemble in different combinations and different locations. But as wildlife becomes increasingly confined to isolated reserves in human-dominated landscapes, the ability of species to adapt to climate change may be severely limited. At the same time, many scientists believe that atmospheric pollution from fossil fuels will increase the levels of greenhouse gases in the atmosphere and lead to a global warming. If these effects prove as

Costa Rican scientists use suction tubes to collect tiny insect specimens in jars. Their work is part of a larger scientific effort to gather data on the species that make up Costa Rica's rain forest ecosystems. In the tropics and elsewhere, such studies are designed to help ecologists develop better methods of protecting entire ecosystems.

significant as scientists predict, we will need to know a great deal more about how atmospheric changes affect Earth's ecosystems, particularly those that have been severely fragmented.

Ecologists are also working to illuminate the relationship between economics and nature. Most people do not realize that biodiversity can be a commodity with economic value. For example, nations and industries tend to place a monetary value on goods and products produced, but not on biodiversity or other natural resources from which they are derived. By trying to assess the economic value of biodiversity, ecologists hope to convince industry and government leaders of the significance of conservation goals.

Establishing conservation priorities

Despite efforts to demonstrate the economic value of biodiversity, many scientists believe that funding for conservation is inadequate and likely to remain so for some time. This problem leads to another important area of research—setting conservation priorities.

Some ecologists say that the best approach is to try to save the widest variety of species. For exam-ple, they would devote conservation funds to a project to save a species that is very different from others, rather than a project to save a plant or animal that is similar to species found in abundance. According to this reasoning, a platypus, which is highly unique, might receive more attention than one of the many species of beetles.

Another approach is based on protecting so-called "charismatic" species, usually large mammals and birds. The notion is that efforts to protect tigers, wolves, or grizzly bears will end up protecting the multitudes of other species that occur in the same habitat.

More and more scientists are beginning to believe that placing priorities on only certain species cannot solve the worldwide problem of extinction. And limiting scientific efforts to such measures may cause us to overlook more critical issues that can only be addressed by looking at an ecosystem as a whole. Such issues include the relationship of biodiversity to the state of an ecosystem and the likelihood that one extinction will lead to another. Factors such as these leave little doubt in the minds of most scientists that conserving whole ecosystems will prove far and away the most effective method for saving most species. 🐞

Reading and Study Guide

For further reading:

Durrell, Lee. *Gaia: State of the Ark Atlas.* Gaia Books Limited, 1986.

Eldredge, Niles. *The Miner's Canary.* Prentice Hall Press, 1991.

Mann, Charles C. and Plummer, Mark L. *Noah's Choice: The Future of Endangered Species.* Alfred A. Knopf, 1995.

Myers, Norman. *Gaia: An Atlas of Planet Management.* Gaia Books Limited, 1993.

Myers, Norman. *The Sinking Ark.* Pergamon Press, 1979.

Schaller, George B. *The Last Panda.* The University of Chicago Press, 1993.

Ward, Peter. *The End of Evolution: On Mass Extinctions and the Preservation of Biodiversity.* Bantam Books, 1994.

Wilson, Edward O. *The Diversity of Life.* Harvard University Press, 1992.

Worldwatch Institute. *State of the World.* Norton, 1992: "Conserving Biological Diversity," pp. 9-26.

Questions for thought and discussion:

1. How do scientists define an episode of mass extinction? At what other times and in what other ways do species become extinct?

2. Imagine that you are having a discussion with a friend about the mass extinction the Earth now faces. Your friend points out that several other mass extinctions have occurred in previous eras. This episode is no different than any of the past episodes, your friend claims, and extinction today is therefore a perfectly natural process. Is your friend right or wrong? What evidence supports your answer?

3. Scientists do not know how many species exist on Earth, so they must rely on special methods to estimate the world's rate of extinction. Describe those methods.

4. Imagine that you are the governor of a heavily forested state. Logging is your state's largest industry. However, an environmental group has been pressuring you to restrict logging to save the habitat of a critically endangered species of squirrel. Logging companies warn that they would be forced to lay off thousands of workers if their industry's activities are restricted.

   One of the loggers' chief arguments is that the survival of one type of squirrel is not as important as the well-being of many families. How would you respond to that argument? Can you suggest actions that might forge a compromise?

5. Give a few examples of "ecosystem services" that species provide. Why are the services important? When is it necessary to save a species in order to keep an ecosystem functioning?

6. Name some events or trends that contributed to increased public concern for wildlife in the United States during the late 1800's. What kind of government action did this concern help to eventually bring about?

7. What factors make conservation a complicated issue in nonindustrial nations?

8. Pretend you are a U.S. senator and head of a special congressional committee on biodiversity. In its next meeting, the committee will review two proposals for use of its limited budget. One proposes that you apply most of your budget to maintaining captive populations of animals that are extinct in the wild. The other proposes that you withdraw funds for captive breeding and spend most of your budget on research for improving national wildlife refuges.

   Explain the advantages and disadvantages of the two proposals. In which direction would you lead the committee? Is a compromise possible? If so, describe it.

For more information:

IUCN–The World Conservation Union
  Ave du Mont Blanc
  CH-1196 Gland, Switzerland

Izaac Walton League of America
  1401 Wilson Boulevard, Level B
  Arlington, VA 22209

National Audubon Society
  950 Third Avenue
  New York, NY 10022

National Wildlife Federation
  1400 16th Street NW
  Washington, DC 20036

Nature Conservancy
  1815 N. Lynn Street
  Arlington, VA 22209

Sierra Club
  730 Polk Street
  San Francisco, CA 94109

World Wildlife Fund/Conservation Foundation
  1250 24th Street NW
  Washington, DC 20037

Science Year contributors report on the year's major developments in their respective fields. The articles in this section are arranged alphabetically.

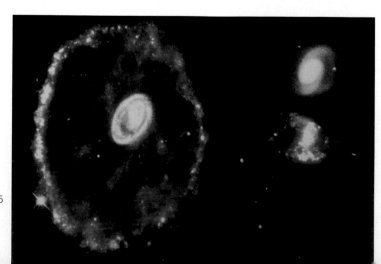

Page 232

Page 259

Seedless watermelons may become more abundant and affordable at the supermarket, thanks to a new, rapid method to produce seeds for watermelon plants. Developmental biologist Dennis Gray and his associate Michael Compton at the Leesburg Center for the University of Florida's Institute of Food and Agricultural Sciences reported the new method in June 1994.

Seedless watermelons yield more fruit per plant compared to seeded varieties and last longer in the supermarket than melons with seeds. Agricultural scientists have known how to produce seedless watermelons since the early 1950's, but the seeds for the plants are expensive—as much as $1,200 per pound, compared with only $15 to $200 per pound for ordinary seeds.

A time-consuming process had been used to produce the plants that bear the seeds. In this process, scientists for commercial seed producers chemically altered hundreds of normal watermelon seedlings in order to produce plants called *tetraploids*. A tetraploid rarely occurs in nature. It has four sets of *chromo-*

somes (tiny structures that carry genes, the units of heredity) instead of the normal two sets. The scientists then cross the tetraploids with normal plants. Some of the offspring are *triploids*, which have three sets of chromosomes. The triploids produce the sterile watermelons that are called seedless. In actuality, sterile watermelons do contain seeds, but they are small, white, and edible—similar to the seeds in cucumbers.

According to seed producers, the current method of producing seeds results in a very low yield. The Florida scientists streamlined the process and increased seed yield by using a tissue-culture technique to create the tetraploids from normal seeded watermelon plants.

The scientists cultured pieces of *cotyledon* (an embryo leaf from inside a seed) from normal seeds in a laboratory dish. The cultured cotyledon pieces produce normal and tetraploid shoots. But scientists rooted only the tetraploid shoots and grew them into plants for crossing with diploid plants. The new method also allows scientists to more quickly produce improved seedless varieties.

The student inventors of totally biodegradable crayons pose on a pile of soybeans, the major ingredient in the crayons, which won a 1994 contest sponsored by Purdue University in West Lafayette, Ind., and the Indiana Soybean Development Council. The students developed a crayon manufacturing process using soybean oil instead of petroleum-based paraffin, the waxy ingredient in commercial crayons. In 1995, they applied for a patent on their "Earth Colors" crayons.

Putting Tobacco to Good Use

To many Americans, the tobacco plant is a loathsome crop, the source of health-impairing cigarettes, cigars, and pipe and chewing tobacco. But several groups of scientists were working to rehabilitate the plant's reputation in 1994 and 1995. Their hope was to use tobacco as a source of food protein, drugs, and other products that are not dangerous to public health.

Tobacco is a small crop in the United States, compared with many food crops, but it can be highly profitable. In 1994, according to the U.S. Department of Agriculture, tobacco grew on 272,000 hectares (673,000 acres), mostly in the Southeastern states. That compares with 1.5 million hectares (3.8 million acres) of corn grown in only one state, Wisconsin. However, many rural Southern communities are economically dependent on the tobacco harvest, and agricultural researchers such as Raymond C. Long at North Carolina State University in Raleigh say that finding other uses for tobacco is vital.

Interest in using tobacco for purposes other than smoking products dates to the early 1900's, when British scientists considered using a protein found in tobacco for food. The protein, known as Fraction 1, is colorless and odorless, and it could be added to foods to boost protein content without altering the foods' taste or smell.

In the late 1970's, biologist Samuel G. Wildman helped build an experimental production facility in North Carolina to extract Fraction 1 from tobacco. But food companies showed no interest in developing the process further, partly because they were not convinced it could be done economically. Since then, advances in biotechnology—including the ability to insert genes into plants to produce various products—may have changed that economic picture. (Genes, the units of heredity, contain the chemical codes for the production of proteins.)

Scientists today call tobacco "the laboratory rat of the plant kingdom" because they know a great deal about its biochemistry, physiology, and genetics. As a result, they can experiment on it easily. Tobacco also grows quickly and is easy to harvest and process. Moreover, it produces large amounts of plant tissue, which means it can churn out large amounts of its proteins and other biochemicals.

In 1995, a team of biologists with Biosource Technologies of Vacaville, Calif., worked to develop tobacco plants that produce compounds useful as a vaccine against malaria, a mosquito-borne parasitic disease that is common in tropical and subtropical areas. The scientists inserted genes from the parasite that causes malaria into a virus called the tobacco mosaic virus. The researchers then infected tobacco plants with the modified virus. The virus duplicated itself thousands of times in the plants, and each new copy produced the proteins coded for by the parasite genes. The researchers believe that if such proteins are extracted from the tobacco plants and injected into human beings, the compounds will cause the human immune system to manufacture disease-fighting proteins called antibodies. The antibodies should be capable of warding off future infections with the actual malaria parasite.

Biosource Technologies also experimented with using tobacco plants as "living factories" for producing disease-fighting molecules called defensins. The company hoped to be able to extract these molecules and sell them as antibiotics.

In North Carolina, biologists used genetic engineering techniques in 1994 to create tobacco plants that produced a cow protein called bovine lysozyme. Laboratory tests had shown that the protein was capable of killing certain types of bacteria that infect plants.

Halfway around the world, Karin Herbers and other scientists at the Institute for Plant Genetics and Tissue Culture in Gattersleben, Germany, were in 1995 genetically altering tobacco plants to produce xylanase. Xylanase is an enzyme used in the production of paper.

Before these or any other alternative uses of tobacco become reality, researchers must determine if the crop can be grown economically for such purposes. Some experts argue that is unlikely, because tobacco requires a great deal of fertilizer and pesticides. And if tobacco is grown for its protein or as a kind of "green factory," it may be intensively cultivated and harvested several times a growing season, a practice that may deplete the soil of nutrients.

Another issue may keep tobacco from finding use as a source of food protein. Considering its bad reputation, people may not want to eat baked goods fortified with tobacco protein, fearing a dose of nicotine in every bite. In fact, the level of nicotine in Fraction 1 is about 1,000 times below what the U.S. Food and Drug Administration (FDA) allows in poultry fat, which becomes contaminated due to nicotine-containing insecticides. Fraction 1 also contains far less nicotine than is found naturally in tomatoes and green peppers. And agricultural researchers say that ultimately, consumers can rest assured that any products derived from tobacco will be approved by the FDA before reaching the market.   [Harvey Black]

Agriculture continued

Antibiotics for soybeans. A bacterium has been found that protects soybean plants from root diseases in a novel way. It produces two antibiotics that inhibit the growth of fungi that cause the diseases. Plant pathologist Jo Handelsman at the University of Wisconsin in Madison discovered the bacterium, called UW85, and LiphaTech Inc. presented the results of five years of field tests to the U.S. Environmental Protection Agency (EPA) in October 1994.

The EPA must approve the use of UW85, or any biological agent, before it can be used against plant diseases. If approved, UW85 could save soybean growers nationwide an estimated $2 million per year, the amount currently spent on chemical *fungicides* (substances that kill or inhibit fungi).

Handelsman found that soybean plants without the bacterium on their root systems developed such diseases as root rot, but those with UW85 were protected. Analysis revealed that UW85 produces zwittermicin A, a type of antibiotic called an aminopolyol. The bacterium also produces another antibiotic whose chemical structure has not yet been fully defined.

Harvesting plastic. In just two years, botanists have succeeded in engineering a 100-fold increase in the amount of plastic produced by certain plants in the laboratory, according to research announced in December 1994. The increase may make "growing" plastic economical for the first time.

Researchers at Carnegie Institution of Washington in Washington, D.C., first produced plastic from a genetically modified mustard plant, *Arabidopsis thaliana*, in 1992. To modify the plant, the scientists gave it three genes from a bacterium found in soil. Under certain conditions, the bacterium produces granules of a natural plastic material called polyhydroxybutyrate (PHB). PHB is similar to the petroleum-based plastics that are used to make milk jugs and soda bottles, but PHB is highly biodegradable. In the 1992 project, the genetically altered *Arabidopsis* plants were severely stunted and produced only small amounts of PHB granules throughout their roots, stems, and leaves.

Pacific coho salmon given genes of sockeye salmon are more than 11 times larger (right) than normal coho at the same age (left). Marine biologists reported their success in using genetic manipulation to boost salmon growth in September 1994. The process could enable fish farms to more quickly produce salmon of marketable size.

In 1994, the researchers genetically altered *Arabidopsis* plants so that the plastic granules would be concentrated only in the *chloroplasts,* the structures in a plant cell where photosynthesis occurs. The change produced plants of normal size and, more importantly, dramatically increased PHB production. The scientists said that their success at retargeting PHB production suggests that they should be able to genetically alter crop plants such as potatoes and soybeans to concentrate PHB production in easily harvested parts of the plants.

Improving legumes. Legume plants such as alfalfa, beans, and peanuts could be more nutritionally valuable to human beings and grazing animals worldwide if they provided a better balance of amino acids, the building blocks of proteins. Researchers reported in January 1995 that they had boosted the food value of legumes by giving them a gene from corn plants.

Human beings and grazing animals need 20 amino acids to build tissues. Human beings must get at least 9 amino acids from their food, but no plant in nature has all of them. Legumes are high in one essential amino acid—lysine—but deficient in two others—methionine and cysteine. Corn, on the other hand, is low in lysine and rich in methionine and cysteine.

Plant geneticists at New Mexico State University's Plant Genetic Engineering Laboratory in Las Cruces sought to redress the deficiency in legumes. They gave a number of food and forage plants a gene that directs the production and storage of a protein in corn plants.

The modified plants produced high levels of corn protein that contained methionine and cysteine. The corn protein was stored in the leaf cells of the transgenic plants, so the protein would be easily accessible to grazing animals that ate the leaves.

The scientists said they hoped their procedure would also work with rice, and perhaps wheat, barley, and potatoes. More-nutritional rice would be especially beneficial because about two-thirds of the world's population relies on rice as the major source of food.

Industrial ash improves soils. A by-product of burning coal—coal fly ash—can increase crop yields when applied to sandy, drought-prone soils, according to soil specialists at the University of Delaware in Newark who announced this finding in December 1994. Because many power companies in the United States and in other nations burn coal to produce electricity, coal fly ash is abundant.

The Delaware soil scientists found that the ash improved the soil in test sites in several ways. The fine particles that make up the ash enhanced the soil's capacity for holding moisture and thus reduced the amount of runoff after rain. The ash also contained all the nutrients that growing plants require except nitrogen. Finally, the ash acted as a liming material, which neutralizes acidic soils.

Experts said the crops most likely to benefit from ash applications to the soil are corn and wheat. The Delaware researchers had begun to investigate any potentially hazardous components of the ash that would affect growing plants. They predicted that by the year 2000, they should have some on-farm testing projects underway.

Trapping cotton weevils. Farmers had a new weapon in 1995 to battle the boll weevil, a major cotton pest. Entomologists from the U.S. Department of Agriculture and the Agriculture Research Service in Mississippi, who developed the device, presented it at the annual meeting of the American Association for Advancement of Science held in Atlanta, Ga., in February 1995.

The device is a heavy cardboard tube coated with a mixture of shellac and the insecticide malathion. Before taking the device into the field, a farmer puts a boll weevil pheromone inside the tube. A pheromone is a chemical substance released by animals to attract or in some other way communicate with other members of their species. Boll weevils are attracted by the pheromone, enter the tube, and die from exposure to the malathion.

The pheromone attracts only boll weevils, leaving beneficial insects to control boll worms and other pests that destroy cotton. The stick requires only 5 to 10 percent of the insecticides used in most spray applications, which makes it more economical and safer for the environment.   [Steve Cain]

In WORLD BOOK, see AGRICULTURE.

Fossils discovered in Ethiopia belong to a new prehuman species that lived more than 4 million years ago, making it the earliest known human ancestor, according to a report published in September 1994. Tim D. White, an anthropologist at the University of California at Berkeley, and his colleagues unearthed the fossils at Aramis, Ethiopia, beginning in late 1992. The new species lived relatively soon after the last shared ancestor of hominids and apes lived. (Hominids include human beings and their close prehuman ancestors.) Many anthropologists believe the last shared ancestor lived 5 million to 6 million years ago.

Oldest ancestor. White and his colleagues dubbed the new species *Australopithecus ramidus*. They took the name *ramidus* from the word for *root* in the language of the Afar people, who live near Aramis. The fossils, which include four arm bones, skull and jaw fragments, and teeth from at least 17 individuals, are about 4.4 million years old. The scientists determined the age of the fossils by dating layers of volcanic ash found below the deposits.

Before the Aramis discovery, the oldest known hominid was *Australopithecus afarensis*, which evolved beginning about 3.9 million years ago. *A. afarensis* walked on two legs like later hominids, but it retained numerous apelike features, notably its long arms and the shape of its skull and *canine teeth* (pointed teeth next to the incisors).

The Aramis fossils show that *A. ramidus* was even more apelike than *A. afarensis*. However, the fossils exhibit several humanlike features. One is the shape of the canine teeth, which are smaller and less pointed than the daggerlike canines of apes such as chimpanzees, the animals most closely related to human beings. Another feature is the location of the *foramen magnum*, a hole at the base of the skull through which nerve fibers pass from the brain to the spinal cord. In *A. ramidus*, as in later hominids, the foramen magnum lies closer to the front of the skull than in chimpanzees and other apes.

The position of the foramen magnum is particularly important because it could mean that *A. ramidus* balanced its

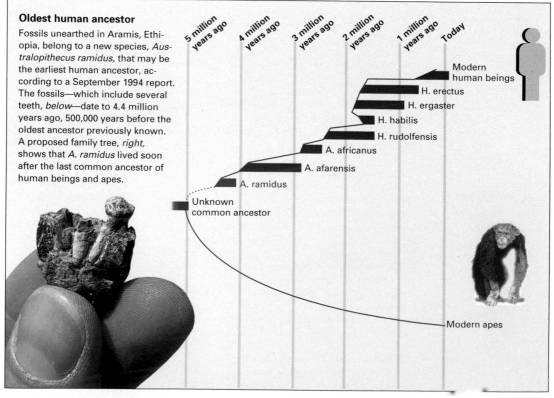

Oldest human ancestor

Fossils unearthed in Aramis, Ethiopia, belong to a new species, *Australopithecus ramidus,* that may be the earliest human ancestor, according to a September 1994 report. The fossils—which include several teeth, *below*—date to 4.4 million years ago, 500,000 years before the oldest ancestor previously known. A proposed family tree, *right,* shows that *A. ramidus* lived soon after the last common ancestor of human beings and apes.

5 million years ago · 4 million years ago · 3 million years ago · 2 million years ago · 1 million years ago · Today

Modern human beings
H. erectus
H. ergaster
H. habilis
H. rudolfensis
A. africanus
A. afarensis
A. ramidus
Unknown common ancestor
Modern apes

head atop its spinal column in roughly the way that living people do. Only by balancing its head in this way could *A. ramidus* walk *bipedally* (on two feet). Most anthropologists have believed that bipedalism evolved among hominids that dwelt in the *savanna* (grassland with scattered trees), where an upright stance would allow individuals to see predators at greater distances. However, animal and plant fossils found near the *A. ramidus* remains indicate that *A. ramidus* may have lived in a woodland habitat. This suggests that an open environment may not have been required for upright walking to evolve.

Only bones from the pelvis or legs can show conclusively that an individual was bipedal, and the initial Aramis finds did not include such bones. This gap was filled in late 1994, when White and his team revisited Aramis and recovered more than two-thirds of a single *A. ramidus* skeleton, including leg bones. An analysis of these bones was expected to resolve any questions about the place of *A. ramidus* in the human family.

The peopling of Eurasia. Fossil evidence from the former Soviet republic of Georgia suggests that human beings had arrived at the boundary of Asia and Europe by nearly 1.8 million years ago, according to a February 1995 report. The new evidence bolsters the view, first raised in 1994, that human beings began migrating from their African homeland into Asia and, perhaps, Europe earlier than had been thought.

Most researchers believe the first migrants were members of *Homo erectus,* which arose in Africa about 1.8 million years ago. (*H. erectus* is thought to be the most recent ancestor of *Homo sapiens,* the species that includes modern and early modern human beings.) In the traditional view, *H. erectus* left Africa between 1.4 million and 1 million years ago. In 1994, scientists who analyzed *H. erectus* fossil beds from Java, Indonesia, suggested that the species had reached Java by about 1.8 million years ago, soon after it evolved. But the Javan dates are controversial, and many specialists believe that no human fossils from Asia are older than about 1 million years.

In their 1995 report, Georgian paleobiologists described finds—stone tools and a human lower jaw from Dmanisi, Georgia—that appear to support the Javan dates. The scientists reached this conclusion after calculating that volcanic rock from just below the finds was formed about 1.8 million years ago. In addition, animal fossils found with the remains resemble 1.8-million- to 1.6-million-year-old fossils previously unearthed elsewhere in Eurasia.

The character of the Dmanisi stone tools seems to fit the estimate of their age. The tools resemble pebble tools made between 2.5 million and 1.7 million years ago at Tanzania's Olduvai Gorge and other African sites. Also, the Dmanisi tools do not include double-edged cutting tools called hand axes, which first appeared in Africa 1.7 million to 1.4 million years ago—after *H. erectus* supposedly migrated to the Georgian site.

However, some anthropologists question whether the Dmanisi jaw is actually 1.8 million years old. These scientists say the jaw appears less primitive than *H. erectus* jaws of that age or even younger from Africa and Asia.

Another problem with the Dmanisi date is that it is much earlier than the time human beings apparently migrated to Europe. Excavators have found no European site that is clearly older than 1 million years, and some archaeologists have concluded that people reached Europe only about 500,000 years ago.

If new studies confirm the Dmanisi date, then anthropologists will need to explain the lack of equally ancient evidence for human migration into Europe. Either researchers have overlooked such evidence, or some aspect of climate or environment kept people out of Europe for a long time after they reached its eastern frontier.

Toolmakers' thumbs. For years, anthropologists have believed that members of the genus *Homo,* the group of species to which modern human beings belong, were the only hominids able to produce stone tools. They thought the first toolmaker was *Homo habilis,* the species that gave rise to *H. erectus.* In September 1994, a researcher challenged this view, arguing that a more apelike species called *Paranthropus robustus* also was able to make such tools. (Some anthropologists believe *P. robustus* should be known as *Australopithecus robustus.*) *P. robustus* became extinct about 1 million years ago. Researchers

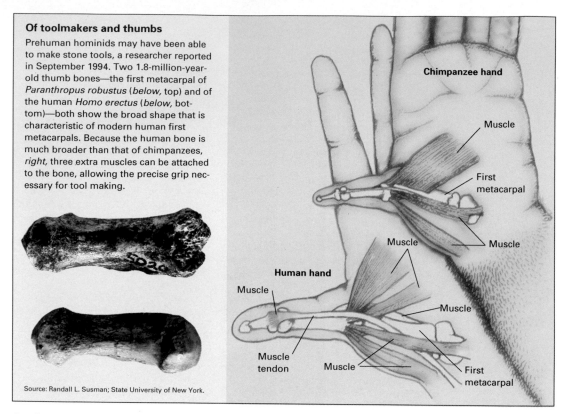

Of toolmakers and thumbs

Prehuman hominids may have been able to make stone tools, a researcher reported in September 1994. Two 1.8-million-year-old thumb bones—the first metacarpal of *Paranthropus robustus* (*below,* top) and of the human *Homo erectus* (*below,* bottom)—both show the broad shape that is characteristic of modern human first metacarpals. Because the human bone is much broader than that of chimpanzees, *right,* three extra muscles can be attached to the bone, allowing the precise grip necessary for tool making.

Chimpanzee hand

Muscle

First metacarpal

Muscle

Muscle

Human hand

Muscle

Muscle

Muscle tendon

Muscle

First metacarpal

Source: Randall L. Susman; State University of New York.

Anthropology continued

believe that a common ancestor of *P. robustus* and *H. habilis* lived between 3 million and 2.5 million years ago.

The oldest stone tools consist of stone flakes and flaked pebbles of the Oldowan culture, which appeared about 2.5 million years ago. At Olduvai Gorge and other African sites, Oldowan artifacts were found together with *H. habilis* fossils. Anthropologists who studied the *H. habilis* finds believed it was a meat-eater, who used the tools it made to kill or scavenge animals such as wildebeest and giraffe. At some sites, however, Oldowan artifacts were also found with *P. robustus* fossils. This species had a smaller brain and larger chewing teeth than *H. habilis,* supporting the idea that it was neither a toolmaker nor a meat-eater.

The researcher who challenged this view, Randall L. Susman of the State University of New York at Stony Brook, based his analysis on the shape of the first metacarpal, a bone that lies at the base of the thumb. In human beings, the first metacarpal is broader than in chimpanzees, providing room to attach three extra muscles and enabling people to grip objects precisely—a requirement for toolmaking.

Susman analyzed a first metacarpal of *P. robustus* found in the 1980's at the site of Swartkrans Cave, South Africa. He determined that the bone's shape was fundamentally human. *P. robustus,* he reasoned, thus had a typically human grip and could have produced some of the stone tools found at Swartkrans and other sites.

Susman's conclusion remains controversial, however. The main objection is that the metacarpal he analyzed may not have come from *P. robustus.* Of the 130 skull remains found at Swartkrans, 97 percent were identified as belonging to *P. robustus.* But others came from *H. erectus*—a species that would be expected to have a fundamentally human first metacarpal. Observers said a full test of Susman's hypothesis would not be possible until many more human metacarpals were found at Swartkrans and other early sites.   [Richard G. Klein]

See also ARCHAEOLOGY. In WORLD BOOK, see ANTHROPOLOGY; PREHISTORIC PEOPLE.

Archaeology

Ancient Egyptian tomb

The statue of the Egyptian god Osiris, *below*, marks the end of the main corridor in a recently discovered tomb that may be the burial place of the sons of Ramses II, one of the most powerful rulers of ancient Egypt. The tomb lies in the Valley of the Kings, an ancient burial ground where Egyptian royalty were buried from 1600 to 1000 B.C. Within the tomb are wall inscriptions, *bottom*, and thousands of artifacts.

The discovery of an enormous tomb that may contain the burials of up to 50 sons of Ramses II, one of the most powerful rulers of ancient Egypt, was announced in May 1995 by Kent R. Weeks, an Egyptologist with the American University in Cairo. The tomb is part of the large burial ground known as Valley of the Kings, where Egyptian royalty were buried from 1600 to 1000 B.C. The tomb is about 30 meters (100 feet) from where Ramses II himself was buried.

Ramses II reigned over an empire that stretched from what is now Libya in the west to the Tigres and Euphrates rivers in the east and from the areas that are now Turkey in the north to Sudan in the south. He began his rule in 1279 B.C. Over the course of his 67-year reign, Ramses II built more structures and was said to have fathered more children than any other pharaoh.

The entrance to the tomb was unearthed in 1820 by a British traveler, who ventured into a few of the outermost chambers. In 1922, English archaeologist Howard Carter unintentionally obscured the entrance with debris from his excavation of the nearby treasure-filled tomb of the ancient Egyptian king Tutankhamen.

In the late 1980's, Weeks and other archaeologists, pursuing clues from old travelers' diaries and ancient manuscripts, uncovered the tomb's entrance. Behind the entrance was a large pillared room, and beyond that was a long corridor lined with doors leading to smaller chambers and ending with a statue of Osiris, Egyptian god of the afterlife.

The archaeologists found more corridors branching off the main hallway, and they suspect that there may be a lower level. Archaeologists noted that the tomb had one of the most unusual floor plans ever encountered in an Egyptian tomb. Most such tombs have a single corridor and few chambers.

The floors of the tomb are littered with thousands of artifacts, including pottery and statue fragments, jewelry, beads, and mummified human body parts. Inscriptions in the tomb indicate that at least four of Ramses's sons were buried in the tomb, but much of the tomb has yet to be explored. Archaeologists said they were confident that the find will yield invaluable insights into a powerful ancient Egyptian family.

One of the oldest known depictions of warfare—a cave painting of a human figure wielding a barbed spear—is among several ancient images of violence found in Australia, according to an October 1994 report. The paintings were drawn by prehistoric hunters and gatherers up to 10,000 years ago, refuting the theory that warfare began with agricultural peoples about 5,000 years ago.

Archaeology continued

Spectacular cave paintings. The discovery in France of a cave containing more than 300 ancient painted and engraved images was announced in January 1995 by Jean Clottes, a specialist in prehistoric cave paintings. The site, named Grotto Chauvet, lies just outside the town of Vallon-Pont-d'Arc in southwestern France. Archaeologists believe some images are up to 32,000 years old, making them the oldest paintings ever found. They date to a period called the Upper Paleolithic.

The prehistoric people who lived during the Paleolithic era, called Cro-Magnons, have long been known for their striking depictions of Ice Age animals. Other caves contain paintings of bison, horse, and mammoth. Experts say the Grotto Chauvet is a unique find because its walls display an even wider array of animals, including woolly rhinos, wild oxen, lions, hyenas, bears, and a panther.

According to cave specialists, the Grotto Chauvet also provides clues about the people who made the art. Outlines of handprints appear in red or black on the cave walls. Footprints of Paleolithic people mark the cave floor. Littered about the floor are remnants of torches, animal-fat lamps, brushes, and pigments used in making paints. A bear skull was also found on a rock ledge.

Experts are puzzled about why Cro-Magnon artists painted the scenes in such a dark, remote place. Some archaeologists suggested that the cave was a type of cathedral, and that the rock ledge with the bear skull was an altar. Other rock art specialists think the dark cave, with the paintings seen only by flickering torchlight, could have been the setting for initiation ceremonies. Whatever the cave's function, experts agreed that the intricacy and splendor of the artwork shows a sophistication in the Cro-Magnons' symbolism and artistic expression. (See also CLOSE-UP.)

Oldest tools found in Africa. The earliest known artifacts made by human beings or their ancestors are 2.6 million years old, according to an announcement by Sileshi Semaw, an Ethiopian graduate student at Rutgers University in New Jersey in March 1995. Semaw's adviser, J. W. K. Harris, anthropology professor at Rutgers, had found some of the tools near the Gona River in

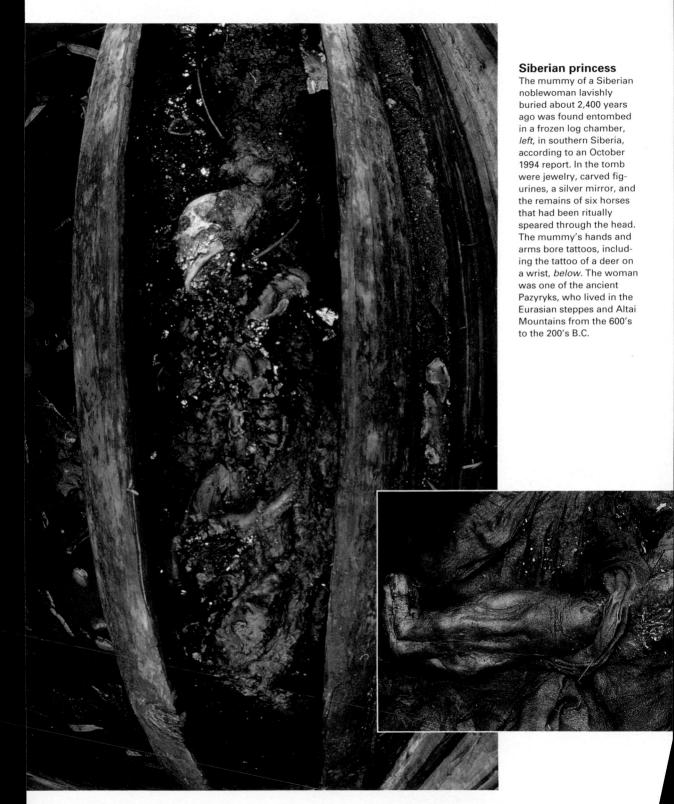

Siberian princess
The mummy of a Siberian noblewoman lavishly buried about 2,400 years ago was found entombed in a frozen log chamber, *left*, in southern Siberia, according to an October 1994 report. In the tomb were jewelry, carved figurines, a silver mirror, and the remains of six horses that had been ritually speared through the head. The mummy's hands and arms bore tattoos, including the tattoo of a deer on a wrist, *below*. The woman was one of the ancient Pazyryks, who lived in the Eurasian steppes and Altai Mountains from the 600's to the 200's B.C.

Ancient Images Illuminate the Past

In January 1995, French officials announced a spectacular discovery: More than 300 painted and engraved images created during the Paleolithic era had been found in a cave in southern France. The images include striking depictions of a wide array of animals, vividly painted in blacks and reds. In June, archaeologists reported that the dazzling find included paintings more than 30,000 years old—the oldest ever discovered.

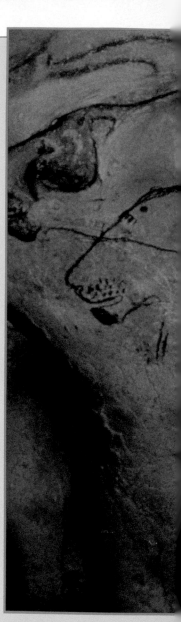

The cave contains rare images of flesh-eating animals, including a panther (lower right). Most other cave paintings of the region represent plant-eating animals commonly hunted for food, not animals dangerous to people. Prominent images of predators including bears, lions, and hyenas in the newly discovered cave may undercut archaeologists' theory that Paleolithic artists sought to depict primarily the food of the hunt.

Images of a horse (left) and a woolly mammoth (right) are etched into a cave wall.

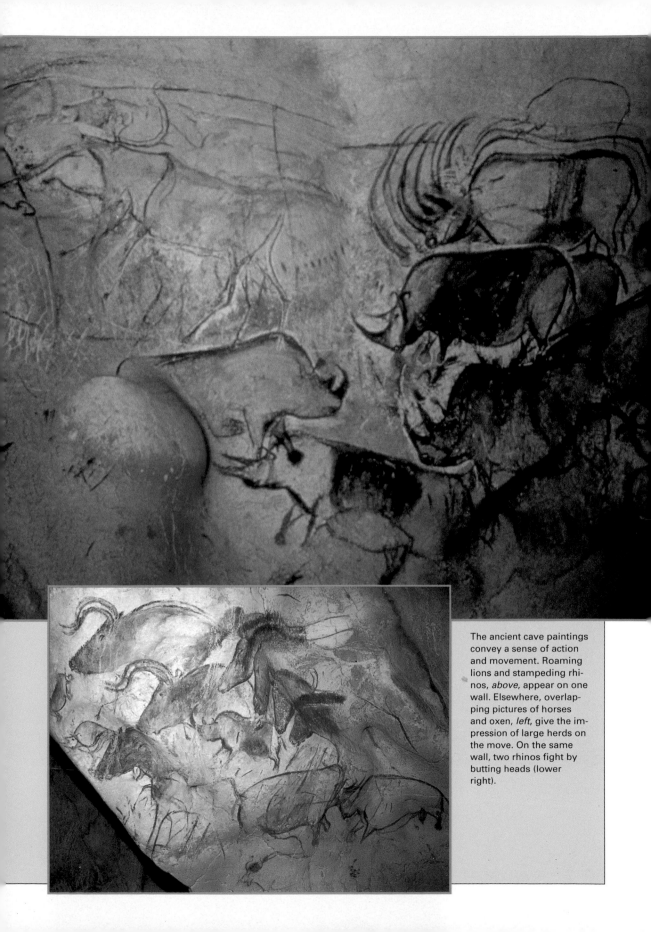

The ancient cave paintings convey a sense of action and movement. Roaming lions and stampeding rhinos, *above*, appear on one wall. Elsewhere, overlapping pictures of horses and oxen, *left*, give the impression of large herds on the move. On the same wall, two rhinos fight by butting heads (lower right).

Archaeology continued

Ethiopia in the 1970's. Early analysis of the tools could not uncover their age.

In 1992, Harris and Semaw began systematic surveys of the Gona region and found thousands of stone tools. Most of the artifacts were crude scraping tools made of volcanic rock. The tools had been formed by striking them against a second stone. Scholars dated the tools by analyzing the sediment in which they were found. They used a technique known as argon-argon single crystal laser fusion, in which a laser melts crystals found in volcanic rock until they release trapped internal gases. The quantities of two of these gases—forms of argon—change over time. By measuring the ratio between the two, scientists dated the rocks.

The new findings could help settle questions over when human beings or their ancestors first produced tools. A standard hypothesis is that tools were first created 2 million years ago by the human species *Homo habilis*, whose name means *toolmaker*. Another theory says that human ancestors began using tools as soon as they walked upright, a posture that left the hands free to manipulate objects. According to this theory, the earliest tools could be even older than 2.6 million years. Archaeologists are now hoping to find remains of the species that used the tools.

Lavish jade offering. A cache of hundreds of jade artifacts was discovered in northwestern Belize, according to a report by archaeologist Thomas Guderjan of St. Mary's University in San Antonio, Tex., in November 1994. The artifacts were attributed to the Maya, a Native American people who created one of the great civilizations of the New World. Their culture flourished from about A.D. 250 to 900. The ancient Maya lived in what are now southern Mexico and Central America.

Offerings of jade, a stone considered sacred by the Maya, are often found in the burials of ruling Maya families. Archaeologists speculate that jade was also used in special rituals, ceremonies, and building dedications.

Guderjan said that the find in Belize was probably an offering made in a dedication ceremony for a building. Excava-

A 1995 space shuttle radar image of the area around Angkor, Cambodia, *left*, shows subtle variations in the texture of the dense jungle area and reveals ancient structures beneath the forest canopy. The dark rectangles are believed to be part of an ancient system of canals and reservoirs that serviced ancient Angkor. The small, darkly outlined square is the excavated Angkor Wat (temple), *below*.

tors working at the site found the jade in a stone-lined shaft 5.6 meters (18.4 feet) deep. The shaft was capped with a limestone disk that was topped with a large stone monument called a stele.

Among the objects found were about 900 pieces of jade, including beads and a head of the Maya jester god, depicted with his tongue sticking out. There were also pottery vessels, pieces of volcanic glass known as obsidian, bone beads, and scattered human bones, though archaeologists believe the offering is not part of a tomb. Based on the pottery types, Guderjan estimated that the offering was made around A.D. 500, during the peak of the Maya culture.

From pithouse to pueblo. A new look at the changing architecture of ancient dwellings in southwestern New Mexico was reported in March 1995 by Harry J. Shafer, archaeologist at Texas A&M University in College Station. The site of Shafer's study, called the NAN ruin, was a village belonging to the Mimbres people, part of the widespread Mogollon culture that flourished along the Mimbres River between A.D. 900 and 1025.

Excavations at the site revealed 33 structures. Twenty-three of the dwellings were pithouses, characterized by recessed floors, circular cooking pits, and side entrances. The other structures showed the transition from pithouses to surface structures called pueblos. In early transitional structures, the pithouse side entrances were blocked off and a ceiling entrance with a ladder was apparently used. The surface pueblos were characterized by rectangular hearths lined with sun-dried bricks or stone, sunken-floor rooms with brick walls, and ceiling entrances.

Beneath the floors of many of the structures, archaeologists found evidence of human burials, including pieces of broken pottery and bones. In some of the burials, perforated ceramic bowls had been placed over the head of the corpse.

Some archaeologists link the changes in architecture to the Mimbres' increasing population, which led to intensified agricultural practices and changes in the methods of food storage. Other experts theorize that the changes in housing, hearth type, and mortuary customs may also reflect changes in beliefs about

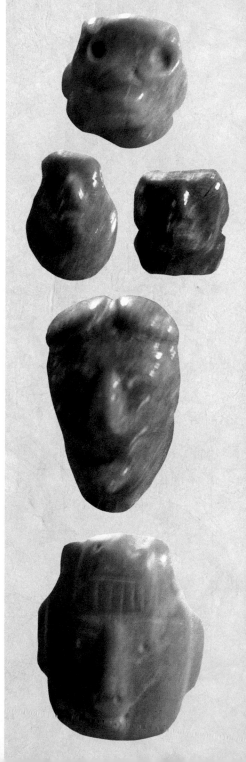

Exquisite jade beads and pendants dating from about A.D. 500 were recovered from a Mayan structure in northwestern Belize, according to a November 1994 report. Among the finds were pieces carved with human features, including a jester god pendant with its tongue sticking out (second from bottom). The collection of jade may be among the largest ever found.

the world. According to this theory, each Mimbres house may have symbolized the living world, or Middleworld. The area beneath the floor, where the dead were placed, was symbolic of the Underworld. The bowls placed over the skulls of the dead were perforated to permit souls to emerge into the Underworld. An Otherworld existed in the space above the room or house and access to it was symbolized by a ladder that extended to a hatchway in the roof.

New dates for early agriculture. In 1994 and 1995, three groups of scientists reported new findings about the development of agriculture in Central America. The researchers produced a new date for the introduction of *maize* (corn) cultivation and evidence of ancient farming tools. The reports help shed light on the transition from a primitive culture of hunters and gatherers to the establishment of early Maya settlements based on agriculture.

Gayle Fritz, a paleoethnobotanist at Washington University in St. Louis, Mo., reported in June 1994 that ancient maize specimens from the Tehuacan Valley of southern Mexico were grown about 2,500 to 3,000 B.C., rather than the previous estimate—3,500 to 5,000 B.C. Because the maize specimens are among the oldest known samples of cultivated crops, the new date indicates that people began cultivating maize in the region at least 500 years later than had been thought.

The maize Fritz examined had been excavated in the 1960's. At that time, none of the original maize fragments was precisely dated, because the traditional dating process, which determines the ratio of two forms of carbon in the sample, would have destroyed much of the small corn cobs. Instead, researchers determined the age of the maize by dating artifacts found with it. To provide the more direct evidence of the age of the maize, Fritz used a process called accelerator mass spectrometry radiocarbon dating, which requires very small pieces of a sample to determine the ratio of the forms of carbon in it.

Based on the new dates for maize agriculture, Fritz suggested that the first farmers in Central America may have been hunters and gatherers who camped long enough to raise and harvest a maize crop before moving on to take advantage of good hunting elsewhere. Earlier views have held that migratory lifestyles suddenly changed into settled Maya culture with the introduction of agriculture. Fritz's findings suggest the transition from migration to settlement in the New World followed the same pattern many archaeologists believe occurred in the Old World.

Fritz's dates were supported by the discovery of another ancient sample of maize, along with a sample of the root crop manioc, that date to 2,500 B.C. Both came from the Cobweb Swamp of the Maya lowlands in Belize. John G. Jones, an expert in plant spores and pollen with the Smithsonian Tropical Research Institute in Panama, reported the finds in December 1994.

Distinctive stone tools that date to about 2,500 B.C. were excavated near the Cobweb Swamp by an archaeological team led by Thomas R. Hester, anthropologist at the University of Texas at Austin, according to a February 1995 report. Careful analysis of the tools indicated that they were used in clearing vegetation and for digging. The users of the tools might have been the first Maya in the region, or they might have been hunters and gatherers who farmed occasionally, as Fritz's research suggested.

Craft specialization among Indians. Evidence of craft specialization in bead making by the Chumash Indians was reported by archaeologist Jeanne Arnold of the University of California at Los Angeles in December 1994. The Chumash Indians began living on the southern California coast about 1,000 to 1,500 years ago. They built large boats and were skilled navigators. They were also known for their involvement in widespread trade with other California Indians, especially the exchange of shell beads, a form of currency.

Arnold examined large deposits of flint on the Channel Islands off the coast of southern California. The Chumash used flint to make tiny rodlike drills to make beads by perforating a cone-shaped shell known as Olivella. Arnold found that between the years 1150 and 1300, the Chumash on the Channel Islands mass-produced the flint drills, leaving behind vast deposits of flint-working debris.

Arnold's research indicates that the bead manufacturers were craft specialists who produced millions of beads for the Chumash trade system. The Chumash elite probably were able to control the marketing of the shells to buyers on the mainland, because the elite owned the canoes that had access to the islands. This complex system of production and distribution was unequaled in most early agricultural societies, archaeologists believe.

Efforts to halt looting in Peru. Peruvian police and scholars have joined forces in an effort to stop the sacking of ancient sites in Peru, according to an August 1994 report by Walter Alva, archaeologist at the Bruning Archaeological Museum in Lambayeque, Peru. Experts say the rich archaeological record of Peru is being destroyed at a rate perhaps faster than in any other place in the world. In 1987, for example, looters at a site near the northern village of Sipán robbed many tombs of spectacular artifacts of gold, silver, and turquoise. In 1993, near Lima, 600-year-old burials of the Ichma culture were looted and the grave offerings sold.

The market for pre-Columbian artifacts, which date before the year 1500, reaches billions of dollars worldwide. Dealers and collectors of such artifacts are found in many places around the world.

Archaeologists say looting is hardly a recent phenomenon. In the 1960's, intense looting episodes took place at a site called Vicus in northern Peru, where an estimated 2,000 tombs were ransacked.

Peru's new antilooting plan focused on public education. Villagers were told of the economic benefits of tourism if the antiquities are preserved, rather than dug up and sold. Police also offered rewards for information on people involved in looting, and officials attempted to identify dealers illegally trading antiquities. In addition, the Peruvian Air Force began flying occasional surveillance missions over ancient sites that often attract looters. Through these efforts, Peruvian authorities and scholars hoped to stop the destruction of Peru's past.

[Thomas R. Hester]

See also ANTHROPOLOGY. In WORLD BOOK, see ARCHAEOLOGY.

Astronomy

The impact of Comet Shoemaker-Levy 9 fragments on Jupiter in July 1994 was one of the most important astronomical events ever witnessed by planetary scientists. In 1995, researchers continued to observe Jupiter, which still bore traces of the impacts, and to study data from the collisions.

Observational data of the collisions, including information recorded by instruments aboard the Hubble Space Telescope, revealed a large amount of ammonia in the planet's upper atmosphere in the vicinity of the impacts. The amount of water, on the other hand, was relatively small. These findings suggested that the comet fragments plunged deep enough into Jupiter's atmosphere before disintegrating to stir up material from high-level ammonia clouds but not far enough to disrupt low-lying water clouds.

Observers also detected concentrations of sulfur, carbon disulfide, and ammonium hydrosulfide around the collision sites. The high levels of these substances indicate that they came from both Jupiter's stirred-up atmosphere and the comet. Comets are known to contain sulfur and sulfur compounds, as does Jupiter's atmosphere.

But planetary scientists do not know the relative percentages of sulfur and sulfur compounds in a typical comet or in Jupiter's lower atmosphere. Thus, it will be difficult to sort out how much of each substance was already in Jupiter's atmosphere and how much was added by the comet. That is just one of the many questions about the collisions investigators will be trying to answer. (In the Special Reports section, see WHEN WORLDS AND COMETS COLLIDE.)

Learning more about the moon. The first scientific results from the space probe Clementine, which orbited the moon in a polar orbit from mid-February to early May 1994, were released in December 1994. The probe surveyed the entire lunar surface and revealed new information about Earth's satellite.

The Clementine mission was a cooperative venture between the United States Department of Defense and the National Aeronautics and Space Administration (NASA) aimed in part at demonstrating that planetary exploration could be done relatively cheaply, with small spacecraft and lightweight instruments. Although the mission was successful, a computer malfunction prevented Clementine from conducting the second of its planned missions, a survey of the asteroid Geographos.

The scientific value of the moon mission lay in the probe's ability to map the entire lunar surface with advanced instruments. A comprehensive survey of the moon's features and composition had never been conducted before.

Among Clementine's many findings was the discovery that a large depressed region near the lunar south pole, called the South Pole-Aitken Basin, is a multiring basin several billion years old. A multiring basin is formed when a violent impact from a large asteroid or other object folds the surface into several circular mountain ranges centered on the point of collision.

The Aitken Basin is enormous, extending about 2,700 kilometers (1,700 miles) from rim to rim. From computer analyses of the size of the impact re-

quired to produce such a feature, geologists estimate that the colliding object gouged out material from as deep as 130 kilometers (80 miles) below the lunar surface. That depth extends into the mantle, the region of the lunar interior directly beneath the outer crust. The possibility of collecting rock that was ejected from the mantle now makes this section of the moon's surface an attractive site for future missions to collect samples of lunar soil.

The many photographs that Clementine sent to Earth included images of another multiring basin, called the Schrödinger Basin. The basin is so free of impact craters, which accumulate over the eons as the moon is hit by objects, that it must be one of the youngest such formations on the moon. Scientists calculated that the basin is no more than 1 billion to 2 billion years old.

Clementine images also revealed a broad depression directly around the moon's south pole. Because the polar regions receive only a scant amount of sunlight, many parts of the depression are in darkness most of the time. This

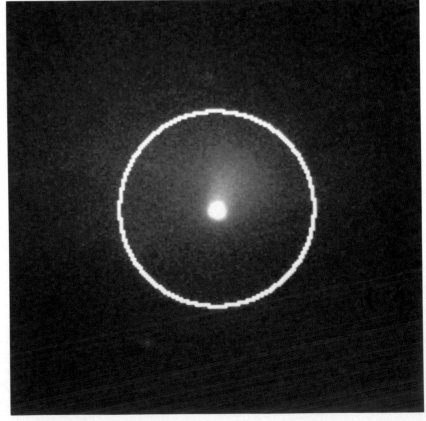

New research explains the mysterious *coma* (halo) of gas surrounding comet Schwassmann-Wachmann 1 (SW1) and other unusual comets. Most comets have a core of primarily water ice, and their comae form when solar heat vaporizes some of the core. But SW1 orbits too far from the sun for ice to be vaporized. Astronomers in Hawaii solved the mystery in September 1994 after analyzing a portion of the light from the coma (within the white circle) and detecting the presence of carbon monoxide. In addition to water ice, SW1's core must contain frozen carbon monoxide, which vaporizes at a much lower temperature than water ice.

A series of photographs of Jupiter taken over a six-day period in July 1994 shows the evolution of impact sites where three fragments of Comet Shoemaker-Levy 9 smashed into the giant planet. The first picture (lower left), taken on July 18 just five minutes after a large fragment known as G struck Jupiter, shows a plume rising over the planet's rim from the explosion. In the second picture, made about 90 minutes later, the impact site has rotated into view. Three days later (third image), the G site and the site of an impact that occurred on July 20 have expanded into large, dark smudges. The final image shows the sites on July 23.

area may be a good place for future moon missions to search for possible ice deposits. (See also SPACE TECHNOLOGY.)

Images of Titan. The surface of Titan, Saturn's largest moon, was revealed for the first time in August 1994 by the Hubble Space Telescope. Titan's surface is hidden by perpetual haze, but the Hubble telescope cut through that obscuring blanket by looking at near-infrared wavelengths of light reflected from Titan. That light, just beyond the red end of the visible spectrum, is able to penetrate the haze. Planetary scientist Peter Smith and his colleagues at the University of Arizona in Tucson produced the images.

Titan, the second-largest moon in the solar system, has an atmosphere of nitrogen and methane that is three times denser than Earth's atmosphere. Because Titan's surface is so cold (−177 °C [−287 °F]), methane in the lower atmosphere condenses to form clouds—the source of some of the haze—and might also be on the surface in the form of seas and lakes.

Making up most of the haze on Titan is an orange atmospheric layer of heavy *organic* (carbon-containing) molecules called hydrocarbons and nitriles. These substances are created when sunlight splits molecules of methane and nitrogen. The organic material sinks to Titan's surface, where it forms a dense layer less than 1 kilometer (0.6 mile) thick.

The Hubble images show a single bright, continent-sized area on Titan surrounded by darker regions. The bright area might be a land mass that rises above the layer of organic material or it could be a huge expanse of water ice that has erupted from the moon's interior. The darker areas are undoubtedly the hydrocarbons, probably in both liquid and solid form.

A joint U.S.-European mission called Cassini-Huygens will explore Titan in detail in the year 2004. An unmanned probe will descend to Titan's surface at or close to the shore of the bright "continent."

Turbulent weather on Neptune. The Hubble Space Telescope scored another coup in April 1995 with pictures revealing big changes on the planet Neptune.

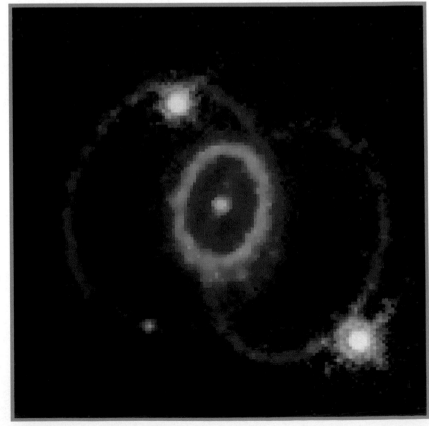

The exploding star called Supernova 1987A is surrounded by three mysterious rings of glowing gas in a Hubble Space Telescope image made in 1994. The rings lie in different planes, with one large ring in front of the star and the other behind it. Astronomers offering theories of how the rings formed said that the small ring could be a remnant of the gas cloud from which the original star formed. The larger rings might be illuminated portions of two bubbles of gas expanding from the supernova. Radiation beams from an unseen companion star might be causing those portions to light up.

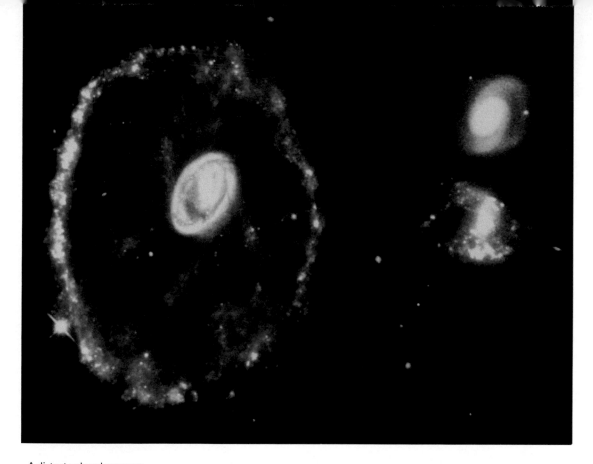

A distant galaxy known as the Cartwheel Galaxy (left) is surrounded by an enormous ring of young stars in a Hubble telescope photograph released in January 1995. The ring, wider than our own Milky Way, was created when another galaxy—probably one of the two at the right—plowed through the Cartwheel Galaxy. The collision created a shock wave that, like a ripple in a pond, pushed clouds of gas and dust outward and gave birth to billions of new stars.

Astronomer Heidi Hammel of the Massachusetts Institute of Technology in Cambridge, who made the images, found new evidence that the eighth planet from the sun is a dynamic and unpredictable place.

Hammel discovered that a huge storm system in Neptune's southern atmosphere called the Great Dark Spot, seen by the Voyager 2 spacecraft in 1989, is now gone. In its place, a similar feature has apparently developed in the northern hemisphere. Bright clouds, which are thought to be made of methane and which indicate stormy activity akin to thunderstorms on Earth, now pepper the northern hemisphere.

Physicists had earlier proposed that the Great Dark Spot and other atmospheric phenomena seen on Neptune by Voyager 2 might appear and disappear unpredictably. The Hubble images seem to bear that out.

Because Neptune has such an active atmosphere, it must have a powerful source of energy in its interior that is adding heat to the atmosphere. The sunlight that the planet receives is too weak to be creating the atmospheric effects that have been observed. But what that energy source might be is uncertain. Planetary scientists think the probable source of the energy is heat left over from the planet's formation some 4.6 billion years ago.

The age of the universe. How old is the universe? Astronomers had long thought they had a pretty good answer to that question—between 15 billion and 20 billion years—but research reported in 1995 cast doubt on that figure. The age of the universe has once again become a hot issue in astronomy.

Attempts to date the age of the universe began in the late 1920's, when the American astronomer Edwin Hubble discovered that the universe is expanding. Hubble found that all the galaxies in the universe are moving apart at speeds that can be measured from the *red shift* of light from the galaxies—a shift of the galaxies' light toward longer, redder wavelengths.

This phenomenon occurs because light waves from a galaxy (or any other light source) that is moving away from an observer become stretched out. The faster a galaxy is receding from the observer, the redder the light becomes.

Hubble found that the farther away galaxies are from Earth, the greater are their red shifts. That is, the farther away they are, the faster they are moving away from us. This increase is exactly proportional to distance—a galaxy that is twice as far away as another galaxy is receding from us at twice the speed.

Determining the age of the universe requires calculating the length of time it has taken for the galaxies to get to their present positions since the *big bang*, the enormous explosion of matter and energy that gave birth to the universe. Galaxies evolved from the matter created in the big bang and were carried ever farther apart as the universe expanded.

But to establish how long it has taken the galaxies to get to where we now observe them, astronomers must determine the overall expansion rate of the universe. And that has been a difficult figure to nail down.

Debating the Hubble constant. The universe's expansion rate is usually ex-pressed in terms of a quantity called the *Hubble constant*, abbreviated H_0. But astronomers have never been able to agree on the exact value of H_0, and so they have been unable to settle the issue of how old the universe is. In 1995, two large groups of astronomers presented observational results that led to divergent conclusions on the value for H_0. The two groups' findings set the stage for one of the most perplexing and intriguing controversies in astronomy since the expansion was discovered.

In order to calculate H_0, astronomers must establish the distances from Earth to a number of galaxies whose red-shift velocities have been measured. The Hubble constant is derived by dividing the galaxies' velocities by their distances. (Because the expansion rate of the universe has been slowing since the big bang, the value of the Hubble constant has changed through time.)

Making accurate distance measurements has been a tricky proposition, however. Astronomers measure distances by looking for certain kinds of stars and other bright celestial objects

A nearby but previously unknown spiral galaxy (arrow), which had been hidden by the disk of the Milky Way, was reported in November 1994 by astronomers in Dwingeloo, the Netherlands. The galaxy, dubbed Dwingeloo 1, was found with the aid of a radio telescope. The photograph of the galaxy is a composite image made with a telescope that views the heavens in infrared light. Astronomers say many more galaxies may be waiting to be discovered by looking through the plane of the Milky Way's disk.

whose energy output is known and then measuring their apparent brightness. How far away each object is can be calculated by determining how much its light has been diminished by distance.

This method is like looking at a number of 100-watt light bulbs shining in the night and deciding how far away each is by how bright it looks. Such a calculation is simple as long as you know that the light sources you are observing are 100-watt bulbs.

Astronomers have identified several types of stars and other objects that are sufficiently uniform in brightness to serve as celestial 100-watt bulbs. Among these objects, which are referred to as *standard candles*, are pulsating stars called Cepheid variables and one kind of *supernova* (exploding star). Cepheids are giant stars and can be observed by the Hubble Space Telescope in other galaxies nearly 100 million *light-years* away. Supernovae are far brighter and can be seen at distances of billions of light-years. A light-year is the distance light travels in one year—about 9.5 trillion kilometers (5.9 trillion miles).

One group of researchers, led by astronomer Allan R. Sandage of the Carnegie Observatories in Pasadena, Calif., used the Hubble Space Telescope to observe Cepheids in some relatively nearby galaxies where supernovae had been seen. By using the Cepheids to learn the supernovae's distances, the astronomers were able to calculate the supernovae's energy output, something that was not known with precision until then. In other words, they used Cepheids to calibrate the supernovae as standard candles. The astronomers then determined the distances to much more faraway galaxies where supernovae could be observed.

Based on their supernova studies, Sandage and his associates reported in January 1995 that the universe has a relatively low expansion rate. At the rate they calculated, the universe would have taken 16 billion to 20 billion years to reach its present size. That figure agrees with the age of the universe that most astronomers had accepted.

But just down the hall from Sandage's group at the Carnegie Observatories, astronomer Wendy L. Freedman, the leader of another research team, came up with quite different results. Freedman

and her colleagues used the superior resolving power of the Hubble telescope to identify Cepheids in a galaxy some 75 million light-years from Earth, far enough away to be useful in measuring the Hubble constant. Astronomers had previously been unable to search for Cepheids in galaxies that far away because no telescope could distinguish individual stars in them.

In October 1994, Freedman and her colleagues arrived at a much higher value for the constant than Sandage's group had calculated. If their figure is correct, the universe is much younger than astronomers had thought—8 billion to 12 billion years old.

Investigators are hoping that further data from the Hubble will soon resolve the disagreement between the two research groups. But if the findings of Freedman's group are upheld, it will create a real problem for astronomers, because many stars in the universe are thought to be more than 12 billion years old. Since the universe cannot be younger than the stars it contains, astronomers would have to rethink their theories about how stars evolve.

The formation of galaxies. Another goal of astronomers using the Hubble Space Telescope is to learn how galaxies formed in the early universe. In December 1994, astronomer Alan Dressler of the Carnegie Observatories, together with investigators from two other U.S. institutions, announced findings from the Hubble telescope that provided new insights into the evolution of galaxies.

A telescope is a sort of time machine, because in looking far across space, it is also looking back in time. The reason for this is that it takes light time to travel to the Earth from distant sources. For example, if we observe a galaxy that is 100 million light-years away, we are seeing that galaxy as it was 100 million years ago. Astronomers refer to this as the "look-back" time. The fine image quality of the Hubble, coupled with its great sensitivity in detecting faint objects, gives astronomers look-back times in the billions of years, back to the formative era of the universe.

Dressler and colleagues from Yale University in New Haven, Conn., and the Space Telescope Science Institute in Baltimore released images of galaxy clusters representing several look-back times. Some of the clusters are so far away that the astronomers were seeing them as they were when the universe was only about one-tenth its present age.

There are two primary classes of galaxies: *spirals,* disk-shaped galaxies with trailing spiral arms, like our own Milky Way; and *ellipticals,* which lack a disk and have a rounded appearance. An estimated 70 to 80 percent of known galaxies in today's universe are spirals, but ellipticals are far more numerous in large, dense clusters of galaxies.

The earliest clusters observed by the three research teams contained elliptical galaxies but no spirals. Clusters from a later epoch in the history of the universe—about 5 billion years ago—included many spiral galaxies as well as great numbers of ellipticals. The ellipticals appeared fully formed in all the clusters, no matter how far back in time the astronomers looked. In contrast, the spirals in the later clusters always had an incomplete, fragmented appearance.

These observations showed that elliptical galaxies formed quickly in the early universe, but the mature spirals we see

today took much longer to evolve. One possible explanation for the unsettled look of the spiral galaxies in the 5-billion-year-old clusters is that they were being torn apart by the gravitational pull of neighboring galaxies after only a short life span as spirals. It may be common for spirals in crowded clusters to be "rounded off" in this way to become ellipticals, which would help explain why ellipticals predominate in today's dense clusters. Alternatively, some of the ragged-looking spiral galaxies may have been in the process of formation.

The observation that mature elliptical galaxies existed so soon after the big bang came as a surprise to astronomers. It suggests that the early universe was expanding at a leisurely enough rate to allow for large numbers of stars to form quickly and gather together into galaxies. Thus, the most widely accepted age for the universe—15 billion to 20 billion years—may be correct.

Galactic black holes. During the 1990's, astronomers have reported evidence that the central regions of many galaxies harbor enormous energy-emit-

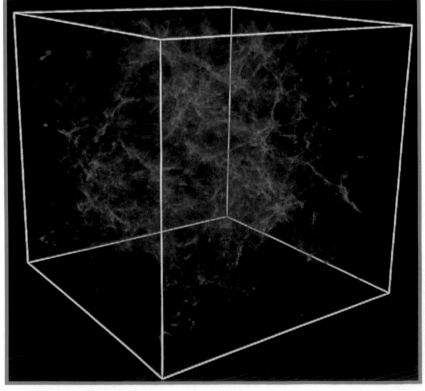

A 1994 computer simulation depicts the distribution of galaxy clusters in the universe with fairly good accuracy, according to its creators at the University of Illinois at Urbana-Champaign. High-density regions are red and low-density regions are blue. The cube is 500 million light-years on a side. (A light-year is the distance light travels in one year.) The simulation was based on calculations that 10 percent of the mass of the universe is ordinary matter, 30 percent is *hot dark matter* (light, fast moving particles) that cannot be seen with telescopes, and 60 percent is slower-moving unseen particles called *cold dark matter.*

ting objects that may be supermassive black hole. In January 1995, astronomer James M. Moran and his colleagues at the Harvard-Smithsonian Center for Astrophysics in Cambridge, Mass., announced finding a probable supermassive black hole in a galaxy named NGC 4258. Many astronomers hailed the discovery as the most conclusive evidence yet that black holes do indeed reside at the core of many galaxies.

A black hole is a region in space in which matter has been compressed into such a small volume that an intense gravitational field is generated. The gravity of a black hole is so strong that not even light can escape its grasp.

According to theory, some black holes form when massive stars collapse at the end of their normal lifetime and their remaining matter contracts from its own gravity. Supermassive black holes, as the name suggests, are much larger. Astronomers think most of them formed in the early universe when huge streams of gas and stars merged.

Because a black hole emits no light, it cannot be observed directly, but its existence can be inferred by observing the effect of its gravity on surrounding matter. Stars and clouds of interstellar gas orbiting a supermassive black hole would be compressed into a disk of matter—known as an *accretion disk*—spiraling into the hole at high speed. The orbital speed of matter in the disk is related to the mass of the central object. Astronomers can determine these orbital speeds by measuring the changing wavelengths of light emanating from the accretion disk.

The Harvard-Smithsonian researchers used an array of 10 widely separated radio telescopes to make detailed observations of gas clouds close to the center of NGC 4258, which lies some 21 million light-years from Earth. By combining the data from the telescopes, the astronomers produced images of the galaxy that were more detailed than they could have obtained using the Hubble telescope.

The observational information allowed Moran and his co-workers to measure the speed at which gas clouds in a disk surrounding the center of NGC 4258 were spiraling into the core of the galaxy. They found that the innermost portion of the disk, a region with a ra-dius of no more than one-third of a light-year, contains a *mass* (quantity of matter) equal to nearly a billion suns. Astronomers know of nothing other than a black hole that could contain that much mass in so small a volume.

Black hole in the Milky Way? Astronomers had also become increasingly convinced in recent years that a supermassive black hole lurks at the center of our own Milky Way galaxy. In February 1995, astronomers Laird M. Close, Donald W. McCarthy, Jr., and Fulvio Melia of the University of Arizona's Steward Observatory near Tucson reported findings indicating that there may indeed be a black hole there.

The astronomers made infrared observations of the galactic center with greater precision and over a wider range of wavelengths than any previously obtained. Infrared radiation is identical to visible light except that it has longer wavelengths and cannot be seen by the human eye. The advantage of using infrared light for observing the center of the Milky Way is that it passes through the clouds of gas and dust that block the view of telescopes using visible light.

There are a number of sources of intense radio waves near the center of the Milky Way, and one of them, called Sagittarius A* (Sgr A*), is thought to be the nucleus of the galaxy—the point about which the entire disk of the galaxy rotates. Some astronomers have speculated that Sgr A* might be an accretion disk surrounding a huge black hole.

The Arizona astronomers set out to test that possibility. They found that the infrared energy coming from Sgr A* fit the expectations for such emissions from an accretion disk.

Still, their observations did not prove that Sgr A* is a black hole. The investigators pointed out that the infrared emissions they detected could just as well have come from a massive cluster of normal stars. Moreover, they said, infrared emissions from an accretion disk would most likely rise and fall in intensity over time, and they did not observe any such variation. Thus, the question of whether a supermassive black hole lies at the heart of the Milky Way remains unanswered. [Jonathan I. Lunine and Theodore P. Snow]

In WORLD BOOK, see ASTRONOMY.

El Niño surprised atmospheric scientists and oceanographers by persisting into 1995—its fourth consecutive year. It thus became the longest El Niño in recorded history.

El Niño is a vast cycle of atmospheric and ocean conditions. It usually occurs every three to seven years, when trade winds that normally blow west from South America along the equator weaken. A huge pool of warm water that normally rests in the western Pacific Ocean then moves east along the equator. This warm water helps produce more clouds and thunderstorms than usual over the central Pacific Ocean. The resulting mass of warm air also disrupts the jet streams that circle the Earth in the mid-latitudes, affecting weather in many areas of the world, often drastically.

In the absence of El Niño, strong trade winds blow from the east across the Pacific along the equator. The winds push surface water away from the South American coast, allowing cold waters to well up from the deep ocean. Some experts call this situation La Niña, and the presence of La Niña marks the opposing phase of the weather cycle that produces El Niños. Historically, La Niñas have lasted longer than El Niños.

Five El Niños have occurred since 1976, with the strongest ever recorded happening during 1982 and 1983. Since 1976, however, only one true La Niña has occurred. Some scientists believe that El Niño may have become a permanent feature of the world's weather. Other scientists share this belief but point out that natural climate variability makes it very difficult to validate theories about trends in such large-scale weather patterns.

By carefully monitoring the changing water temperature in the tropical Pacific Ocean, scientists hoped to be able to forecast El Niños and their associated droughts and wet spells months in advance. In January 1995, scientists at the National Meteorological Center in Camp Springs, Md., began issuing a new series of seasonal outlooks that specifically take into account the presence or absence of an El Niño warming in the Pacific Ocean.

A warm 1994. The global average surface temperature for 1994 tied 1987 as the fourth warmest year on record. That was the January 1995 conclusion of atmospheric scientist James E. Hansen of the National Aeronautics and Space Administration's (NASA's) Goddard Institute for Space Studies in New York City. The 1994 average surface temperature was 15.34 °C (59.58 °F), according to Hansen. He based his conclusion on temperature measurements taken at about 200 locations. Such records of Earth's average yearly temperature date from the 1880's.

The high figure for 1994 suggested that Earth may have recovered from the cooling effects of the 1991 eruption of Mount Pinatubo in the Philippines. The eruption ejected some 20 million metric tons (22 million short tons) of ash and gases into Earth's *stratosphere* (upper atmosphere). The gases reacted with water vapor in the air to produce a veil of sulfuric acid droplets that circled the globe and reflected some incoming sunlight back into space. The reflection lowered Earth's global average temperature by about 0.3 Celsius degree (0.6 Fahrenheit degree) in 1992, creating an abrupt drop from the record high global average temperature set in 1990. By mid-1994, about 85 percent of the sulfuric acid droplets had settled out of the stratosphere, and Earth's global average temperature began to rise.

Some scientists view the rebound as evidence that Earth's climate will continue to warm. Many climate researchers anticipate a rise in the global average temperature by 2.8 to 3.3 Celsius degrees (5 to 6 Fahrenheit degrees) by the middle 2000's. The major cause of the warming, many scientists say, will be an enhanced greenhouse effect caused by increases in carbon dioxide and other heat-trapping "greenhouse gases" in the atmosphere. Burning *fossil fuels* (coal, oil, and natural gas) contributes to the buildup of greenhouse gases.

Average global temperatures have risen 0.5 Celsius degree (0.9 Fahrenheit degree) since the late 1800's, but that increase is so small that it may be due entirely to natural variations rather than to the enhanced greenhouse effect, according to many atmospheric scientists. British researchers ascribed as much as a third of the 1994 temperature recovery to the global effect of the current El Niño, for instance.

Atmospheric scientists David Parker of the United Kingdom's Meteorologi-

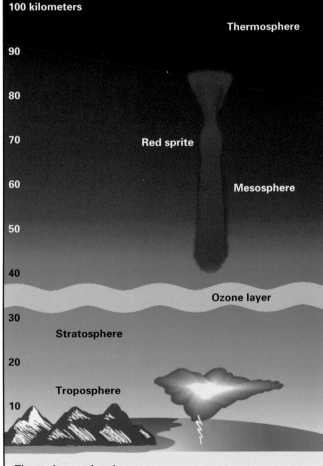

100 kilometers

Thermosphere

90

80

70
Red sprite

60
Mesosphere

50

40
Ozone layer

30
Stratosphere

20

Troposphere
10

The curious red sprite

A newly discovered atmospheric phenomenon called a red sprite, *top*, was reported in August 1994. Scientists are uncertain what causes the shooting red flashes but say that they last only a few thousandths of a second and shoot from the tops of storm clouds to as high as 90 kilometers (56 miles) above Earth's surface, *above*.

Source: The University of Alaska at Fairbanks.

cal Office and Phil Jones of the University of East Anglia found in the late 1980's that an El Niño in the Pacific usually raises Earth's global average temperature by 0.1 to 0.2 Celsius degree (0.2 to 0.4 Fahrenheit degree). Such phenomena have thus far made it impossible for climate researchers to clearly identify a warming trend due to the enhanced greenhouse effect, they said.

Red sprites and blue jets. In summer 1994, researchers captured on videotape two previously undocumented forms of electrical discharge above thunderstorm clouds. Scientists dubbed the new phenomena *red sprites* and *blue jets*. Atmospheric physicists then sought to explain these latest additions to nature's repertoire of electrical curiosities. Pilots and passengers on high-flying aircraft have reported brief, colorful flashes above thunderstorms for years, but scientists have often met such observations with skepticism.

Atmospheric scientist Davis D. Sentman and his colleagues from the University of Alaska at Fairbanks used simultaneous observations from two aircraft to determine where the flashes occur above thunderstorms. They found that sprites—red blobs of light that trail off into bluish tendrils—occur at altitudes of 50 to 90 kilometers (30 to 60 miles). Blue jets are flashes that appear in narrow beams, fans, or cones in the stratosphere, from 20 to 50 kilometers (12 to 30 miles) above Earth's surface. Neither the red sprites nor the blue jets last more than a few thousandths of a second.

The two types of flashes appear to be connected with lightning discharges, but scientists are uncertain exactly how they form. Some atmospheric researchers associate the sprites with a brief strengthening of the electric field near a thunderstorm, following powerful cloud-to-ground lightning strokes.

Heat-hungry clouds. Clouds absorb nearly four times more sunlight than scientists had believed. That was the conclusion of two studies reported in January 1995. Atmospheric scientists Robert Cess of the State University of New York at Stony Brook and Veerabhadran Ramanathan of the Scripps Institution of Oceanography in San Diego reported the findings.

Researchers had thought that clouds

absorb only about 4 percent of the radiation that strikes them. But when the researchers measured the solar radiation above and below the same clouds using satellites and surface instruments, they found that clouds absorb about 15 percent of the radiation that strikes them.

This extra absorption means that about 20 percent less energy reaches Earth's surface than scientists had previously believed, according to the researchers. Experts said the new finding would significantly alter the way in which scientists construct computer models of Earth's climate. Such models attempt to predict how Earth's climate will change in the near future. The models involve complex mathematical formulas that represent essential aspects of Earth's climate, such as ocean currents, seasonal temperature variations, the amount of heat-trapping gases in the atmosphere, and wind patterns.

Near-record ozone depletion. Atmospheric scientists announced in late September 1994 that the levels of ozone above Antarctica fell to near record lows in 1994. Each year since 1987, scientists have observed a thinning of the ozone layer above Antarctica. This annual thinning has become popularly known as the "ozone hole." The 1994 ozone hole approached the record depletion observed in October 1993, according to atmospheric scientists.

Ozone is a molecule made of three oxygen atoms. In Earth's upper atmosphere, ozone protects life by absorbing much of the most damaging ultraviolet radiation from the sun. (In the lower atmosphere, ozone is a pollutant, a byproduct largely of the interaction between automobile exhaust and sunlight. Ozone in the lower atmosphere can damage the lungs and cause other respiratory problems.)

In the upper atmosphere, chlorine from chemicals called chlorofluorocarbons (CFC's) greatly ehances the natural processes that destroy ozone. CFC's are used mainly as coolants in refrigeration and air conditioning systems. International treaties ban the production of most CFC's after 1995.

Ozone destruction requires cold temperatures and sunlight to occur. The destruction begins when the sun rises over Antarctica in September after the Antarctic winter. Sunlight breaks apart

CFC molecules, releasing chlorine atoms. These atoms adhere to the surfaces of ice crystals and begin chemical reactions that quickly destroy ozone in the region of the stratosphere contained within a circular band of winds called the circumpolar vortex. These winds prevent the ozone-rich air in the midlatitudes from moving poleward. Until late October, when the Antarctic circumpolar vortex weakens and the polar stratospheric clouds finally break up, much of the stratosphere over Antarctica remains depleted of ozone.

Researchers calculate ozone destruction in *Dobson units*, which measure the ability of the atmosphere to absorb certain wavelengths of light, especially in the ultraviolet range. Scientists had predicted that 1994's ozone hole would bottom out near 125 Dobson units, slightly more than the record low of 1993, when scientists recorded only 93 Dobson units above Antarctica. By comparison, in the early 1970's, the thickness of the ozone layer at the same time of year was calculated at around 280 Dobson units.

The actual 1994 low of only 102 Dobson units surprised scientists, because a major natural cause of ozone destruction in the early 1990's had largely disappeared. When Mount Pinatubo in the Philippines erupted, it spewed volcanic debris and gases into the stratosphere. The volcanic gases formed sulfuric acid droplets that eventually circled the globe. The droplets enhanced ozone destruction by providing additional surfaces upon which ozone-destroying chemical reactions could occur. By the fall of 1994, most of the volcanic material had settled out of the atmosphere, however, so researchers thought that ozone destruction would lessen.

Researchers speculated that three factors contributed to 1994's ozone loss. The Antarctic winter was 2 to 3 Celsius degrees (3.6 to 5.4 Fahrenheit degrees) colder than normal, a factor that increases the effectiveness with which chlorine destroys ozone. About 15 percent of the volcanic debris also remains in the stratosphere, and that amount may be enough to contribute to ozone destruction. Finally, CFC emissions since 1991 may also have been greater than expected.   [John T. Snow]

In WORLD BOOK, see METEOROLOGY; OZONE.

Awards and Prizes

Advances in developing environmentally safer fuels, in probing the atomic structure of matter, and in understanding how cells in the body respond to biochemical messages led to the awarding of Nobel Prizes in chemistry, physics, and physiology or medicine in October 1994. For students, major prizes were awarded for a biochemistry project on the type of cancer called lymphoma, for the development of an electronic device to help the blind distinguish different currency values, and for many other projects.

The Nobel Prize in chemistry was awarded to George A. Olah, a Hungarian-born organic chemist who directs the Loker Hydrocarbon Research Institute at the University of Southern California in Los Angeles. Olah developed a way to study highly unstable hydrocarbon molecules containing *carbocations* (positively charged carbon atoms). Carbocations (pronounced *car bo CAT ions*) are formed during certain chemical reactions but exist for less than one-millionth of a second, too briefly for chemists to analyze them.

In 1962, Olah discovered that superacids, acids that are trillions of times stronger than sulfuric acid, could stabilize hydrocarbon carbocations long enough for chemists to study them using conventional methods. Olah's finding opened up an entirely new field of hydrocarbon research and led to such practical results as gasoline with high octane ratings. Recent research into ways of producing fuels and plastics that are safer for the environment resulted from Olah's findings.

The physics prize was shared by Canadian Bertram N. Brockhouse of McMaster University in Hamilton, Ontario, and Clifford G. Shull, a former professor at the Massachusetts Institute of Technology (MIT) in Cambridge, now retired. The award recognized work done by Shull in the 1940's and by Brockhouse in the 1950's, using beams of neutrons to explore the atomic structure and properties of matter.

Together, the two scientists helped pioneer neutron scattering, a technique that proved far superior to the use of X rays and other forms of radiation for

American physicist Clifford G. Shull, *right,* a former professor, now retired, at the Massachusetts Institute of Technology (MIT) in Cambridge, takes telephone congratulations after learning in October 1994 that he shared the Nobel Prize in physics with Canadian physicist Bertram N. Brockhouse, *below,* a professor at McMaster University in Hamilton, Ontario. The two men were honored for pioneering the use of neutron beams to probe the structure of matter.

studying molecular structure. Shull's work showed how to deduce the arrangement of atoms in a material by studying how neutrons are diffracted when a neutron beam passes through the material. Brockhouse demonstrated that because neutrons lose energy when a neutron beam passes through a crystal, the motion of atoms in the crystal can be studied. Neutron beam research has thrown light on the structure of many materials, including semiconductors used in the electronics industry and superconducting materials, substances that conduct electricity with little or no resistance.

The prize for physiology or medicine was awarded jointly to Alfred Gilman of the University of Texas Southwestern Medical Center in Dallas and Martin Rodbell, who retired in 1994 from the National Institute of Environmental Health Science near Durham, N.C. The two were recognized for their work in showing how living cells communicate with each other and how they respond to outside stimuli.

In the early 1970's, Rodbell theorized that a substance known as a G protein helps relay the signals a cell receives from other cells or from outside stimuli, such as light. At that time, most scientists rejected Rodbell's theory, but in 1977, Gilman demonstrated that G proteins did, in fact, exist and played the role Rodbell had outlined for them. Scientists have since discovered at least 20 G proteins and have shown that they are involved in the cell's response to certain hormones and medications as well as many other stimuli. Researchers have linked abnormal G proteins to cholera, whooping cough, and other diseases.

Science student awards. Winners in the annual Westinghouse Science Talent Search were announced on March 13, 1995, and winners of the annual International Science and Engineering Fair were named on May 11. Both student competitions are conducted by Science Service, a nonprofit organization based in Washington, D.C. Other student science competitions included international olympiads in chemistry, mathematics, and physics, all held in July 1994.

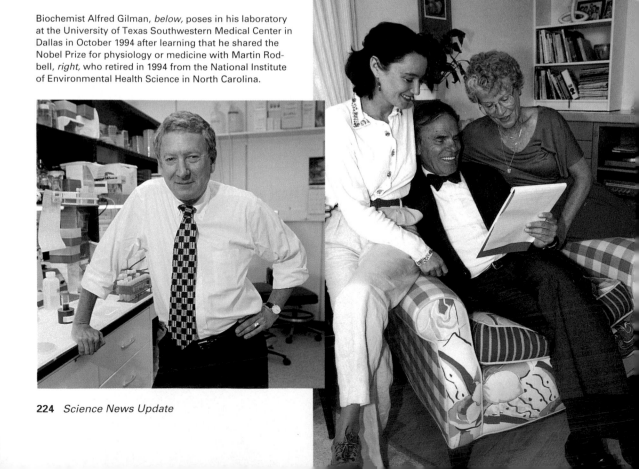

Biochemist Alfred Gilman, *below,* poses in his laboratory at the University of Texas Southwestern Medical Center in Dallas in October 1994 after learning that he shared the Nobel Prize for physiology or medicine with Martin Rodbell, *right,* who retired in 1994 from the National Institute of Environmental Health Science in North Carolina.

Science Talent Search. Forty finalists from a field of 1,667 high school seniors competed in Washington, D.C., for a total of $205,000 in scholarships. The competition was sponsored by Science Service, Inc., and the Westinghouse Electric Corporation.

First place and a $40,000 scholarship went to Irene Ann Chen of San Diego, a student at La Jolla High School, for her biochemistry project on lymphoma cancer. Chen studied two genes isolated from a lymphoma cell line and tried to determine their function in the spread of cancer.

Second place and a $30,000 scholarship were awarded to Tracy Caroline Phillips of Long Beach (N.Y.) High School. Phillips developed an electronic device that helps vision-impaired people distinguish different denominations of paper currency.

The third-place winner of a $20,000 scholarship was Martin Tibor Stiaszny of Overland Park, Kans., a student at Shawnee Mission High School. He investigated dye adsorption into particles called micelles and dendrimers.

Fourth place and a $15,000 scholarship went to Samit Dasgupta of Montgomery Blair High School in Silver Spring, Md.

Fifth place and a $15,000 scholarship were awarded to Deborah Yeh of Plano (Tex.) Senior High School.

Sixth-place winner of a $15,000 scholarship was Gina Petrocelli of Edward R. Murrow High School in Brooklyn, a borough of New York City.

Seventh place and a $10,000 scholarship went to Aleksandr Khazanov of Stuyvesant High School in New York City.

Eighth place and a $10,000 scholarship were awarded to Griffin Weber of Denbigh High School in Newport News, Va.

Ninth-place winner of a $10,000 scholarship was Jordan Cummins of Livingston (N.J.) High School.

Tenth place and a $10,000 scholarship went to Franz Edward Boas, also of La Jolla High School.

In addition, a $5,000 grant went to Jericho High School in Jericho, N.Y., in memory of Soo Yeun Kim. Kim, the competition's first posthumous finalist, was killed in an automobile accident after submitting her project.

Science Fair. More than 1,000 students from the United States, its territories, and over 30 foreign countries competed in the International Science and Engineering Fair, held in Hamilton, Ontario. The seven students who won the highest honors will attend either the 1995 Nobel Prize ceremonies in Stockholm, Sweden; the European Union Contest for Young Scientists in Newcastle upon Tyne, England; or the Tenth Feria Internacional de Ciencia y Technologia Juvenil in Santiago, Chile.

Selected to attend the Nobel ceremonies were Neil Hattangadi of Winter Park High School in Winter Park, Fla., and Tracy Phillips of Long Beach Senior High School. Chosen to attend the European Union contest were Jonathan Edwards and Mani Mahjouri, both of Atholton High School in Columbia, Md. Ben Carter, Michael Ross, and Richard Castle, all of Coleraine Academical Institution in Coleraine, Northern Ireland, won the trip to the science and technology fair in Santiago, Chile.

The First Award winners in 13 disciplinary categories and a team project were:

Behavioral and social sciences. Ann Seiferle-Valencia of Farmington (New Mexico) High School and Miriam Frank of Ward Melville High School in Setauket, N.Y.

Biochemistry. Sarah Vickman of Winona (Minn.) Senior High School and Tekly Ung of Montgomery Blair High School.

Botany. Neil Hattangadi of Winter Park (Fla.) High School; Adam Possner of Dupont Manual Magnet High School in Louisville, Ky.; and Fiona Grant of St. Margaret's School in Victoria, Canada.

Chemistry. Cristiano Krug of Fundacao Escola Tecnica Liberato Salzano Vieira daCunha in Rio Grande do Sul, Brazil.

Computer science. David Slik of Howe Sound Secondary School in Squamish, Canada.

Earth and space sciences. Heather Cameron of Horton District High School in Wolfville, Canada.

Engineering. Tracy Phillips of Long Beach (N.Y.) High School; Paulo Machado of Faculdade de Ciencias in Oporto, Portugal; Daniel Moran of Thomas Edison High School in Tulsa, Okla.; and Setul Patel of Narrows High School in Narrows, Va.

Environmental sciences. Jeremy Kassebaum of Sunnyside (Wash.) Senior High School; Emily Griffin of Adams Central High School in Hastings, Neb.; Katherin Slimak of West Springfield High School in Springfield, Va.; and Olvia Colon of Immaculate Conception Academy in Mayaguez, Puerto Rico.

Mathematics. Benjamin Goetz of Thomas Jefferson High School for Science & Technology in Alexandria, Va., and Claus Soerensen of Skanderborg (Denmark) Amtsgymnasium.

Medicine and health. Jo Ann Guerrero of Astronaut High School in Titusville Fla.; Shivani Grover of Miami (Fla.) Coral Park Senior High School; Christy Berry of Warren Central High School in Vicksburg, Miss.; and Sandra Wong of Central High School in Phoenix, Ariz.

Microbiology. Eden Haverfield of Canterbury School in Fort Myers, Fla.; William Blodgett of Wellington High School in West Palm Beach, Fla.; and Scott Damrauer of Southview High School in Sylvania, Ohio.

Physics. Lawrence Cruciana of West Orange High School in Winter Garden, Fla., and Dorek Alan Biglari of Covenant Christian Academy in Huntsville, Ala.

Zoology. Rebecca Cox of Airline High School in Bossier City, La.; Amy Plummer of Central Bucks High School West in Doylestown, Pa.; and Jessica Wright of Toronto (Canada) French School.

Team project. Ben Carter, Richard Castle, and Michael Ross, all of Coleraine Academical Institution in Coleraine, Northern Ireland.

Chemistry Olympiad. The four-student U.S. team finished in the top three in the International Chemistry Olympiad, held in Oslo, Norway. The other top three teams were from China and the United Kingdom. Gold medals went to Jessen Yu of Thomas Jefferson High School for Science & Technology and Justin McCarty of Amherst (N.Y.) Central High School. Nicholas Loehr of Midlothian (Va.) High School won a silver medal, and James Grimmelman of Horace Mann High School in the Bronx, a borough of New York City, won a bronze medal.

Members of the U.S. team to the International Mathematical Olympiad pose with a statue of physicist Albert Einstein in Washington, D.C., before departing for Hong Kong, where in July 1994 they became the first team in the olympiad's history to register a perfect score.

Math Olympiad. For the first time in the International Mathematical Olympiad's 35-year-history, a team achieved a perfect score. The six-member U.S. team aced a nine-hour examination that tested them on algebra, geometry, and numbers theory. Each member scored a perfect 42 for a perfect team score of 252.

It was also the first victory for a U.S. team since 1986, when an American team tied with the Soviet Union for first-place honors. China and Russia have dominated the Math Olympiad in recent years.

The six-member team competed in Hong Kong against 360 other students from 67 countries. The six winners were Jeremy Bem of Ithaca (N.Y.) High School; Aleksandr Khazanov of Stuyvesant High School in New York City; Jacob A. Lurie of Montgomery Blair High School in Silver Spring, Md.; Noam M. Shazeer of Swampscott (Mass.) High School; Stephen S. Wang of Illinois Mathematics and Science Academy in Aurora; and Jonathan Weinstein of Lexington (Mass.) High School.

Physics Olympiad. The five-member U.S. team placed third at the XXV International Physics Olympiad held in Beijing. China won first place, and Germany took second place. Those two countries won 9 of the 11 gold and silver medals, with the United Kingdom and Poland winning the remainder. The third-place finish was the highest ever for a U.S. team, which competed against 224 other students from 46 countries.

Andrew Frey of the North Carolina School of Science and Mathematics in Winston-Salem placed 15th in the competition. Daniel Schepler of Beavercreek (Ohio) High School finished 16th overall, and Andy Neitzke of Harriton High School in Narberth, Pa., placed 25th overall. All three students received bronze medals and special gold medals. Geoffrey Park of Tenafly (N.J.) High School tied for 50th place and received an honorable mention and a special bronze medal. Charlene Ahn, also of the North Carolina School of Science and Mathematics, placed 82nd overall and received a special bronze medal.

[Rod Such]

Biology

The jolt of adrenaline a person feels when frightened or threatened helps imprint the fearful or threatening event in a special kind of emotional memory. That was the conclusion reported in October 1994 by neurobiologist Larry Cahill and his co-workers at the University of California at Irvine.

For years, researchers had suspected that the brain processes emotionally charged memories in a different manner than it handles memories of situations that do not induce strong emotions. Evidence supporting this view came, in part, from patients who had suffered injury to a pair of almond-shaped structures in the brain called the amygdalae. Such patients often recall emotion-laden memories less effectively than do people with normal amygdalae.

Researchers had also found that emotionally charged memories may be enhanced by stress hormones, such as adrenaline. Such hormones are produced during fearful situations and lead to the "fight-or-flight" syndrome, involving higher heart rates and respiration rates and increased muscle tension.

Cahill and his colleagues tested the effect of adrenaline on emotional memory. They showed two groups of people a series of slides accompanied by either a sad and suspenseful story or a story without any emotional component. The latter story described a boy's visit to a hospital to watch a routine series of drills and exercises. The other story told of a desperate attempt to save a boy's life after an automobile accident.

Some of the participants in both groups were given propranolol, a chemical that blocks the body's production of adrenaline in response to stress. A week later, the researchers tested the subjects' recollection. Those given propranolol who heard the story of the routine hospital visit were unaffected in their ability to recall the story compared to subjects not given the drug. But the subjects given the drug who heard the suspenseful story showed impaired ability to recall the story compared to subjects not given the drug

The results indicated that the heightened memory that normally accompanies highly emotional experiences de-

Biology continued

pends on the action of adrenaline or other stress hormones. Memories of ordinary events, on the other hand, do not require hormonal activity.

The researchers said that the memories associated with fearful or stressful experiences appear to be stored in a different way or in a different part of the brain than other memories. How many different kinds of memory-storage systems does the brain have? The answer from this study seems to indicate at least two memory systems. Experts say that more may be awaiting discovery.

Living prehistoric trees. A group of conifers of a type thought to have become extinct 50 million years ago were discovered in Australia, according to a December 1994 announcement. Botanists classified the trees as a new genus belonging to the Araucariaceae family, a primitive family of conifers related to modern pine trees.

A worker with the Australian National Parks and Wildlife Service discovered one of the trees while on a hike in the Wollemi National Park in August 1994. It was noticeable because of its great height and unusual fernlike branches. The worker took a branch to paleobotanists Ken Hill and Barbara Briggs of the Royal Botanic Garden in Sydney, who made the identification.

The Wollemi pines, as the newly discovered trees are being called, grow in a single, secluded area less than half a hectare in size within a damp gorge. The botanists found 23 adult trees and 16 juveniles. The tallest was 40 meters (130 feet) high. The leaves vary in color from bright lime green on the younger trees to yellow-olive green on the older trees. Hill said the oldest specimen is about 400 years old.

Millions of years ago, primitive conifers related to Wollemi pines were a dominant form of plant life on Earth. Today, they are known mostly from their fossil remains. However, a few related species still exist, including the Norfolk Island pine and the monkey puzzle tree of Chile.

Some botanists compared the Australian discovery with the 1944 discovery that the primitive dawn redwood, or *Metasequoia*, was still growing in China.

A tree whose lineage may date to the age of the dinosaurs stands in a deep gorge in an Australian national park, *below,* where a park worker discovered about 40 specimens of the "living fossils" in August 1994. The conifers have a spongy bark, cones, and drooping fernlike branches. The largest is 40 meters (130 feet) tall.

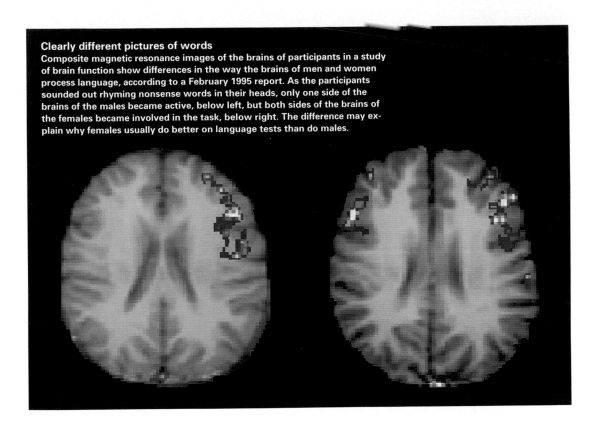

Clearly different pictures of words
Composite magnetic resonance images of the brains of participants in a study of brain function show differences in the way the brains of men and women process language, according to a February 1995 report. As the participants sounded out rhyming nonsense words in their heads, only one side of the brains of the males became active, below left, but both sides of the brains of the females became involved in the task, below right. The difference may explain why females usually do better on language tests than do males.

That tree had also been known only from its fossil record and was thought to be extinct. After the Australian discovery, biologists and conservationists were tantalized by the prospect that the Southern Hemisphere may hold many more examples of "living fossils."

How insects began to fly. By observing how aquatic insects flap their wings to travel across the surface of the water, ecological physiologist James H. Marden of Pennsylvania State University in University Park gained important insights into how insects may have evolved wings some 350 million years ago. (Evolution is the process by which living things develop from simple organisms and change through the ages.) In October 1994, Marden reported that the evolution of the insect wing may have started with a form of locomotion called surface skimming. Surface skimming is intermediate between swimming and flying: The insect stays in contact with the surface of the water while flapping its wings to propel itself rapidly forward.

About 400 million years ago, long before dinosaurs roamed the Earth, most insects had gills and swam underwater. Within another 100 million years, insects evolved wings, took to the air, and diversified in a frenzy of *speciation* (formation of species). Today, insects account for more than half of the species on Earth. The ability to fly was key to this species multiplication, because it enabled insects to take advantage of the new ecological niches that were created as plant life on land evolved into mixed forests of primitive plants.

Insect flight required not just the evolution of a set of wings, but also the development of muscles to move the wings and of nerves to drive the muscles. How this complex assembly might have evolved together has for years perplexed scientists that study insects. Fossils provide evidence that wings originated as gills and that gills were used for getting oxygen from water as well as for movement. But no one could say just how insects made the evolutionary leap from moving gills to flapping wings.

To find an answer, Marden studied stoneflies, insects that belong to an ancient group that has hardly changed in

Discovering Life Deep in the Earth

Science-fiction writers have fantasized about a hidden realm of life deep underground ever since Jules Verne wrote *A Journey to the Center of the Earth* in 1864. Many biologists now believe that a world, teaming with microorganisms, really does exist in the hellish temperatures and enormous pressures far beneath Earth's surface.

Exploration of this so-called deep biosphere— the lowest portion of Earth's crust where life exists—has become one of the most exciting areas of microbiology. A deep-drilling project sponsored by the United States government found an abundance of microbial life at several sites in America in the 1990's, including a hole drilled to 2.8 kilometers (1.7 miles) in Virginia. By mid-1995, scientists had found microbes thriving among rocks almost 3 kilometers (2 miles) below the surface, at a temperature of 75 °C (167 °F).

The number of such discoveries has convinced some scientists that a vast, if primitive, living world exists beneath our feet. These experts believe that the microbes living in the upper few miles of Earth's crust may be so numerous that they literally outweigh all the plants, animals, fungi, and microorganisms that live in all the world's surface ecosystems. One scientist has proposed that if the dwellers of the deep were gathered up and spread over the surface, they would form a layer about 1.2 meters (4 feet) thick.

The discovery of the deep biosphere interests scientists in several fields. Evolutionary biologists say the findings challenge conventional ideas about how life emerged on Earth. For planetary astronomers, the microbes' existence raises the intriguing possibility that life could exist on planets whose environments are much harsher than Earth's. And molecular biologists think the strange microorganisms may one day prove to have practical applications in biotechnology. For instance, the microbes may be treasure troves of previously unknown *enzymes* (proteins that catalyze biochemical reactions) that could be used for industrial processes as well as for the development of new drugs to fight infections, cancer, or other diseases.

Biologists describe the biosphere as the thin shell of atmosphere, water, and soil where living things dwell. The outer edge of the shell is the highest altitude where birds fly and where seeds and pollen are swept by the wind. For most of the 1900's, scientists thought the inner edge of the biosphere was at the surface of the Earth, which included the soil, where worms, insects, microbes, molds, and fungi live, as well as caves. Scientists regarded the deep ocean and the rocky areas below Earth's surface as biological wastelands, virtually devoid of life.

But those ideas were challenged when scientists began to find organisms thriving in extremely hostile environments. In 1977, for example, scientists discovered an oasis of life in the abyss of the Pacific Ocean northeast of the Galapagos Islands, about 2.6 kilometers (1.6 miles) below the surface. Through the "eyes" of a research submarine called *Alvin*, the scientists saw giant tube worms, clams, mussels, shrimp, and other creatures thriving in the inky darkness in numbers previously thought to be impossible in the deep sea.

The animals lived around a hydrothermal vent, a deep-sea hot spring that occurs along ridges on the sea floor where giant plates in Earth's crust are slowly spreading apart. Below the spreading plates, molten rock wells up from Earth's fiery interior. The molten rock heats the seawater that constantly seeps into the ocean floor. The water leaches minerals from the rock and undergoes chemical changes that cause it to discolor. The water rises and spews out of the sea-floor vents, often in a thick, black smokelike fluid that is rich in hydrogen sulfide and other chemical compounds.

The temperature of the water coming from a vent can exceed 360 °C (680 °F), hot enough to melt lead. Nevertheless, the water does not boil, because of the crushing pressure at the sea floor. The water does, however, warm the surrounding area to 10 to 20 °C (50 to 68 °F), compared with 2 to 4 °C (36 to 39 °F) in most of the deep ocean.

As scientists discovered hydrothermal vent communities in other parts of the sea floor, they struggled to understand how animals could survive in the utter darkness, where there are no green plants to provide a source of food. In other biological communities, green plants anchor the food chain, because they are capable of photosynthesis—using energy from sunlight to convert carbon dioxide and water into sugars and other nutrients.

Researchers found to their surprise that the tube worms and other animals in the vent communities were feeding on bacteria. Furthermore, the microbes were using a chemical compound— hydrogen sulfide—as their energy source. This finding meant that the bacteria lived not by photosynthesis, as green plants do, but by a mechanism called *chemosynthesis*. Such microorganisms harness the chemical energy of hydrogen sulfide, methane, or other compounds by combining them with oxygen in a process called oxidation. The energy released when the chemicals are oxidized is used to fuel the organism's growth and activities.

The vent microbes also proved to be *hyperthermophiles* ("high-heat lovers") that can thrive in temperatures up to 110 °C (230 °F). Most surface bacteria die at temperatures above 100 °C (212 °F), the boiling point of water at sea level.

After the discoveries at ocean vents, scientists found hyperthermophilic microbes in surface hot springs and volcanic craters. In 1993, researchers reported detecting heat-loving microbes even in hot petroleum. Oil drillers found the microorganisms in petroleum deposits in the North Sea and in the North Slope of Alaska. The microbes were nearly 3.2 kilometers (2 miles) below the surface at a temperature of 110 °C (230 °F).

After examining the heat-loving microbes, biologists classified some as members of a newly recognized branch on the tree of life. The branch is a kingdom of organisms termed *archaebacteria* or *Archaea*, from the Greek word for ancient. Archaebacteria are like other bacteria in that their single cell lacks a central nucleus. But biologists say they are as different from bacteria in evolutionary terms as they are from human beings. Archaebacteria and "true" bacteria apparently diverged from a common ancestor soon after life appeared on Earth about 4 billion years ago. Ancestors of green plants and animals later split off from the archaebacteria.

How the microbes came to live in their subterranean environment is not known. Some scientists think that the deep microbes are descendants of ancient surface life forms that found their way underground by seeping in surface water through cracks in the soil and rock. As those microorganisms descended, successive generations gradually adapted to life at high temperatures.

Other experts view the deep biosphere as the place where life first appeared. Chemosynthesis is a simpler biological process than photosynthesis, and thus it may have been the first energy-capturing technique used by living things. The subterranean world would have provided a comfortable haven with an abundant food supply in the form of hydrogen sulfide, hydrogen, and methane. The microbes would have been shielded from high levels of ultraviolet light from the sun and other harsh surface conditions on the young Earth. Eventually, the organisms of the deep biosphere could have populated the surface by rising through hydrothermal vents or by percolating up through surface cracks. The new surface-dwellers would have evolved to thrive at lower surface temperatures and in the absence of the compounds used for chemosynthesis.

A final intriguing implication of the discovery of the subterranean realm involves life on other worlds. Astronomer Thomas Gold of Cornell University in Ithaca, N.Y., and others believe that planets with hostile surface conditions may have subsurface conditions where microbial life could thrive, just as Earth does. Space probes, such as the Viking spacecraft that America landed on Mars in the 1970's, could not detect that subsurface life, but future missions might. If so, Gold suggests, Earth's surface life, based on photosynthesis and moderate temperatures, may turn out to be "just one strange branch of life" and not its most common expression. [Michael Woods]

Life in a deep, hot realm

Scientists have found heat-loving microbes in the superheated water rising from vents along ridges in the ocean floor, in the steamy spray of geysers, and in the craters of active volcanoes, *right*. Some scientists think the microbes are descendants of ancient surface bacteria that adapted to the extreme heat below. Other scientists think underground bacteria were Earth's first life forms and that microbes that reached the surface gave rise to the more common bacteria seen today.

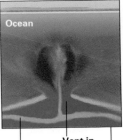

Ocean

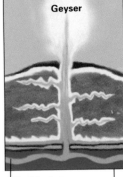

Heat-loving bacteria | Vent in an ocean ridge

Geyser

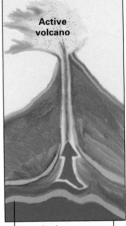

Heat-loving bacteria

Active volcano

Heat-loving bacteria

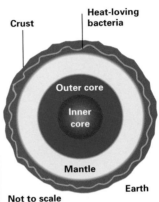

Crust | Heat-loving bacteria

Outer core

Inner core

Mantle

Earth

Not to scale

Some microbiologists theorize that microbes occupy even the deep crust of Earth, *above*. The thickness of the crust varies from about 8 kilometers (5 miles) under the oceans to about 40 kilometers (25 miles) under the continents, and temperatures in the deepest part of the crust may reach 870 °C (1,600 °F).

Biology continued

millions of years. Stoneflies can skim across water, but they are weak fliers. Marden trimmed the stoneflies' wings and found that the insects were still able to skim across the water, but at slower speeds.

Marden speculated that the aquatic ancestors of insects could have been surface skimmers with small winglike structures. Evolution would have favored the development of bigger, stronger wings, because they would be more effective than small wings for skimming across the water. Over many generations, the wings would have become large enough to enable the insects to fly.

Thus, in Marden's view, surface skimming provided the evolutionary stepping stone needed to alter the gill into a primitive wing. He also suggested that when we look at surface-skimming stoneflies today, we may be seeing insect life as it was 400 million years ago.

How cabbage became cauliflower. Defective cabbage genes were responsible for the development of the cauliflower thousands of years ago, according to a team of plant molecular biologists headed by Martin F. Yanofsky at the University of California, San Diego. Their work, reported in January 1995, was part of a research program aimed at understanding the genetic basis for plant development. (Genes, the units of heredity, contain coded information for making proteins.)

The origins of cauliflower can be traced to the domestication of the wild cabbage species *Brassica oleracea* in the coastal areas of northern Europe more than 8,000 years ago. Prehistoric farmers selected and cultivated *mutated* (genetically changed) plants that occasionally appeared in plantings of the wild cabbage. In this way, the wild cabbage gave rise to such diverse vegetables as the heading cabbage, cauliflower, broccoli, Brussel sprouts, kale, kohlrabi, turnip, rutabaga, and mustard greens. The wide array of plants from a single species attests to the ability of minor genetic changes to alter the development of a plant form.

The experiments by Yanofsky and his colleagues began not with cauliflower, but with a distant relative known as

A new species of tree kangaroo resembles a black-and-white koala bear. The kangaroo was discovered in a densely forested mountain range in New Guinea, according to a June 1994 announcement. Researchers from Australia and Indonesia who discovered the timid creature said that a large adult male might reach 76 centimeters (30 inches) in height and weigh 14 kilograms (30 pounds). When frightened, the kangaroo makes a whistling noise and lifts its forelimbs to display its white belly fur.

Arabidopsis thaliana. Plant geneticists and molecular biologists have long used this small plant in the cabbage family for experiments because it has a short life cycle and a small amount of genetic material in the nucleus of its cells. These properties make feasible many genetic experiments that are impossible to carry out in other plants.

Yanofsky's team first identified a genetic mutant of *A. thaliana* with a tight cluster of buds that never properly developed into flowers. Normal *A. thaliana* have single flowers spaced individually along the stem. Because the mutant cluster of buds closely resembled cauliflower, Yanofsky's team named the *A. thaliana* gene responsible for this growth *cauliflower*.

The researchers then made copies of the gene and determined the chemical makeup of the protein it produces. That analysis revealed that the gene encoded a *transcription factor*, a protein with the ability to bind to genes and by so doing, to alter the activity of the gene. The researchers concluded that the normal form of the *cauliflower* gene controls the activity of other genes, and a mutated *cauliflower* gene fails to regulate these other genes properly. The other genes have not yet been identified, but the researchers believe they control the pattern of flower bud formation.

Yanofsky's team used the *cauliflower* gene from *A. thaliana* to identify and study the corresponding gene in cauliflower plants. They found that this gene also coded for a defective protein.

The new research suggests that when prehistoric farmers chose cauliflower-like cabbage plants for cultivation, they were selecting plants that had defects in the gene responsible for the transcription factor. By extending Yanofsky's results, botanists surmise that Brussel sprouts and other plants of the cabbage family have similar defects in genes for other transcription factors.

Abalone rapidly adapt. Abalone, marine mollusks that live along coasts throughout the world, contain a protein that is evolving at an unusually fast rate in successive generations of the organism. That finding was reported in February 1995 by a team of molecular evolutionists and marine biologists headed by Victor D. Vacquier of the Scripps Institution of Oceanography in La Jolla,

Calif. Vacquier's team examined the abalone protein lysin—which is carried in the sperm—in 20 different species of abalone throughout the world.

Abalone produce young by releasing eggs and sperm into the surrounding water and leaving it to the sperm to find the eggs. Abalone eggs are surrounded by a protein coat called the vitelline layer. When sperm and egg meet, the sperm cell releases its package of lysin, which makes a hole in the vitelline layer that allows the sperm to pass through and fuse with the egg to form an embryo. In earlier work, Vacquier and his colleagues found that each abalone species had a version of lysin protein that worked best on the vitelline layer of eggs belonging to its own species, but poorly, if at all, on the vitelline layer of other abalone species.

In February 1995, Vacquier's group reported that the abalone gene that encodes the lysin protein was changing from generation to generation in an unusual manner. A species' genetic material can change in two ways. One way, called silent substitution, does not affect the chemical makeup of the protein coded for by the gene. The second type, called nonsilent substitution, does result in a changed protein. Normally, the rate of silent substitutions in a species is as great or greater than the rate of nonsilent substitutions.

Vacquier's group found just the opposite occurring in the abalone DNA. The rate of protein-altering substitutions in the lysin gene was greater than the rate of silent substitutions.

What could promote rapid change in the chemical makeup of the abalone lysin? The researchers speculated that the need to avoid crossbreeding between two different abalone species was the agent of change. In many coastal areas such as the Pacific coast of North America, several species of abalone have overlapping habitats and breeding seasons. Crossbreeding is reduced if the chemical makeup of the lysin protein and the vitelline layer of each abalone species changes rapidly. In that way, many abalone species can coexist in the environment without losing their identity in what otherwise would be a random mix-or-match fertilization between species.   [Daniel J. Cosgrove]

In WORLD BOOK, see BIOLOGY.

Books About Science

Here are 18 important new science books suitable for the general reader. They have been selected from books published in 1994 and 1995.

Anthropology. *The Man in the Ice: The Discovery of a 5,000-Year-Old Body Reveals the Secrets of the Stone Age* by Konrad Spindler. Spindler was the lead archaeologist on a team of scientists who recovered an ancient corpse that had been found in 1991 intact and preserved in a glacier in the Austrian Alps.

Spindler's account attempts to unravel the mysteries that surround the life and death of this particular Stone Age man. Through meticulous investigation of the man's clothing, equipment, and physical remains, the author also probes what human life must have been like in Europe during the late Neolithic Period (New Stone Age). (Harmony Books, 1995. 305 pp. illus. $25)

The Origin of Humankind by anthropologist Richard Leakey examines the best-known theories about how *hominids* (a group of species that includes human beings and their apelike human ancestors) came to be *bipedal* (moving about on only two feet) and how social organization and culture originated. Most of Leakey's conclusions are based on his studies of some of the earliest hominid fossils found in Africa. (BasicBooks, 1994. 171 pp. illus. $20)

Archaeology. *Time Detectives: How Archaeologists Use Technology to Recapture the Past* by Brian Fagan takes readers to some of the most important archaeological finds in recent years, including an ancient Mayan village and a Bronze Age shipwreck.

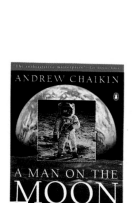

Fagan shows how archaeologists use modern scientific techniques to learn about the past, such as determining the diets of ancient humans by examining bone collagen from their remains. Fagan also probes how the knowledge gained from archaeological digs has influenced modern human society. (Simon & Schuster, 1995. 288 pp. illus. $24)

Astronomy. *A Man on the Moon: The Voyages of the Apollo Astronauts* by Andrew Chaikin highlights his exhaustive interviews with astronauts who took part in the Apollo missions to the moon. Recently declassified information, such as the astronauts' on-board voice tapes, helps recapture in vivid detail the first manned lunar explorations. (Viking, 1994. 670 pp. illus. $27.95)

The Cambridge Atlas of Astronomy edited by Jean Audouze and Guy Israël provides extensive illustrations and descriptions of the science of astronomy. The articles are written by some of the most prominent researchers in their respective fields. Among the subjects covered are the planets and current theories about how the stars and the universe itself originated. The illustrations include photographs from recent space probes, such as the Magellan mission to Venus. (Cambridge University Press, 1994. 470 pp. illus. $75)

Pale Blue Dot: A Vision of the Human Future in Space by Carl Sagan argues that we should continue to explore our solar system. The Cornell University astronomer suggests that human survival may ultimately depend on our ability to colonize our neighboring planets. (Random House, 1994. 429 pp. illus. $35)

Biology. *Bugs in the System: Insects and Their Impact on Human Affairs* by entomologist May Berenbaum examines the impact that insects have on human life. The importance of insects to the pollination of crops is just one of many examples of how deeply insects are entwined in human affairs. (Addison-Wesley, 1995. 377 pp. illus. $25)

The Book of Man: The Human Genome Project and the Quest to Discover Our Genetic Heritage by Walter Bodmer and Robin McKie tackles both the practical and ethical issues involved in the Human Genome Project, the effort to map the 100,000 or so genes that make up human chromosomes. The authors explain what DNA (deoxyribonucleic acid) is and give a historical account of how its molecular structure was discovered. They also discuss the advances genetic medicine may bring, including cures for cystic fibrosis and Alzheimer's disease. (Scribner, 1994. 259 pp. illus. $25)

Chemistry. *Designing the Molecular World: Chemistry at the Frontier* by Philip Ball discusses some of the most important recent advances in chemistry and shows how these advances are being applied in other fields, such as biology, electronics, and atmospheric science. The author cites the creation of superconducting ceramics for brain scanners and liquid-crystal flat screens for televisions as examples of how chemical research is being applied. (Princeton University Press, 1994. 376 pp. illus. $29.95)

Cosmology. *The Origin of the Universe* by John D. Barrow addresses current theories about the birth of the universe. Barrow also discusses the tools astronomers use to investigate those theories, such as the Cosmic Background Explorer (COBE) satellite. COBE went aloft in 1989 to study the cosmic background radiation that scientists believe is the remnant of the big bang, the event that scientists think created the universe. Barrow suggests that particle detectors buried deep underground may gather the evidence that will explain how the galaxies originated. (BasicBooks, 1994. 150 pp. illus. $20)

General Science. *Shadows of the Mind: A Search for the Missing Science of Consciousness* by Roger Penrose. Penrose, a British mathematician, continues his quest, begun in an earlier work, *The Emperor's New Mind,* to explain human consciousness on the basis of physical principles. Penrose attacks current efforts in the field of artificial intelligence, arguing that the endeavor is pointless because consciousness is not computational. (Oxford University Press, 1994. 457 pp. illus. $25)

Geology. *Minerals: An Illustrated Exploration of the Dynamic World of Minerals and Their Properties* by George W. Robinson explores the world of minerals. The author focuses on four of the most important crystal-forming processes found in nature: magmatism, precipitation from solution, chemical alteration, and recrystallization. The results of these processes are shown in illustrations that display the many shapes, structures, and colors of minerals. (Simon & Schuster, 1994. 208 pp. illus. $40)

Mathematics. *The Mathematical Universe: An Alphabetical Journey Through the Great Proofs, Problems, and Personalities* by William Dunham is organized alphabetically, as its title implies. The book begins conveniently with a general history of arithmetic, and ends with z, the symbol for complex numbers. Dunham profiles several mathematical pioneers, including Leonhard Euler, a Swiss mathematician of the 1700's; and Pierre de Fermat, a French mathematician of the 1600's whose proof for a mathematical proposition known as "Fermat's last theorem" eluded mathematicians until

1993. (Wiley, 1994. 314 pp. illus. $22.95)

Natural History. *Journey to the Ants: A Story of Scientific Exploration* by entomologists Bert Hölldobler and Edward O. Wilson recounts the authors' experiences during a lifetime of studying ants. They present a concise summary of the findings of *myrmecology* (the study of ants), describing in particular the intriguing social organization of these incredibly adaptable creatures. (Belknap/Harvard University Press, 1994. 228 pp. illus. $24.95)

The Beak of the Finch: A Story of Evolution in Our Time by Jonathan Weiner won the Pulitzer Prize for general non-fiction in 1995. Weiner reports on the work of two evolutionary biologists who returned every year for 20 years to the isolated, uninhabited island of Daphne Major in the Galapagos Islands chain to monitor changes in the 13 species of finch that live there. Their data demonstrated that evolutionary change can occur rapidly. Each new generation of finch showed some new adaptation to its environment. (Knopf, 1994. 332 pp. illus. $25)

Physics. *About Time: Einstein's Unfinished Revolution* by Paul Davies pursues ideas about the nature of time that were first raised by German-born physicist Albert Einstein. Was there a beginning of time, and will there be an end? What makes time flow from past to present to future? These are just a few of the issues Davies addresses as he discusses research in quantum mechanics and cosmology to dispute some current theories about time. (Simon & Schuster, 1995. 316 pp. $24)

Public Health. *The Coming Plague: Newly Emerging Diseases in a World Out of Balance* by Laurie Garrett is a well-researched history of infectious diseases that argues that new strains of infectious agents, often resistant to antibiotics, pose a worldwide threat to human health. (Farrar, Straus & Giroux, 1994. 750 pp. $25)

Technology. *The Sand Dollar and the Slide Rule: Drawing Blueprints from Nature* by Delta Willis investigates how architects and engineers have looked to structural designs found in nature—the shape of the sand dollar, for example– to get ideas for their own design techniques. (Addison-Wesley, 1995. 234 pp. $23) [Caitlin Anth

New elements with atomic numbers 110 and 111 were created by scientists at the Heavy Ion Research Center in Darmstadt, Germany, researchers announced in November and December 1994. The two elements were the heaviest ever reported. (See PHYSICS.)

Artificial blood. A promising synthetic substitute for whole blood was described in December 1994 by chemist Kenneth S. Suslick of the University of Illinois in Urbana-Champaign. Because whole blood is highly perishable and can carry disease-causing microbes, scientists have long sought such substitutes.

One form of artificial blood, a water *emulsion* (liquid containing finely dispersed particles) of fluorocarbons, is used during some surgical procedures, but its oxygen-carrying ability is limited. Hemoglobin, the protein in red blood cells that carries oxygen, has not been used as a whole blood substitute because single hemoglobin molecules become toxic when broken down in the body.

The blood substitute Suslick developed is a water emulsion containing microscopic bubbles made up of more than a million hemoglobin molecules. The hemoglobin bubbles form when *ultrasound* (high-frequency sound) waves are directed at a solution of hemoglobin and oxygen in water. Left to themselves, these bubbles would soon break apart. But the energy of the sound waves creates millions of tiny bubbles of water vapor that rapidly collapse, releasing heat. The heat causes excess oxygen in the solution to react with water, forming a highly reactive chemical called hydrogen superoxide. This compound causes chemical groups on the hemoglobin molecules to join together, strengthening the structure of the hemoglobin bubbles so that they do not break apart.

Experiments in test tubes showed that the hemoglobin bubbles readily absorb and release oxygen in a manner like that of natural red blood cells. The microbubbles also seem to be much more stable than whole blood. After Suslik's team stored the emulsions for six months at 4 °C (39 °F), less than a quarter of the bubbles had broken down. (Stored whole blood usually lasts only about six weeks.) However, Suslick

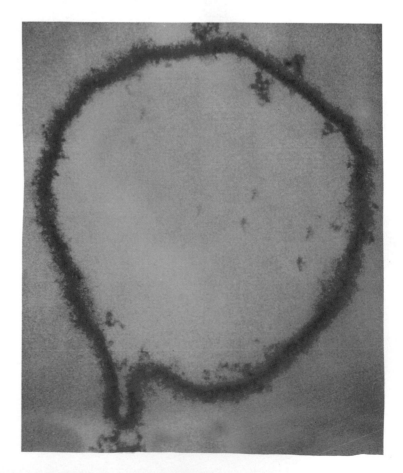

A potential synthetic blood substitute consisting of microscopic bubbles of hemoglobin, the oxygen-carrying protein in red blood cells, was developed by Illinois chemists, according to a December 1994 report. A hemoglobin microbubble, shown in a thin slice, *right,* is about one-fifth the size of a red blood cell.

A simple synthetic molecule that replicates itself was created by chemists at the Massachusetts Institute of Technology in Cambridge. In October 1994, the scientists reported that when the molecule (red) is placed in a chemical solution, it attracts molecular subunits (green and yellow) that form a mirror-image compound held in place by hydrogen bonds (purple dots). Studies of the molecule may improve understanding of the development of DNA and RNA, the self-replicating nucleic acids that are the basis of all life forms.

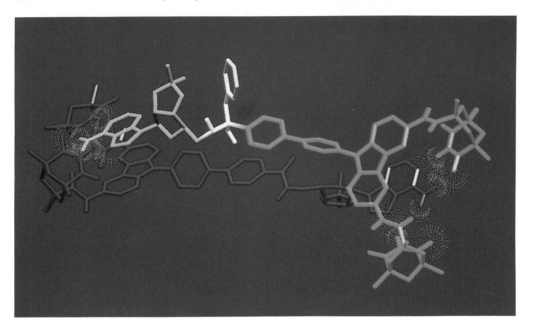

cautioned, the emulsions must still be tested in living organisms for effectiveness and safety. It could be years before the emulsions are approved for human use.

Elastic plastic. A new process that adds elasticity to a plastic used in carpets, clothing, appliances, and many other items was described in January 1995 by chemist Robert M. Waymouth of Stanford University in California. Current manufacturing processes can make the plastic, called polypropylene, stretchable, but the degree of elasticity is hard to control.

Polypropylene is a *polymer* (chain of molecules) composed of three-carbon chemical building blocks called *propylene*. The plastic is made by mixing the propylene with a *catalyst* (a compound that causes a chemical reaction without itself being changed). The catalyst causes the propylene molecules to link up into long chains. But the catalysts currently in use—generally mixtures of aluminum and titanium compounds—produce polymers in which rows of *methyl groups* (groups of three hydrogen atoms bonded to one carbon atom) project from the same side of the chain. Such polymers are strong but are not very stretchable.

The catalyst discovered by Waymouth and his colleagues contains the metal zirconium. This catalyst produces a polymer in which segments containing methyl groups on the same side of the chain alternate with segments containing methyl groups randomly arranged around the chain.

The resulting materials are strong, yet they can be stretched like rubber. Moreover, by varying the pressure applied while the polymer is being formed, chemists can control the lengths of each segment in the chain. This, in turn, allows them to precisely control the elasticity of the polymer.

The Stanford research is still in the experimental stage. However, industrial chemists said the new technology could lead to strong, low-cost rubberlike plastics that could be melted and reused. Such materials would have an advantage over rubber, which cannot be recycled and is often disposed of in waste dumps.

Chemistry continued

Light-carrying molecule. The creation of an unusual elongated molecule that absorbs light at one end and emits it at the other was reported by a team of chemists in October 1994. The scientists, headed by Jonathan S. Lindsey of Carnegie Mellon University in Pittsburgh, Pa., said the molecule resembles optical fibers, hair-thin strands of glass used to transmit telephone messages and computer data on beams of light. But the new molecule—called a photonic wire—is millions of times thinner than the average optical fiber. In principle, bundles of the molecules could carry far more information than the optical fiber systems available today.

The light-carrying molecule consists of five rings of atoms arranged in a straight line. Each ring contains carbon, hydrogen, and nitrogen atoms. The three middle rings have zinc atoms at their centers, and a ring at one end of the string possesses boron and fluorine atoms. The rings' structures resemble that of the plant pigment chlorophyll, which enables plants to absorb light.

The light-transmitting molecules are only 9 nanometers (0.00000035 inch) long—far too short to be made into practical optical devices. But Lindsey said it should be possible to synthesize much longer photonic wires. Researchers also must find ways to switch light transmission on and off through the wires. This might open the door to molecular-scale optical computers, which could potentially store thousands of times more information than present computers. Other possible outgrowths of the wires are artificial retinas that would enable blind people to detect visual patterns, and ultrasensitive light detectors for scientific applications.

Improving chips with fullerenes. What may be the first practical application for fullerenes—soccer-ball shaped molecules made of carbon atoms—was reported by engineers at the Lawrence Livermore National Laboratory in Livermore, Calif., in October 1994. The investigators used fullerenes to form coats of an ultrahard, heat-resistant compound called silicon carbide on the surfaces of silicon wafers. (Such wafers are used to manufacture the semiconductor chips found in computers and other electronic devices.) Mechanical engineer Mehdi Balooch and chemical engineer Alex Hamza, who led the Livermore team, said the process could make it possible to manufacture semiconductor chips able to withstand high temperatures and severe impacts that would ruin chips made from silicon alone.

To prepare the coated wafers, the Livermore team first used a technique called photolithography to create a pattern of tiny electronic circuits on the wafer surface. (In photolithography, light is beamed onto a chemically treated surface through a screen bearing a transparent pattern on a black background. Light passes through the transparent areas, etching the desired pattern in the surface.) This process caused the silicon in the light-treated areas of the wafer to react with oxygen, forming silicon dioxide.

Next, the scientists heated the patterned chip and bombarded it with a stream of fullerene molecules. When the spherical molecules came into contact with the heated silicon, they opened up and reacted with the silicon to form a layer of silicon carbide. But the fullerenes bounced off the silicon dioxide without reacting. The engineers then cooled the wafers and dipped them in hydrofluoric acid. The acid dissolved the silicon dioxide, exposing channels of silicon underneath. The resulting chips could in principle be used for tough, heat-resistant electronic devices.

The scientists suggested several applications for their chips. One possibility is a pressure sensor that would be placed inside car engines to control fuel injection, improving fuel economy and reducing harmful emissions. Other potential uses include flameout detectors in aircraft engines and tiny automotive engine parts built on microchips.

Superconducting tape. The development of a flexible, high-temperature superconducting tape was announced by materials scientists at Los Alamos National Laboratory in Los Alamos, N. Mex., in April 1995. The tape can carry nearly 100 times as much electric current as any previous superconducting tape or wire. The discovery could have practical benefits in areas ranging from medical diagnosis to mass transit.

High-temperature superconductors, first discovered in 1987, are ceramic materials that become *superconducting*—capable of carrying an electric current without resistance—at temperatures much higher than required by the first known superconductors, which had to be cooled nearly to absolute zero (−273 °C or −459 °F). The tapes developed by the Los Alamos team, in contrast, require chilling to a comparatively balmy −196 °C (−321 °F), the temperature of liquid nitrogen.

The Los Alamos team, led by Stephen R. Foltyn, made the new tape from a material known as YBCO, named for its component elements *y*ttrium, *b*arium, *c*opper, and *o*xygen. YBCO, though strongly superconducting, is brittle and hard to process. Foltyn and his co-workers solved this problem by depositing a thin layer of YBCO crystals onto the surface of a tape made from a flexible and inexpensive *alloy* (mixture of metals) composed mostly of nickel.

In order to deposit the YBCO on the alloy, however, the researchers had to build a framework on which the crystals could be aligned. To make this framework, the scientists coated the alloy with cubic zirconia, a mineral consisting of zirconium and oxygen that is used to make artificial diamonds. The researchers used a beam of argon *ions* (charged particles) to sweep cubic zirconia particles onto the alloy. Finally, they deposited the YBCO layer on the coated alloy by exposing the alloy to gases containing yttrium, barium, copper, and oxygen atoms. When lasers were beamed into the gases, the gases decomposed, causing the atoms to be deposited as crystals on the zirconia framework.

When the researchers immersed the resulting tape in liquid nitrogen, it became superconducting, with an ability to carry more than 1 million amperes of current per square centimeter. Potentially, the researchers said, the tape could be wound into coils to make tiny, powerful electromagnets. These might be used to make miniature magnetic resonance imaging (MRI) devices for medical purposes. Other possible applications include low-loss electrical transmission lines, magnetically levitated trains, and equipment to attract toxic metals and remove them from contaminated soil.   [Gordon Graff]

In WORLD BOOK, see CHEMISTRY.

Computers and Electronics

A flaw in a popular and powerful computer chip cast one of the few shadows over the personal computer industry in late 1994. The flaw came to light when the Intel Corporation of Santa Clara, Calif., announced in November 1994 that its Pentium microprocessor performed inaccurately in certain mathematical operations.

Pentium flaw. The microprocessor, or "brain" of the personal computer, is the device that performs the calculations and other operations required by software programs. Microprocessors, which are also called computer chips, consist of millions of minuscule circuits etched onto tiny squares, or chips, of silicon. Intel is the world's largest manufacturer of microprocessors, and Intel chips are used in as many as 80 percent of all personal computers worldwide.

The latest generation of Intel microprocessors is called the Pentium processor. Pentium processors are capable of millions of mathematical operations per second and make possible many advanced computing features, such as enhanced graphics, animation, and video presentations. Pentium's speed and power have made computers built around the processor popular all over the world. Millions of machines with Pentium processors were sold in 1994 alone, the first year it was introduced.

The flaw was located in the Pentium's floating point unit (FPU), which is a special circuitry designed for calculating numbers that contain a decimal point. When certain combinations of numbers were divided using the flawed FPU, the microprocessor produced inaccurate answers.

Intel estimated that the circumstances resulting in the errors would occur in only 1 in 9 billion mathematical operations. So, at first, Intel claimed there was no need to correct the problem in existing Pentium computers. But news of the flaw made headlines around the world. Public concern, fueled by the heavy media coverage, persuaded Intel in December 1994 to offer free replacement of the flawed processor.

Although the FPU error in the Pentium was an obscure flaw, its announcement prompted much reflection and analysis on the part of consumers and reporters, many of whom had become accustomed to thinking of computers as incapable of such errors.

New Pentium processor. Intel recovered from its stumble over a flawed product, and in late March 1995, the company announced the fastest Pentium microprocessor yet. The new Pentium operates at 120 megahertz (MHz). (The megahertz is a unit of wave frequency used to describe the speed of transistor operation in microprocessors.) Other Pentium chips operated at a variety of speeds below 120 MHz.

The performance increase was made possible by a new manufacturing technology that enabled manufacturers to dramatically shrink the size of their chips. The smaller the space occupied by the millions of transistors that make up a microprocessor, the greater the microprocessor's speed and the better its performance.

As computer software becomes more dependent on the presentation of sophisticated graphics, animation, and video, increased speed and power become more important. Observers also noted that the introduction of powerful new chips tends to be followed by dramatic price reductions in already established chips, making the previous generation of personal computers more affordable to more people.

Falling prices boost consumption. Personal computer hardware and software prices fell an average of 20 percent in 1994. One result of the falling prices was that throughout 1994 and 1995 the personal computer hardware and software industries enjoyed explosive growth and increasing popularity.

Industry analysts estimated that more than 8 million personal computers would be sold to North American consumers in 1995. About 3 million were sold in 1994. According to some estimates, more than 25 percent of American homes contained a personal computer in 1995. By the end of 1994, typical home computer prices were under $2,000.

Going multimedia. By late 1994, CD-ROM (*c*ompact *d*isk-*r*ead *o*nly *m*emory) had became the dominant format for

A multilayer compact disc under development at IBM's Almaden Research Center in San Jose, Calif., could hold up to 10 times more information than conventional compact discs. The new discs are made of 2 to 10 transparent layers and are capable of storing the equivalent of more than a million pages of text.

computer software, and most new personal computers sold included CD-ROM drives. The blend of audio, video, animation, still pictures, and text created through CD-ROM technology is called multimedia. (In the Science You Can Use section, see CD-ROM's: Multimedia Computing on a Silver Platter.)

Game machines. Multimedia presentation affected all types of software in 1995. But its greatest impact was on computer and video games. In 1994, sales of such games exceeded $14 billion, which is more than twice the amount spent in the United States on tickets to motion pictures.

Video game machines, taking on increasingly computer-like speed and power, took a leap in May 1995 with the introduction of the Sega Corporation's Saturn machine. Priced at about $399, the Saturn plays CD-ROM games at a far faster speed and with better resolution of graphics than previous machines.

Sega's largest competitor, Nintendo of America, announced in May 1995 that its own advanced video game machine, which was expected to come on the market in 1995, would be delayed until spring 1996.

Personal digital assistant. The latest attempt at creating a small computer called a personal digital assistant (PDA) hit the market in September 1994 with the introduction of Magic Link PIC 1000 from Sony Electronics. The device was priced at about $1,000 when it first appeared in computer stores.

Like most PDA's, the Magic Link PIC 1000 (PIC stands for Personal Intelligent Communicator) is about the size of a fat paperback book and is capable of performing fairly sophisticated computing tasks, including word processing and sending and receiving faxes and electronic mail.

Using the Magic Link, a person can also make airline reservations, log appointments, check stock quotes, pay bills, do financial analysis and scheduling, and run standard personal computer software, such as Lotus 1-2-3. The PDA also has a built-in modem, which allows users to plug into telephone lines and connect to on-line services.

A "digital ink" feature allows the user to write on the screen and fax the message in its handwritten form. The messages cannot be translated into computer text, however. To write in computer text, users must tap on a keyboard on the screen or type on a separate keyboard.

Special software in the device was designed to make it "user friendly," with touch-screen menus and icons such as a telephone, postcard, Rolodex, date book, in-box, out-box, and file cabinet, all representing programs and functions. To fax a message, for example, the user taps on the postcard, which opens up a message form. A tap on the Rolodex can bring up the addressee's name. The user can then write on the message form with digital ink or type out a message on the machine's keyboard, and then hit the Send button.

Magic Link will also have access to PersonaLink, a new on-line service from AT&T. For a small monthly charge, PersonaLink allows the user to customize tasks and deliver electronic messages.

Experts said that most users found the device easy to use. Some, however, found the screen too dim, the memory capacity too small, and the price too high.

More laptops. A new laptop computer that includes a full-size keyboard was introduced by IBM (International Business Machines Corporation) of Armonk, N.Y., in early 1995. Laptops, also known as notebook and subnotebook computers, are portable computers about the size of a briefcase. In the 1990's, laptops increasingly took on the characteristics and power of desktop machines, with full-color displays, fast modems, and CD-ROM drives built into the portable unit.

A drawback of the computers has been that their smaller keyboards are awkward and sometimes lead to typing errors. IBM's new laptop attempted to solve that problem with a two-part keyboard that extends out to spread over an area larger than the computer itself when the laptop's case is opened. Because of its two-part, winglike keyboard, the computer was quickly nicknamed the "Butterfly."

Heavy traffic on the Internet. Home computer users created telecommunications traffic in great numbers in 1994 and 1995. Part of the increase could be attributed to the trend of personal computers being sold with modems, which enable computers to dial out to a variety of telecommunication services and organizations.

The largest source of telecommunications traffic in 1994 and 1995 was the Internet, a global connection of computer networks belonging to universities, government, industry, and individuals. Originally created by the United States government as an emergency computer network, the Internet has become a vast electronic meeting place for sharing information, images, opinions, and conversation. The Internet is the heart of what has come to be called the information superhighway, a communications network that will ultimately link computers and televisions in businesses, institutions, and homes into one gigantic electronic network.

Traffic on the information superhighway takes many forms. Businesses share information among computers on the superhighway. Researchers and scientists can compare notes and findings with colleagues around the world. Physicians can consult with each other and electronically examine patients at great distances. Students can examine the holdings of libraries and museums without leaving their school. During 1994 and 1995, however, it was individual users that dominated the traffic on the information superhighway. Some estimates placed the number of individuals on the Internet as high as 30 million.

One aspect of the Internet attracting a great deal of attention from home computer users, as well as business and institutional users, was the World Wide Web, a portion of the Internet that has graphics, animation, and sound capabilities in addition to text. By mid-1995, the Web contained thousands of sites that offered everything from digital magazines to clips of motion pictures to live tours of museums and other institutions.

Freedom of speech on the "Net." The benefits of free exchange of information on the Internet were called into question in 1995. In the wake of the April 1995 bombing of the Oklahoma

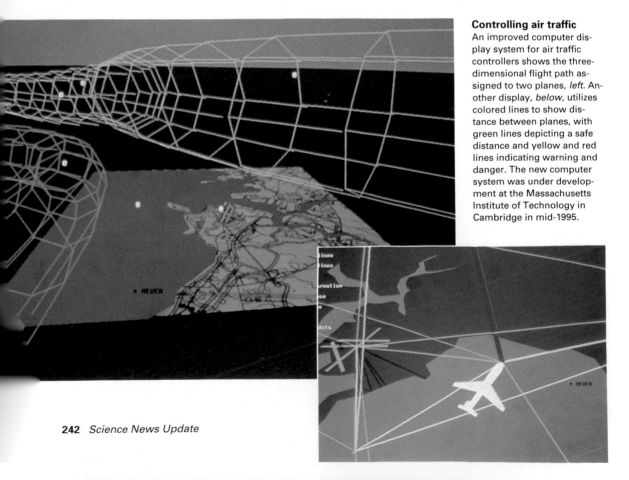

Controlling air traffic
An improved computer display system for air traffic controllers shows the three-dimensional flight path assigned to two planes, *left.* Another display, *below,* utilizes colored lines to show distance between planes, with green lines depicting a safe distance and yellow and red lines indicating warning and danger. The new computer system was under development at the Massachusetts Institute of Technology in Cambridge in mid-1995.

Bob, a software program designed to make personal computers easier to use, was introduced by Microsoft Corporation of Redmond, Wash., in spring 1995. Users click on simple icons to open programs, and cartoon characters on the display screen offer assistance.

City Federal Building, U.S. officials grew concerned about the amount of potentially dangerous information, such as instructions on how to construct explosive devices, available via the Internet.

A debate over possible restrictions on Internet content sprang up in Congress and spread rapidly throughout the media and across the Internet itself. Experts debating the issue generally felt that the Internet was so diffuse and widespread that effectively regulating its contents by legislation would be nearly impossible. (See also SCIENCE AND SOCIETY.)

Software industry news. The biggest news in computer software in 1994 and 1995 had to do with mergers and acquisitions rather than bits and bytes.

Microsoft Corporation of Redmond, Wash., announced in October 1994 its intention to acquire Intuit, a software publisher based in Menlo Park, Calif. The deal was reportedly worth more than $2 billion. It would have been the largest and perhaps most significant merger in software industry history.

Microsoft dominates many types of software publishing, particularly operating systems, the software that coordinates the operation of such computer hardware as the microprocessor and disk drives. Microsoft's Windows software is the world's most popular personal computer software, with tens of millions of copies in use around the world. Intuit dominates personal finance software with its software product Quicken. By using Quicken along with a modem, users can pay bills electronically, check bank accounts, transfer funds, and even pay taxes.

Many in the software industry felt that the combination of Microsoft's leadership in operating system software and Intuit's in financial software would have given the merged companies an all-but-unbeatable lead in the electronic banking industry. Through the merger with Intuit, Microsoft could potentially have participated in a large percentage of the world's financial transactions.

Then, in April 1995, the United States Justice Department filed suit to stop the merger due to concerns that Microsoft's potential to dominate the industry would hinder competition. Rather than face courtroom hearings and legal presentations that could take years to resolve, Microsoft dropped its attempt to acquire Intuit in May 1995.

In an earlier development, Microsoft reached a settlement with the U.S. Justice Department in July 1994, after four years of investigations into alleged antitrust practices. Microsoft had been accused of stifling competition in software, particularly software that runs the operating systems of all IBM-type personal computers.

Rival software companies said that Microsoft tried to block competition by using unfair licensing practices and other tactics. Critics also complained of the company's use of "vaporware," a practice by which the company announced a product several months before it would be available on the market. Then instead of purchasing the competition's product, customers waited for the arrival of the Microsoft product.

According to the settlement, Microsoft would have to modify certain licensing practices. Many in the computer software industry considered the settlement too lenient. In February 1995, Federal District Court Judge Stanley Sporkin found the settlement was too favorable to Microsoft and threw open the case again. Both Microsoft and the Justice Department appealed the judge's decision. In June, a federal appeals court reinstated the settlement.

In another major development in the computer industry, IBM acquired the Lotus Development Corporation, a software company, in June 1995 for more than $3.5 billion. Industry analysts said the acquisition of successful Lotus personal computer programs, including a spreadsheet and word processor, would help IBM sell personal computers. A popular program called Lotus Notes, which allows individual users to work together on the same material across networks, would make IBM a leader in the emerging market of so-called "groupware" programs.   [Keith Ferrell]

In WORLD BOOK, see COMPACT DISC; COMPUTER; ELECTRONICS.

Conservation

Conservation policies in the United States in 1994 and 1995 included both the killing and the protection of wolves. Alaska ended a program to eliminate wolves as a way of increasing caribou herds in a small area of the state. And wolves were reintroduced in Yellowstone National Park in a program to restore the major species that once lived there.

Alaska ends wolf control. In February 1995, Alaska Governor Tony Knowles ended his state's controversial two-year program of killing gray wolves on a 10,440-square-kilometer (4,030-square-mile) area south of Fairbanks. The Alaska Department of Fish and Game (ADFG) had hoped to increase the caribou population by killing wolves.

The caribou are important to Alaska's tourist industry, but the number of animals in the area had dropped from about 10,700 in 1989 to about 4,000 in 1993. Some biologists believed wolves, which prey on caribou, were primarily responsible for the decrease, but other experts believed additional factors were also at work. As many as 7,000 gray wolves live throughout Alaska, the only state besides Minnesota where the gray wolf is not on an official endangered species list.

The ADFG originally planned to shoot wolves from aircraft. In response to animal rights activists who opposed aerial shooting, the ADFG authorized the use of snares instead. More than 1,700 snares were set. Unfortunately, some caught animals other than wolves, including moose, foxes, eagles, and even caribou.

In November 1994, a wildlife biologist videotaped an ADFG official shooting a snared wolf several times before it was killed. The disturbing video was shown on television worldwide. Public reaction against the killing led to an investigation by the Alaska Department of Public Safety. The agency's report stated that the snares did not always catch the wolves around the neck and kill them quickly. Of the 134 wolves killed in the program, 37 did not die in the snares and had to be shot. The agency's report prompted Governor Knowles to halt the program, saying it had been mismanaged and was inhumane.

Wolves return to Yellowstone. Gray wolves were released in Yellowstone National Park in Wyoming in March 1995 by biologists with the National Park Service and the U.S. Fish and Wildlife Service. The goal was to reestablish a natural community of predators in the park. Wolves had been part of the original wildlife community in the park, but they were hunted to extinction in the western United States in order to protect livestock herds. In 1915, federal law called for the removal of wolves from all federal lands, including Yellowstone. Since then, the numbers of elk, which wolves prey upon, have increased greatly, resulting in overbrowsed vegetation in some areas.

The wolves, 14 animals captured in Canada, were taken to three areas in the park. For several weeks, the gates of holding pens in the areas were left open so that the wolves could leave and return whenever they wished—a technique known as "soft release." The wolves were fitted with radio collars so that biologists could monitor them in the wild.

A conservation group known as Defenders of Wildlife proposed that the first pack formed by the released wolves be named "Aldo's Pack" after the conservationist Aldo Leopold. In the mid-1900's, Leopold's writings described the importance of the wolf and other predators in the balance of nature.

Some ranchers who raise livestock near the park feared that the wolves would kill their sheep and cattle, and they opposed the reintroduction of wolves into Yellowstone. In response to these concerns, Defenders of Wildlife established a compensation fund of more than $100,000 to reimburse ranchers for the market value of any livestock lost to wolf predation.

Salty threat to Florida reefs. Unusually salty water may be the reason that kilometers of coral reefs in the Florida Keys area are degrading, according to evidence presented in August 1994 by marine biologist James Porter of the University of Georgia in Athens. Reef degradation has been in evidence since at least 1988.

Coral reefs are an important part of

Mechanical "mole"
A California wildlife biologist sends a robotic device into a den to monitor burrowing animals while they sleep, *below right*. The device, called the miniature optical lair explorer, or MOLE, *bottom left,* contains a tiny camera for filming animals in their dens. Scientists invented the device in 1994 to monitor endangered San Joaquin kit foxes, burrowing owls, and badgers, all of which are at risk because their California habitat is a testing site for explosives.

Conservation continued

the marine environment in Florida Bay, and any damage they suffer is likely to harm the health of the entire ecosystem. Moreover, because coral reefs are important sites of biological diversity, a large number of species are at risk whenever a reef is damaged.

Porter claimed that the reefs were being harmed by an unusual pattern of water temperatures caused by the influx of salty water. Normally, the temperature of ocean water decreases with depth, so that water at the bottom is cooler than the water at the surface. However, Porter found the seemingly impossible to be the case in the water around the reefs—the warmer water was at the bottom, and the cooler water was at the top.

Porter saw this unusual pattern as an effect of the diversion of huge amounts of fresh water north of south Florida's Everglades National Park area. Instead of flowing southward through the Everglades into Florida Bay, the water ends up in irrigation channels serving farmland. Deprived of fresh water, Florida Bay has become increasingly salty, and the high concentration of dissolved salt increases the density of the water. As the salty water flows southward through the Keys, it sinks below the cool water that normally surrounds the bottom of the reefs. The salty water also carries nutrient-rich sediments, which compound the damage to the reef system. According to Porter, the water is too salty, too hot, too cloudy, and too nutrient-rich to support coral life.

Biologists said that Porter's research shows how ecosystems interact with natural resources. In this case, the fresh water coming from the Everglades is needed to exert a crucial and positive influence on marine species living far away.

"Downlisting" species. Growing numbers of bald eagles, the national symbol of the United States, enabled the U.S. Fish and Wildlife Service to change the bird's status from endangered to threatened in July 1994. However, the reclassification, known as "downlisting," did not apply to bald eagles in Arizona, New Mexico, or parts of Texas and California, where the species is still classified as endangered. The dry climates of these areas present difficulties for the health of young bald eagles. For example, only 18 young eagles were raised in Arizona in 1994, too few to offset the deaths of adult birds in the state.

Compounding the problem is the rapid growth of the human population in the western areas. Bald eagle habitats may be destroyed when land is developed for housing and other human needs.

The overall good news for the bald eagle followed a similar reclassification earlier in 1994 for two other species. The gray whale became the first marine species to be downlisted to threatened, and some populations of peregrine falcons were also reclassified.

New record for Kirtland's warbler. The population of Kirtland's warbler, an endangered bird species that nests only in Michigan, reached a new high in 1994. Researchers counted 633 singing males, up from 485 in 1993. The number of singing males provides biologists with a gauge to the size of the breeding population as a whole.

Kirtland's warblers migrate to the Bahama Islands for the winter months and breed in a limited area in central Michigan. They depend on jack pine forest for nesting habitat, so when about 4 million jack pines were planted on more than 900 hectares (2,000 acres) of state and federal lands in Michigan, conservationists hoped the warbler population would increase. Conservationists said the planting clearly helped.

The population of the warblers hit a record low in 1987, when researchers counted only 167 singing males. The previous record high for the birds occurred in 1961, when 502 singing males were counted, according to the Michigan Department of Natural Resources.

Legal aid for rare deer. In August 1994, a U.S. District Court ruled that the Federal Emergency Management Agency (FEMA) was not exempt from provisions of the Endangered Species Act, as FEMA had contended. At issue was the welfare of the remaining population of Key deer, the smallest subspecies of white-tailed deer that lives only in the Florida Keys.

The ruling affected FEMA'S practice of offering low-cost flood insurance. Over the years, this practice has encouraged development of the flood-prone Florida Keys. But development came at the cost of diminishing the habitat for

Key deer. By the 1950's, only about 25 Key deer survived. In 1995, the herd was still small, numbering between 250 and 300 animals. According to the new court ruling, FEMA cannot offer flood insurance to property owners in areas inhabited by an endangered species.

Protecting California deserts. On Oct. 31, 1994, U.S. President Bill Clinton signed into law the California Desert Protection Act of 1994. The act formally recognizes the unique scenic, historical, archaeological, ecological, scientific, recreational, and wildlife resources provided by desert ecosystems in California.

The act created a new desert wilderness area in California from lands administered by the Bureau of Land Management. The newly designated desert wilderness, which includes parts of two national wildlife refuges, became part of the National Wilderness Preservation System. The large areas of desert thus gained protection from economic or development interests that might exert pressure to use the land in ways that might impair or destroy its public and natural values.

The federal government has been authorized to set aside land as protected wilderness since the Wilderness Act of 1964 was made law. The Wilderness Act declared that large and remote tracts of federally owned land might be maintained and preserved in a natural condition. The act defined wilderness areas as those where "man himself is a visitor who does not remain" and only the forces of nature affect the land.

The 1994 law also changed two national monuments into two national parks—Joshua Tree National Park and Death Valley National Park. Joshua Tree National Park, named after the fragrant yucca tree growing there, is in California, and Death Valley National Park is in both California and Nevada. Death Valley is 86 meters (282 feet) below sea level, the lowest land surface in the Western Hemisphere.

Finally, the law established a new 566,560-hectare (1.4 million-acre) wilderness area known as the Mojave National Preserve. Also in California, this desert region is filled with extinct volcanoes. [Eric G. Bolen]

In the Special Reports section, see HURRICANES—WHIRLWINDS OF CHANGE. In WORLD BOOK, see CONSERVATION.

Falling prey to a mysterious illness
A male lion in the Serengeti National Park in Tanzania begins to falter, *below,* and falls into twitching convulsions, *bottom,* due to a mysterious illness that killed more than 80 lions in the park in 1994. Researchers reported in June 1994 that the disease agent was the virus that causes distemper in dogs. Precisely how the virus came to infect the lions was unclear.

Deaths of Scientists

Notable scientists and engineers who died between June 1, 1994, and June 1, 1995, are listed below. Those listed were Americans unless otherwise indicated.

Alfvén, Hannes (1908-April 2, 1995), Swedish physicist who shared the Nobel Prize in physics in 1970 for his pioneering studies in *magnetohydrodynamics,* the study of electrically conducting fluids moving in a magnetic field. Alfvén predicted in 1942 that magnetic field lines in a *plasma* (ionized gas) could transmit a wave. Such waves were eventually observed and came to be known as Alfvén waves. His work helped explain the shape of the Van Allen radiation belts that encircle the Earth.

Anfinsen, Christian B. (1916-May 14, 1995), biochemist who shared the Nobel Prize in chemistry in 1972 for his contributions to understanding the relationship between a protein's structural properties and its biological function. He was regarded as a pioneer in the field of protein structure and folding, showing how the enzyme ribonuclease folds to create a three-dimensional structure that determines its function.

Butenandt, Adolph (1903-Jan. 18, 1995), German chemist whose work on sex hormones earned him a share of the Nobel Prize in chemistry in 1939. Butenandt was the first person to isolate *estrone,* the hormone that determines sexual development in females. Working with other chemists, he was the first to isolate *androsterone,* a male hormone, and the first to synthesize *testosterone,* the hormone that stimulates male sexual development. The Nazi government in Germany forced Butenandt to decline the Nobel award. He later accepted the Nobel medal and diploma in 1949.

Cain, Stanley A. (1902-April 1, 1995), botanist and conservationist who helped found the science of ecology and who served as an assistant secretary in the United States Department of the Interior in the 1960's.

Fowler, William A. (1911-March 14, 1995), astrophysicist who shared the Nobel Prize in physics in 1983 for his work showing that heavy elements are created in the cores of stars. Fowler showed that virtually all of the elements heavier than hydrogen and helium were produced in the nuclear furnaces of the stars and were dispersed into space during stellar explosions. "All of us are truly and liter-

ally a little bit of stardust," he once said.

Fuller, Calvin S. (1902-Oct. 28, 1994), chemist and co-inventor of the *solar cell,* a device that converts sunlight into electricity. Fuller first demonstrated the solar cell in 1954. In 1962, its use on a communications satellite helped make space exploration practical.

Hodgkin, Dorothy (1910-July 29, 1994), British biochemist and crystallographer who won the Nobel Prize in chemistry in 1964 for her work in using X rays to probe the structures of such complex biochemical compounds as penicillin. Her research helped establish X-ray crystallography as one of the fastest methods of deciphering the chemical constitution of these compounds.

Köhler, Georges J. F. (1946-March 1, 1995), West German-born biochemist who shared the Nobel Prize in physiology or medicine in 1984 for developing a laboratory technique to produce *monoclonal antibodies,* identical copies, or clones, of antibodies that can be directed at cancerous cells without harming normal cells. Köhler's findings also enabled scientists to study how antibodies are made.

Lwoff, André (1902-Sept. 30, 1994), French biochemist who shared the Nobel Prize in physiology or medicine in 1965 for discoveries regarding the genetic control of enzyme activity in living cells. In the 1940's, Lwoff showed that certain enzymes regulate the function of some genes. Lwoff also made pioneering discoveries regarding the role of vitamins in living organisms and did seminal work in the study of viruses that infect bacteria. Lwoff was a hero of the French Resistance during World War II (1939-1945).

Meister, Alton (1922-April 6, 1995), biochemist known for his research on the role played by certain amino acid compounds in the human body's immune system.

Morgan, William W. (1906-June 21, 1994), astronomer who was credited with discovering the spiral shape of our Milky Way Galaxy and who demonstrated the existence of *supergiant galaxies,* galaxies that are many times more massive than most other galaxies.

Needham, Joseph (1900-March 24, 1995), British biochemist and historian of science known for his monumental study of the history of science in China,

Dorothy Hodgkin

André Lwoff

Linus C. Pauling

a collection of 16 volumes entitled *Science and Civilization in China*.

Pappenheimer, Alwin M., Jr. (1908-March 21, 1995), biochemist and immunologist who helped unravel the secrets of bacterial toxins by isolating and identifying the chemical makeup of the diphtheria toxin.

Pauling, Linus C. (1901-Aug. 19, 1994), chemist whose work was widely regarded as having revolutionized the science of chemistry. Pauling won the Nobel Prize in chemistry in 1954 for his work on the nature of *chemical bonds,* the energies that bind atoms and help explain the structure of complex molecules. His research on the molecular structure of proteins laid the groundwork for the later discovery of the structure of the DNA (deoxyribonucleic acid) molecule. Pauling also won the Nobel Peace Prize in 1962 for his efforts to ban nuclear weapons and halt open-air nuclear testing. He later became known for his advocacy of the health benefits of vitamin C.

Popper, Sir Karl (1902-Sept. 17, 1994), Austrian-born British philosopher known for his pioneering work in the philosophy of science.

Schalk, Marshall (1907-Feb. 22, 1995), geologist known for his research on shoreline changes and submarine topography along the Arctic coastline of Alaska.

Schwinger, Julian (1918-July 16, 1994), theoretical physicist who shared the Nobel Prize in physics in 1965 for his "fundamental work" in the field of *quantum electrodynamics,* the study of the interaction between electrons and photons. Schwinger's work helped bring about a revolution in theoretical physics and quantum field theory. His mathematical formulations laid the foundation for understanding the interaction between charged particles and an electromagnetic field. Schwinger was a prodigy who published his first important scientific paper at the age of 18 and received his doctorate at the age of 21.

Stibitz, George R. (1904-Jan. 31, 1995), mathematician who invented the first digital computer in 1940.

Stratton, Julius A. (1901-June 22, 1994), physicist and electrical engineer best known as the president of the Massachusetts Institute of Technology (M.I.T.) in Cambridge from 1959 to

Julian Schwinger

Colin M. Turnbull

Jerome B. Wiesner

1966. There, he introduced a number of curriculum changes, including the creation of interdisciplinary centers for space research and Earth science. He was the chairman of the Ford Foundation from 1966 to 1971.

Swinton, William E. (1901?-June 12, 1994), Canadian paleontologist known for his writings about dinosaurs.

Tamm, Igor (1922-Feb. 6, 1995), virologist noted for his pioneering studies on the composition of viruses and how they replicate in the cells they infect.

Tucker, Albert W. (1905-Jan. 25, 1995), Canadian-born mathematician who created the mathematical foundations of linear programming and was credited with inventing the "Prisoners' Dilemma," a well-known explanation of game theory.

Turnbull, Colin M. (1924-July 28, 1994), British-born anthropologist best known for two studies based on field work in Africa and published as *The Forest People* (1961) and *The Mountain People* (1972).

Weintraub, Harold M. (1945-March 28, 1995), molecular biologist whose research in genetics contributed to an understanding of how cells develop. For example, he helped establish an experimental framework for showing how embryonic cells become specialized cell types.

Wiesner, Jerome B. (1915-Oct. 21, 1994), electrical engineer who helped develop radar in the 1940's and was regarded as an authority on microwave theory but who became better known as science adviser to President John F. Kennedy in the 1960's and as president of M.I.T. from 1971 to 1980.

Wigner, Eugene P. (1902-Jan. 1, 1995), Hungarian-born physicist who shared the Nobel Prize in physics in 1963 for his contributions to the study of atomic nuclei and the complex behavior of electrons. Wigner was also credited with developing the theoretical methods that led to the first controlled nuclear chain reaction in 1942. He was among a group of scientists who persuaded physicist Albert Einstein to write President Franklin D. Roosevelt, warning that Nazi Germany might build an atomic bomb. The letter reportedly inspired the Manhattan Project, the United States effort that succeeded in building the first atomic bomb.   [Rod Such]

New drugs for treating stubborn viruses received approval in the United States in 1994 and 1995. These and other newly approved medications gave patients much-needed treatment alternatives.

Chickenpox vaccine. A vaccine for chickenpox was approved by the U.S. Food and Drug Administration (FDA) in March 1995. Chickenpox, a common contagious childhood disease characterized by skin blisters, affects about 3.5 million people in the United States each year. Although the disease is usually mild, about 9,000 patients experience complications serious enough to require hospitalization, and about 50 to 100 people die each year from the disease.

In April 1995, the American Academy of Pediatrics endorsed use of the vaccine, recommending that it be given routinely to children between the ages of 12 and 18 months and to all older children who had not yet had the disease. Some questions remained regarding the period of immunity provided by the new vaccine, and additional studies were being conducted to address these and other issues. Experts said, however, that the vaccine represented an important advance that would result in a rapid reduction in the number of cases of chickenpox within one or two years.

Easing shingles. A new treatment for shingles, often described as the most painful human infection, came in June 1994 with the FDA approval of a drug called famciclovir. This drug was only the second to be available for shingles.

Varicella-zoster virus (VZV), a type of herpesvirus that causes chickenpox, is also responsible for shingles. After a person has recovered from chickenpox, the VZV remains in the body in an inactive state. In some people, VZV is reactivated later in life and causes herpes zoster, better known as shingles. The virus infects a nerve root and then causes an outbreak of painful, itchy blisters on the skin. The pain often continues after the lesions have healed and can last for months or even years. The infection occurs most frequently in people over 50 years old. About 600,000 Americans suffer an episode each year.

Doctors have treated shingles with pain-relief medicine and a drug called acyclovir. Famciclovir offers the advantage of being administered less frequently: three times per day compared with five times a day for acyclovir. The drug, like acyclovir, cannot cure the disease but lessens its severity.

In research tests, famciclovir also appeared to work against the virus that causes genital herpes infections—herpes simplex virus, type 2. However, its effectiveness against the virus was not determined, and acyclovir continued to be the only drug approved for the treatment of that common sexually transmitted disease.

New drug for HIV infection. In June 1994, the FDA approved a new drug for the treatment of infection by the human immunodeficiency virus (HIV). The virus is the cause of AIDS (acquired immunodeficiency syndrome). The drug, called stavudine, became fourth on the list of HIV drugs, joining zidovudine (also known as AZT), didanosine, and zalcitabine. All four drugs hinder the creation of new viral particles. They cannot cure HIV infection but may prolong an infected person's life and, by reducing complications, improve the quality of life.

Experts consider zidovudine the treatment of first choice for the management of HIV infection. However, some patients experience serious adverse reactions to zidovudine, or their infections continue to worsen despite the treatment. For those patients, stavudine provides an alternative treatment that may be more effective or better tolerated. Some adverse effects were associated with stavudine, the most important of which was nervous-system damage, which causes numbness, tingling, or pain in the feet or hands, and may not be reversible.

Drugs for heart-surgery patients. Two new drugs became available in 1994 and 1995 to help prevent difficulties that can arise during heart surgery. One of the drugs works to reduce clotting and the other reduces bleeding.

In March 1995, abciximab, also called ReoPro, an antibody that reduces blood clotting, became available. The antibody was to be used in conjunction with a procedure called coronary angioplasty, in which doctors open narrowed or blocked arteries. Nearly 30 percent of such patients are at high risk of developing clots that could close the artery following the procedure. Administering abciximab inhibits the formation of blood clots and significantly reduces the risk of complications, including heart attack. However, physicians must monitor patients using the drug closely to avoid major bleeding reactions and the need for transfusions.

A drug called aprotinin became available in mid-1994 to reduce blood loss in patients undergoing coronary artery bypass graft surgery. During this surgery, a patient's blood circulation is assisted by a cardiopulmonary bypass, or heart-lung machine. These patients sometimes bleed excessively, and in some cases, bleeding is severe enough to require multiple blood transfusions.

Aprotinin, derived from animal tissue, helps the blood *coagulate* (thicken), thereby decreasing bleeding. Aprotinin carries a risk of serious allergic reactions, so prospective patients must first receive a small dose of the drug to test for their risk of such reactions.

Alternative for diabetic patients. In December 1994, the FDA approved a new drug, metformin, to help people with Type II diabetes lower their blood sugar levels. Also known as *non-insulin-dependent* or *adult-type* diabetes, Type II is characterized by the body's inability to efficiently process the sugar-controlling hormone insulin. This form of diabetes typically occurs in overweight people over the age of 40. Diabetics whose condition cannot be managed by diet alone can use the new drug as an adjunct to a low-calorie diet to lower their blood glucose concentrations.

The new drug, the first offering of its kind in nearly two decades, provides an alternative to a class of antidiabetic drugs known as sulfonylureas. Metformin may be used in addition to a sulfonylurea in patients who cannot manage their diabetes with one drug alone.

The action of metformin is similar to that of an antidiabetic drug called phenformin that was withdrawn from the market in the late 1970's because of concerns about lactic acidosis, a sometimes-fatal side effect. Rare instances of this side effect occurred with metformin, but the risk of lactic acidosis was much lower than with phenformin.

[Daniel A. Hussar]
In WORLD BOOK, see DRUG.

Ecology

In 1994 and 1995, ecologists reported evidence of climate warming at both poles and in the midlatitudes of the Pacific Ocean. The findings may support the theory that atmospheric emissions of carbon dioxide, a heat-trapping gas, have begun to cause *global warming,* a worldwide rise in average surface temperatures. The new research includes studies of flowering plants in Antarctica, algae fossils from ancient ponds in the Arctic, and marine communities along central California's Pacific Coast.

Antarctica in bloom. Antarctica's only two flowering plant species—Antarctic hair grass and Antarctic pearlwort—are thriving, according to an October 1994 report by plant ecologist Ron Lewis Smith of the British Antarctic Survey. Both plants live on the northern part of the Antarctic Peninsula, which experiences a brief growing season in summertime, when temperatures rise to just above the freezing point, 0 °C (32 °F).

Lewis Smith found that the Antarctic Peninsula's average summer temperature has risen by about 2 Celsius degrees (3.6 Fahrenheit degrees) since 1964, and the rise has lengthened the growing season by about two weeks. The warming has had the greatest effect on flowering plants, because they are more sensitive to small temperature changes than the dominant plants of the region—mosses, lichens, and algae. The number of hair grass plants grew from about 700 in 1964 to 17,500 in 1990, and the pearlwort increased from about 60 plants to 380. Lewis Smith predicted that should this trend continue, additional flowering species would begin to sprout from dormant seeds or from seeds carried to the peninsula on the wind or by birds.

Arctic ponds tell a tale. Evidence of global warming was also discovered at the opposite end of the world, on Ellesmere Island in the Canadian Arctic, according to an October 1994 report by paleoecologist Marianne S. V. Douglas, now at the University of Massachusetts at Amherst, and her colleagues. The scientists studied *diatoms,* microscopic algae with a hard, glasslike outer shell. The shells are usually well preserved, in some cases for thousands of years. In the study, the scientists looked for diatom shells in cores of sediment drilled out of the bottom of ponds on Ellesmere Island. The deepest sediment dated from 8,000 years ago.

The researchers analyzed the diversity and abundance of diatom species in the core samples and found that the diatom communities had changed very little until about 1800. After that time, the population of diatom species previously found in abundance drastically declined while the numbers of some species rarely found before 1800 dramatically increased. The overall number of diatoms in different layers of the sediment was unchanged, however.

The scientists theorized that climate warming caused the changes in the diatom diversity. The researchers ruled out other possible causes, such as acid rain or the thinning of the protective ozone layer, because those changes would have also reduced the overall diatom abundance throughout the cores.

Midlatitude warming. Ecological changes in coastal midlatitudes point to a warming since the 1930's, according to marine ecologist J. P. Barry at the

Monterey Bay Aquarium in Pacific Grove, Calif., and his colleagues. The researchers studied species of *invertebrates* (animals without backbones) that live in a rocky intertidal zone in central California. An intertidal zone is the area between the high-water mark and the low-water mark of tides.

Barry and his colleagues compared data on the intertidal community gathered in 1931 to 1933 with data they collected from 1993 to 1994. Of the 45 species covered by both research studies, 32 had undergone significant population changes. Moreover, eight of the nine southern invertebrate species in the community had widened their ranges northward, and five of the eight northern species had become less abundant. These findings suggest, according to Barry, that the average annual water temperature at the site had risen almost 1 Celsius degree since the early 1930's.

Wolves, moose, and trees. These ecological relationships on Lake Superior's Isle Royale are elegantly simple: The wolves eat moose, and the moose eat needles of balsam fir trees. Ecolo-

Invasion of the spurge
A spreading weed called leafy spurge, *inset,* has crowded out virtually all native plants in a Colorado field, *below.* Native to Europe and Asia, leafy spurge became established in the American West around 1900, and since then has become the "worst of the worst" invaders, according to an August 1994 report by federal land management officials. The weed's 6-meter (20-foot) long roots enable it to survive attempts to kill it by spraying herbicides or plowing it under.

The fly that decapitates fire ants
A tiny parasitic fly, *right,* may one day be used as a natural means of controlling a species of South American fire ant that has invaded 11 Southern states since 1918, scientists reported in November 1994. The female fly lays an egg in the ant's body, and within two days, the developing maggot crawls into the head to seal the mouth and eat the insides. Later, the maggot releases an enzyme that decapitates the ant, *below.* The maggot remains inside the head for two more weeks as it develops into an adult.

gists have long known that the populations of the three species on the well-studied island fluctuate in relation to each other. But which species exerts the greatest influence? In December 1994, wildlife ecologists Brian E. McLaren and Rolf O. Peterson of Michigan Technological University in Houghton reported the answer to that question.

The ecologists sought to discover which of two major population theories best explained life on Isle Royale. The "bottom-up" theory is that species at the lowest level on the food chain of an ecosystem are the key species, regulating the populations of the higher "links." In the "top-down" theory, the highest species is the regulator.

On Isle Royale, the Michigan Tech team checked the growth rings of balsam fir trees by removing a thin cylinder of wood from trees at various locations on the island. A tree adds one growth ring each year, and by measuring the width of the ring, researchers can determine how vigorous the year's growth was. A narrow ring, for example, could indicate that moose had eaten so many

needles that the growth of the tree was hampered.

After comparing each year's tree-ring widths with data on the wolf and moose populations, the ecologists discovered that a drop in the number of wolves in one year was followed in the next with an increase in the moose population. A year or two later the trees grew very little, as evidenced by a narrow ring. That pattern indicates the top-down theory is correct, at least for the simple food chain on Isle Royale.

Disturbance and ecology. In September 1994, ecologist Seth R. Reice of the University of North Carolina at Chapel Hill challenged the popular notion that ecological disturbances exert only a temporary influence on ecosystems. His report, based on research on invertebrate communities in streams, suggested that floods, hurricanes, and other natural disturbances are the major determiners of the structure of ecological communities. (In the Special Reports section, see HURRICANES—WHIRLWINDS OF CHANGE.)   [Robert H. Tamarin]

In WORLD BOOK, see ECOLOGY.

Electronics

See Computers and Electronics

Endangered Species

See Conservation

In October 1994, the United States Department of Energy (DOE) announced plans to build a $1.1-billion fusion energy research facility at the Lawrence Livermore National Laboratory in Livermore, Calif. The National Ignition Facility (NIF) will use immensely powerful lasers to generate about 500 trillion watts released over 3 billionths of a second. The combined power of the NIF lasers will be 40 times greater than the world's most powerful existing laser. Construction was planned to begin in 1997, with operation to begin in 2002.

Nuclear fusion is the process that fuels the sun and other stars. Fusion occurs when *nuclei* (cores) of atoms combine under extremely high temperatures and pressures and release energy. Fusion differs from the standard method of producing nuclear energy—fission—which involves splitting atomic nuclei.

New fusion facility. The heart of the research facility is a spherical chamber 10 meters (33 feet) in diameter. Within the chamber, 192 laser beams will bombard a target no bigger than 5 millimeters (0.2 inch) in diameter. The target is made of deuterium and tritium, two *isotopes* (forms) of the element hydrogen.

The intense concentration of energy is intended to heat the deuterium and tritium nuclei to a temperature high enough to start a fusion reaction. The lasers will heat the target so much that it *implodes* (collapses), forcing the nuclei to fuse and releasing energy in the process. Scientists hope that the reactions at the NIF facility will become self-sustaining, continuing without the addition of energy once the reactions begin. Previous fusion experiments have all consumed more power than they produced.

Engineers are pursuing fusion research because it could prove to be a safe and perhaps one day economical source of energy. Fusion produces far less radioactive waste than does fission, and fusion, unlike fission, cannot cause the uncontrolled chain reactions that can lead to a meltdown at a nuclear reactor.

The DOE chose Lawrence Livermore Laboratory because it has extensive expertise with operating high-powered lasers. Lawrence Livermore already houses NOVA, the world's most powerful laser. As part of the NIF project, a new, more powerful laser called the Petawatt will be installed in the NOVA system by December 1995. The Petawatt will be capable of generating 1,000 times more power than all electric generating facilities in the United States can produce at any given instant, though the Petawatt's burst of energy will last only a trillionth of a second.

World's tallest solar panel. A Canadian firm installed the world's tallest solar panel on a Canadian government building in September 1994. The panel is 61 meters (200 feet) tall and operates as a flat-plate solar collector. Conserval Engineering Inc. of Toronto, Canada, designed and installed the panel.

Solar collectors heat air or water, which engineers pump through a building to heat the interior space. Collectors are usually insulated boxes covered by one or more layers of clear plastic or glass. Inside the box is a plate of black metal or black plastic. The dark plate absorbs sunlight, and its heat is transferred to a fluid that circulates through tubes welded to the plate. The heated fluid then flows to a heat exchanger, a device that transfers the fluid's heat to the air or water used to heat the building.

The Conserval solar panel consists solely of aluminum sheets similar in appearance to the corrugated metal panels used as roofing material in many industrial buildings. The panel has two design modifications to increase its efficiency— the glass or plastic sheet that covers most solar collectors was eliminated, and 2 million holes about 0.75 millimeter (0.03 inch) in diameter were drilled in the solar collector plate.

The glass that covers most solar collectors reflects 10 to 15 percent of the sunlight that strikes the collector. So eliminating the glass increased the amount of sunlight that the Conserval plate can collect and transform into heat. The perforations in the panel increase efficiency by allowing fans to draw air through the panel. The system can thus collect heated air from both sides of the panel. A central fan draws outside air heated by the panel into the channels formed by the panel's metal corrugations. The fan forces the air inside the building through a distribution system to heat the building.

The system preheats air by as much as

30 Celsius degrees (54 Fahrenheit degrees), reducing annual heating costs by $10 to $30 per square meter ($1 to $3 per square foot) of collector wall. The giant panel collects enough solar energy each heating season to save almost $5,000 a year, according to the company. Because the panels lack glass, the collectors cost only about half as much as glazed flat-plate collectors.

Tests on the panels conducted by the DOE turned up refinements that resulted in an improved collector system capable of capturing up to 80 percent of the solar radiation striking it. This compares with about 65 to 70 percent for traditional solar panels.

Ocean-wave energy. A U.S. company announced plans in February 1995 to build a power plant that captures the energy of ocean waves with sheets of a unique plastic anchored to the sea floor. The company—Ocean Power Technology of West Trenton, N.J.—said the small test plant in the Gulf of Mexico should be finished by early 1996.

The plant's operation depends on the piezoelectric effect, which some materials, such as quartz and certain plastics, exhibit. In a piezoelectric material, electric charge builds up along the surface when the material is stretched or compressed along an axis. By coating each side of a piezoelectric plastic sheet with a conducting material, such as silver or aluminum, engineers can use the build-up of charges to drive an electric current that flows through a circuit and performs useful energy.

The Ocean Power Technology plant will use sheets of piezoelectric plastic about 15 meters (50 feet) long, 1 meter (3 feet) wide, and 2.5 centimeters (1 inch) thick. The sheets will be anchored to the sea floor and connected to floats on the surface. As waves move the floats up and down, the sheets will stretch, building up electric charges. The conductive materials will transfer the resulting electric current to undersea cables that will carry it to a power distribution system.   [Pasquale M. Sforza]

In the Special Reports section, see CARS FOR THE YEAR 2000 (AND BEYOND). In WORLD BOOK, see ENERGY SUPPLY; SOLAR ENERGY.

Engineering

Development of the world's smallest and fastest engine was announced by engineers at the Sandia National Laboratories in Albuquerque, N. Mex., in November 1994. The microscopic device could be used to power other miniature machines, such as tiny surgical tools designed to unclog arteries, destroy tumor cells, or repair damage inside the eyes, ears, or brain. In addition, the researchers said, the technology they developed could be applied to the design of other micromachines, including miniature safety devices in nuclear weapons and industrial products.

Microengine. The new engine is about as thick as a few human hairs and may operate at speeds approaching 500,000 revolutions per minute (rpm). Few other mechanical devices can exceed 100,000 rpm, according to engineers Ernest Garcia and Jeff Sniegowski, who developed the engine.

The electrically powered engine converts *linear* (back-and-forth) motion into rotary motion that can provide continuous mechanical power. When viewed through a microscope, the device resembles a connecting rod driving a toothed gear, much like that on an old-fashioned steam locomotive. But the gear is only 50 micrometers (0.002 inch) in diameter.

The new microengine lies on a wafer of silicon, the material used to make the integrated circuit chips used in computers and other electronic devices. The Sandia engineers fabricated the engine using the same techniques that workers employ to etch electronic circuits on computer chips. Eventually, the researchers said, this approach would enable workers to mass-produce the microengine, with thousands or even millions being created at one time.

The prototype Sandia microengine is a free-standing device operated by a computer. In future versions, researchers said, the microengine may be combined with computer circuits, producing a "smart" electromechanical device that could sense and respond to different operating conditions.

Rust-resistant steel. The development of a new type of steel that resists corrosion was reported in January 1995 by engineers at the University of California at Berkeley. The new steel could save billions of dollars now required each year to repair corroded concrete bridges and other structures, according to the engineers.

Most concrete structures are constructed with an internal skeleton of steel reinforcing bars, called "re-bar." Such reinforced structures are much stronger than those made from concrete alone. However, conventional re-bar tends to corrode easily. Corrosion occurs when water and salts seep into concrete from the soil, the ocean, or applied deicing compounds. The water and salt come into contact with the steel, rusting the bars and weakening the concrete structure.

Conventional re-bar steel consists of iron layers interspersed with microscopic "fingers" of carbides, which form when carbon begins to separate from the hot steel as it is cooled. The dissolved salts that leach into concrete conduct a tiny electric current from the iron to the carbides. The process oxidizes iron into rust.

Gareth Thomas, professor emeritus of materials science and mineral engineering at Berkeley, and his colleagues developed the new re-bar, called Fermar. The researchers altered the manufacturing process to replace carbides in the alloy with an iron-containing material called martensite. An electric current does not flow between iron and martensite, even when large amounts of salt and moisture are present.

In tests, the researchers subjected concrete reinforced with Fermar and with conventional steel to moist, salty conditions for one year. Extensive rusting occurred in the ordinary steel, but there was no evidence of rust in Fermar.

A safer trench digger. A new trench-digging device that reduces the risk of cutting buried telephone cables, electrical lines, and gas pipes was unveiled in September 1994. It was developed by engineers at Battelle Memorial Institute, a nonprofit research and development institute based in Columbus, Ohio.

Conventional digging equipment can easily damage buried pipes and cables because of its hard cutting teeth and

A handheld camera that detects both metallic and nonmetallic weapons concealed under people's clothing was unveiled by engineers at Millitech Corporation in South Deerfield, Mass., in April 1995. The camera detects naturally occurring electromagnetic radiation from human beings and from objects of metal, plastic, ceramic, and other materials. A concealed weapon emits less radiation than a human being and so appears white in the image produced by the camera.

The world's longest cable-stayed suspension bridge was inaugurated in Le Havre, France, in January 1995. The bridge, which spans the Seine River from Le Havre to Honfleur, measures 856 meters (2,808 feet) at its central span and is suspended from 186 cable stays.

powerful downward force. Equipment that scoops away upturned soil also can cut cables and pipes near the surface. Such accidents can create a great deal of damage, injuring construction workers and disrupting telephone and utility service for thousands of consumers.

Battelle's device, called the Soft Trencher, moves soil with jets of high-pressure air that travel at supersonic speeds, according to engineer Gary Brawley, who headed the project. The trencher's blasts loosen soil and dislodge small rocks but leave utility pipes and cables unharmed. A vacuum system then sucks up the debris. The Soft Trencher's excavation head is small enough for easy manipulation around exposed cables and pipes, eliminating the need for slow, costly hand-digging around them.

The Soft Trencher can dig trenches with a width of 0.3 to 1.8 meters (1 to 6 feet). It removes 5 to 13 centimeters (2 to 5 inches) of soil on each pass and can vacuum up rocks as large as 18 centimeters (7 inches) in diameter.

Modified versions of the Soft Trench-

er could have several other applications, according to engineers. One version, for example, could be used to vacuum up contaminated soil at toxic waste sites or spills. Such a device could be operated by remote control to protect workers from exposure to the contaminated material. Another version could be mounted on a railroad car and used to clean and maintain railroad tracks. Yet another could replace conventional conveyor systems for loading dump trucks and other vehicles in gravel yards.

Strong metal-clad structures. Buildings constructed from wooden posts and beams that are covered with metal sheets are much stiffer than previously believed, engineers at Cornell University in Ithaca, N.Y., reported in December 1994. Such metal-clad, post-frame buildings are used for agricultural, industrial, and other purposes. The findings suggest that the structures could be built more cheaply—with lighter framing and more shallow foundations than currently allowed—without weakening their resistance to wind and other stresses.

The Cornell project appeared to be

the first time that engineers had actually built a metal-clad, post-frame structure in order to measure its stiffness. Current building standards for the structures are based on simplified, small-scale models, which cannot duplicate the way all components of the structures work together to withstand stress. As a result, engineers did not accurately know whether the standards resulted in buildings that were needlessly strong or too weak.

In the Cornell project, led by agricultural engineer Kifle G. Gebremedhin, researchers built a metal-clad, post-frame structure about 12 meters (40 feet) wide, 24 meters (80 feet) long, and 5 meters (16 feet) high and calculated its stiffness at various stages of construction. The researchers used electronically operated devices to determine how much the building swayed when subjected to forces such as strong winds.

With only the wooden framework in place, portions of the building bowed up to 15 centimeters (6 inches). But the researchers found that application of the sheet-metal skin to the walls and roof made the structure much stiffer than anticipated, reducing bowing to less than 1.3 centimeters (0.5 inch). The researchers concluded that metal-clad buildings with light framing would be able to withstand winds of 95 to 115 kilometers (60 to 70 miles) per hour.

Improved recycling. A new technique that increases the amount of aluminum recovered from recycled beverage cans was announced in January 1995 by researchers at Ohio State University in Columbus. Materials engineer Yogesh Sahai, developer of the technique, said it could permit recovery of almost 20 percent more aluminum from each batch of cans than current methods do. The process could make aluminum recycling more profitable and stimulate efforts to recycle used beverage cans.

In the traditional recycling process, shredded cans are first heated to about 500 °C (930 °F) to burn away their coatings of lacquer and paint. The cans then go into a hotter furnace containing sodium chloride, potassium chloride, and fluoride. This mixture, known as a salt cake, collects and traps impurities from the cans. Pure aluminum settles to the furnace bottom, where it is drained away and used to make new cans.

But about 20 percent of each batch of aluminum becomes trapped in the thick salt cake. By squeezing the cake, metal companies can recover about 10 percent of the trapped aluminum. However, the rest remains unusable.

Sahai's technique enables almost all the trapped aluminum to be recovered, with the added benefit of increasing the number of times a salt cake can be used. In the technique, workers pass an electric current through the salt cake. The current gives aluminum particles suspended in the cake a negative electric charge. The aluminum particles then migrate toward positively charged electrodes at the furnace bottom. This aluminum is then drained away along with the rest of the molten metal.

New use for waste gas. A new technique for using biogas, a by-product of wastewater treatment, could reduce electricity bills at municipal sewage treatment plants around the country. The technique was announced by engineers at Syracuse University in New York in January 1995.

Sewage treatment plants produce biogas during the removal of organic materials from wastewater. The substance is about 65 percent methane, the main component of natural gas, and about 35 percent carbon dioxide, along with some sulfur dioxide and other gases.

Treatment facilities now burn some biogas to heat their buildings. But large amounts of biogas cannot be used in boilers and other equipment because the carbon dioxide and sulfur dioxide produce impurities that corrode the equipment. As a result, treatment plants simply burn up most biogas and allow the heat and impurities to escape into the atmosphere.

The new process, developed by chemical engineer S. Alexander Stern and environmental engineer Alexander A. Friedman, removes impurities from biogas by passing the gas through a plastic membrane. Because the impurities pass through the membrane more rapidly than methane, they can be collected and removed. The result is purer methane suitable for burning in an internal combustion engine. Wastewater treatment plants could save thousands of dollars each year by using the process to generate their own electricity, according to engineers.   [Michael Woods]

In WORLD BOOK, see ENGINEERING.

One of the worst oil spills in history occurred in Russia in late August and early September 1994. As many as 2 million barrels of oil leaked from a pipeline between Vozey and Usinsk in the remote Arctic republic of Komi. The oil leaked from a series of holes in the pipeline and washed into two tributaries of the salmon-rich Pechora River, which flows into the Arctic Ocean. Officials at the United States Department of Energy (DOE) estimated that the spill was about eight times bigger than the *Exxon Valdez* spill in Alaska's Prince William Sound in 1989.

The pipeline had apparently been leaking from several holes since February 1994. Workers built a dike 8 meters (25 feet) high to contain the growing spill, but heavy rain washed out the dike in August. DOE officials estimated the spill was eventually 1 meter (3.3 feet) deep, 12 meters (40 feet) wide, and 10 to 11 kilometers (about 7 miles) long.

Ecologists believe the spill could devastate the area's fragile ecosystem. Plants grow slowly in the Arctic climate, making ecological recovery slow or impossible. Oil spilling into the river and the Arctic Ocean could cause considerable additional environmental damage.

Dioxin's dangers reaffirmed. In September 1994, the U.S. Environmental Protection Agency (EPA) affirmed findings that highly toxic chemicals called dioxins are probably *carcinogenic* (cancer causing) in human beings. Most dioxins in the environment are produced as a by-product of incinerating municipal and medical solid waste.

The 1994 report strengthened the EPA's tentative 1985 conclusion that dioxins are a "probable human carcinogen." At that time, many chemical manufacturers and industries asked the government to reevaluate the data linking dioxins to cancer. The EPA began the reassessment in 1991.

The new report, which was based on the views of more than 100 scientists, also linked dioxins to other health problems. Dioxins may suppress the immune system, disrupt hormonal function, and cause abnormal growth of reproductive organs in animals, the report said.

According to the EPA, dioxins are

Russian oil spill

Black smoke billows from a burning oil spill in Komi, a Russian republic in the Arctic, in October 1994, *below*. The oil spilled from a ruptured pipeline and contaminated the Pechora River, which flows into the Arctic Ocean. Russian workers attempting to clean up the spill are hampered by snow and ice, *left*. The United States Department of Energy estimated that the spill was eight times larger than the *Exxon Valdez* accident in Alaska's Prince William Sound in 1989.

generally found only in trace amounts in the environment. Wind can carry dioxins in incinerator emissions to distant sites, however, and the compounds may settle on plants and grasses that are eaten by livestock.

For people in the United States, the most common means of exposure to dioxide is by consuming beef and cow's milk. According to the EPA, people who eat a balanced diet need not fear dioxin contamination, because most adverse health effects occur at exposure levels 10 to 100 times greater than those experienced by the average American.

The EPA was expected to release its final draft of the report in late 1995. The agency may then move to reduce the allowable levels of dioxin emissions from incinerators and other sources.

Ultrasound cleans polluted water. Ultrasonic waves may prove useful in destroying common *organic* (carbon-containing) water pollutants, according to an August 1994 report by chemical engineers Michael Cheung and Ashish Batnagar of the University of Akron in Ohio. Ultrasonic waves, or ultrasound, are sound waves with frequencies higher than the range of human hearing.

In their findings, Cheung and Batnagar reported that ultrasound successfully broke down seven common industrial water pollutants, all of them chlorine-containing compounds called organochlorines. The pollutants included chloroform, carbon tetrachloride, and methylene chloride.

According to the EPA, even extremely small quantities of organochlorines in drinking water present a long-term health risk to humans. The pollutants under study are released from a variety of sources, primarily manufacturing plants that produce paints, solvents, dyes, inks, and pesticides.

The researchers reported that ultrasound broke down 72 to 99.9 percent of the pollutant molecules, depending on the type. The high-frequency waves created microscopic bubbles of superheated liquid that expand rapidly in water-based solutions. After the bubbles reached a critical size, they *imploded* (burst inward). Gas and vapor in the bubbles compress during the implosion, generating very high temperatures and pressures and breaking the organochlorines into relatively harmless by-prod-

ucts, including weak hydrochloric acid, carbon dioxide, and water.

Asthma and urban pollution. Medical researchers in September 1994 reported growing evidence of a connection between air pollution and the increasing incidence of asthma in smoggy cities. Asthma is a condition that narrows air passages in the lungs and makes breathing difficult. The researchers, at a meeting on urban air pollution and public health in London, reported several studies indicating that auto exhaust may be partly responsible for a doubling of the incidence of asthma attacks since 1974 in the United Kingdom.

One such study was described by Jon Ayres, a respirologist at the Chest Research Institute at Birmingham Heartlands Hospital in the United Kingdom. Ayres reported that patients with mild asthma caused by allergies to dust mites had more severe symptoms if they inhaled nitrogen dioxide, a major component of automobile exhaust and smokestack emissions from power plants and factories. Ayres's research supports the results of other studies that demonstrate a correlation between inhaling nitrogen dioxide and asthma attacks.

Ayers's work did not show that nitrogen dioxide itself stimulated the asthma attacks, however. Instead, according to Ayres, nitrogen dioxide makes the respiratory tract more sensitive to dust mites and other allergy-provoking substances that can trigger asthma. Nitrogen dioxide also causes inflammation of the lining of the respiratory tract, which prevents it from expelling the allergy-causing agents.

Indoor air pollution damage. Scientists reported in November 1994 that certain indoor air pollutants may damage electronic equipment. In addition, the researchers found that indoor air pollutants may arise from outside of buildings and exist in higher-than-expected concentrations. A team of researchers at Bell Communications Research in Red Bank, N.J., reported the findings.

Researchers have studied indoor air pollution for years, primarily for its effect on human health. Most research has focused on pollutants generated within buildings, from combustion sources such as furnaces and stoves, building products such as plywood, and furniture and furnishings such as sofas and carpeting.

Charles J. Weschler and his Bell Communications co-workers discovered that three common outdoor air pollutants—ozone, nitric oxide, and nitrogen dioxide—were found inside a telephone switching facility in California in levels much higher than anticipated. The team also found that ozone and nitrogen dioxide reacted inside the facility, producing a by-product that reacted in turn with compounds in the atmosphere to create nitric acid.

Nitric acid is a corrosive chemical known to damage electronic circuitry. Nitric acid also reacts with other chemicals to form nitrate salts. The salts can build up on sensitive electronic switches, causing computer-processing glitches and, in some cases, disrupting electric circuits.

Home pesticides. Chemical products used to kill insects in the home are known to cause nausea, headaches, eye and lung irritation, and other symptoms among frequent users. According to a March 1995 study, these health effects may be caused by chemical additives in the mixture, not by the pest-killing compounds themselves, as researchers had previously assumed. John A. Bukowski and Leroy W. Meyer of the New Jersey Department of Environmental Protection in Trenton authored the study.

Pesticide chemicals make up only 5 percent or less of the weight of a typical product for indoor use. The rest of the mixture contains inactive ingredients, including *emulsifiers* (compounds that help liquids mix), spray propellants, and many types of solvents such as kerosene and xylene, according to the scientists.

The researchers simulated pesticide use in homes and found that the solvent additives typically became airborne more quickly and remained in the air for a longer time than the heavier pesticides. The study found that in unventilated rooms, the levels of the solvent fumes became high enough to cause adverse health effects in otherwise healthy adults who inhaled them.

[Daniel D. Chiras]

In WORLD BOOK, see ENVIRONMENTAL POLLUTION.

Fossil Studies

The Cambrian Period in Earth's history, which began about 545 million years ago, was a time of extraordinary diversification in marine life, when all the major body plans known in animals evolved. For years, the cause of the so-called "Cambrian explosion" remained elusive. But discoveries reported in June 1994 by Nicholas Butterfield, a paleontologist at Cambridge University in England, may shed light on the origin of this evolutionary burst.

The source of Butterfield's insight was a simple mistake. Butterfield had intended to look for microscopic fossils in 1-billion-year-old rock from Canada's Northwest Territories. But he accidentally ordered Early Cambrian rock samples instead. After dissolving the rock with hydrofluoric acid, Butterfield used a powerful microscope to examine the fossils, discovering a broad array of ancient animals, among them small crustaceans. Butterfield observed that many of the crustaceans possessed rows of tiny bristles on their limbs. In this, they resembled modern crustaceans such as branchiopods, which use their bristles to filter small food particles from sea water. The discovery suggested that filter feeding may have been a common strategy in the Early Cambrian.

In modern oceans, filter-feeding crustaceans form one of the most critical links in the marine food chain. These animals feed on small floating algae and, in turn, serve as a major food source for larger organisms. Butterfield speculated that the evolution of tiny filter-feeding animals at the start of the Cambrian Period may have sparked the rapid appearance of many other animals that relied on them for food.

Dinosaur embryo. The discovery of the first fossilized embryo of a meat-eating dinosaur was reported in November 1994 by paleontologist Mark Norell of the American Museum of Natural History in New York. The find overturned a long-standing case of mistaken identity.

The 75-million-year-old embryo was unearthed at Ukhaa Tolgod, a region of fossil-rich sandstone beds in Mongolia's Gobi Desert that was discovered in 1993. Among the site's offerings was a cluster of 13-centimeter- (5-inch-) long dino-

The dinosaur and the egg

The first fossilized embryo of a meat-eating dinosaur—and one of fewer than 10 known dinosaur embryos of any kind—was discovered in Mongolia's Gobi Desert, according to a November 1994 announcement. The 75-million-year-old skeleton, exposed when part of the egg it lay in eroded away, was missing only a piece of the skull and part of the tail, *below*. An artist's sketch shows the complete embryo, *bottom*. Paleontologists determined that the embryo belonged to a group of dinosaurs known as oviraptorids.

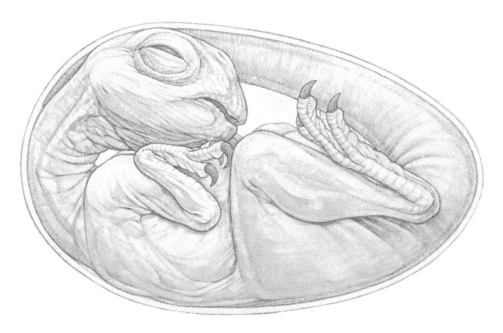

saur eggs. The top of one egg had eroded away, revealing the skeleton inside.

According to Norell, the Ukhaa Tolgod eggs resembled a nest of eggs found at the Gobi Desert site of Flaming Cliffs, which was excavated in the 1920's by the well-known paleontologist Roy Chapman Andrews. Andrews and other scientists assumed the eggs belonged to *Protoceratops*, a small horned dinosaur whose remains were abundant at the site. Associated with the eggs were the bones of a then-unknown meat-eating dinosaur. Paleontologists named the meat-eater *Oviraptor*, meaning *egg-stealer*, because they thought it had died—perhaps in a sandstorm—while sucking the eggs.

When Norell examined the embryonic skeleton from Ukhaa Tolgod, he found to his surprise that it belonged not to *Protoceratops* but to *Oviraptor*. Norell concluded that Chapman's *Oviraptor* died while protecting the eggs at Flaming Cliffs, not eating them.

The Ukhaa Tolgod find is expected to shed light on the way at least some dinosaur species nurtured their young. In another surprising discovery, two skulls

of a small meat-eating dinosaur related to *Velociraptor* were found in the nest with the *Oviraptor* embryo. The researchers suggested that these may represent the remains of prey brought to the nest by the parental *Oviraptor*.

Early tetrapods. Two new *tetrapods* (four-limbed vertebrates) were reported in 1994 and 1995. In July 1994, Edward B. Daeschler and Keith Thomson, paleontologists with Philadelphia's Academy of Natural Sciences, described *Hynerpeton bassetti*, a fossil amphibian that was one of the earliest vertebrates to emerge onto dry land. The fossil, which was found in 365-million-year-old Devonian sediments near Williamsport, Pa., represents the oldest known North American amphibian.

The small partial skeleton includes parts of the skull and a well-preserved shoulder. The relatively strong shoulder bones indicate that *Hynerpeton* had well-developed limb muscles capable of supporting the animal's body on land. The researchers found the skeletons of large predatory fish in nearby swamp deposits of the same age as *Hynerpeton*. *Hynerpe-*

Ancient amphibian
Fossil bones found in Pennsylvania belong to the oldest known North American amphibian, according to a report in July 1994. The 365-million-year-old bones included a sturdy shoulder bone, *right*. The animal's strong shoulders supported well-developed limb muscles capable of bearing the animal's weight on land, *below*.

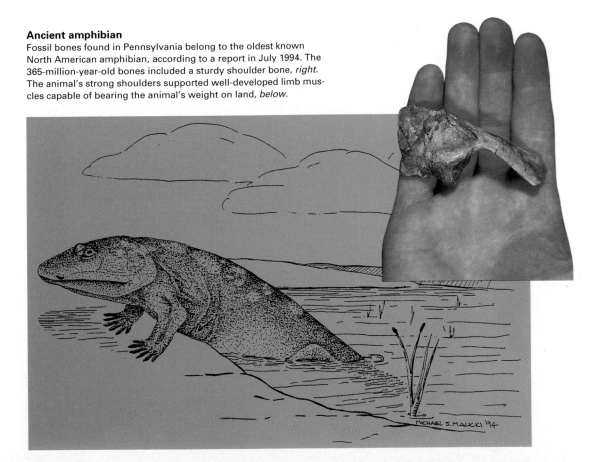

MICHAEL J. MALICKI '94

ton may have emerged from the water to escape intense predation by these fish, according to Daeschler.

An even older tetrapod skeleton, from 368-million-year-old lake deposits in Scotland, was described in February 1995 by paleontologists at The British Museum of Natural History in London. The new species, named *Elginerpeton,* shows fishlike and amphibian features and was an animal that lived shortly after the split between these two groups.

African dinosaurs. Excavations in Africa's Sahara Desert yielded fossils of two previously unknown dinosaur species dating to about 130 million years ago, the early Cretaceous Period. The finds were described by paleontologist Paul Sereno of the University of Chicago in October 1994. The fossils represent some of the first known Cretaceous dinosaurs from the African continent.

The paleontologists unearthed a nearly complete skeleton of a dinosaur they called *Afrovenator abakensis* ("African Hunter from In Abaka"), named for the site in Niger where the bones were found. *Afrovenator* belonged to the

group of dinosaurs known as *theropods*— meat-eating dinosaurs that walked upright on two legs. According to the paleontologists, the dinosaur was related to *Allosaurus,* a well-known theropod that lived in the western United States about 150 million years ago, in the Late Jurassic Period. *Afrovenator* stood about 2 meters (7 feet) tall at the hip and measured 8 meters (26 feet) from head to tail. Several three-toed footprints found at a nearby site may have been made by *Afrovenator,* the researchers said.

The second dinosaur species was one of the *sauropods,* large plant-eating dinosaurs with long necks. Well-known sauropods include *Apatosaurus* (formerly known as *Brontosaurus)* and *Brachiosaurus.* The new African specimen was about 17 meters (56 feet) long. It had broad teeth for crushing plants and a skull resembling that of *Camarosaurus,* a large sauropod that, like *Allosaurus,* lived near the end of the Jurassic Period in the western United States. Scientists had believed that broad-toothed sauropods like *Camarosaurus* had died out by the late Jurassic, some 20 million years be-

The reconstructed skeleton of a meat-eating, upright dinosaur, *below,* represents one of two newly discovered dinosaur species whose remains were found in Africa's Sahara Desert, researchers announced in October 1994. The two dinosaurs, which lived about 130 million years ago, are among the first known African dinosaurs dating to the Cretaceous Period.

fore the new African sauropod lived.

The two dinosaurs species lived at a time when the Sahara was a warm, humid, tropical environment. Fossils found at the excavation site indicate that *conifers* (cone-bearing shrubs and trees) dominated the vegetation in the area. The fossilized conifer woods that Sereno's team found lacked growth rings, suggesting that the temperature and humidity varied little through the seasons. Growth rings form when trees are subjected to regular cycles of wet, rainy seasons followed by dry periods.

One surprise was the fossils' close relation to Jurassic Period dinosaurs of North America. In contrast, the African fossils bear little resemblance to contemporary Early Cretaceous dinosaurs from South America—even though Africa was at the time still partially connected to that continent. Geologists believe that Africa and North America had drifted apart by the Middle Jurassic. The paleontologists concluded that theropod and sauropod dinosaurs must have spread into Africa before the continents separated and lived on there after their extinction in the north.

Permian extinctions. Research in 1994 and 1995 provided missing details about the transition between the Permian and Triassic periods, some 250 million years ago. This interval, called the Permo-Triassic boundary, has long been known for the greatest mass extinction in the history of marine life. In most parts of the world, however, the geologic record is marked by gaps at the Permo-Triassic boundary, and so details of the mass extinction have been obscured.

In November 1994, paleontologists reported on fossil distribution from a number of intact Permo-Triassic boundary sections, particularly in China. The researchers, Steven Stanley of Johns Hopkins University in Baltimore and X Yang of China's Nanjing University, found evidence that up to 80 percent of marine species were killed off at the very end of the Permian. The scientists also documented another mass extinction, which occurred about 5 million years earlier. That extinction eliminated up to 70 percent of species of marine invertebrates. It was relatively short-lived, however. As a result, a number of animal groups began to rediversify in the last 5 million years of the Permian Period.

In February 1995, paleontologist Gregory Retallack of the University of Oregon in Eugene described *terrestrial* (land-dwelling) plant fossils from Permo-Triassic boundary sections in southeastern Australia. Retallack observed that a widespread and diverse array of seed-bearing ferns suddenly disappeared at the boundary. They were replaced by a relatively small number of conifer and moss species.

Scientists have proposed a number of hypotheses to account for the Permo-Triassic extinctions. One possibility is that oceans worldwide retreated from the continents around this time, causing harsher, more seasonally variable climates. Another possibility, affecting at least the final extinction, is that intense volcanic activity raised clouds of ash that blocked the sun, causing abrupt cooling of the climate. Support for this theory came in early 1995, when geologists reported that massive outpourings of volcanic rock in Siberia date precisely to the time of the final Permo-Triassic extinction.

Dinosaur DNA? The possibility of studying dinosaur DNA (deoxyribonucleic acid, the molecule of which genes are made) may have come a step closer to reality in 1994. Geneticist Scott Woodward of Brigham Young University in Provo, Utah, and his colleagues recovered 80-million-year-old fossil bones from a Utah coal mine and extracted fragments of DNA from the bones. Analysis showed that the DNA had been contained in cellular structures called mitochondria. After comparing the fragments of DNA with mitochondrial DNA from modern organisms, the scientists reported that the fragments were not the result of contamination by human beings or bacteria.

Surprisingly, the ancient DNA does not closely resemble that of birds or crocodiles, two groups thought to be close relatives of dinosaurs. That discovery raised serious doubts about whether the investigators had indeed recovered dinosaur DNA. It may instead be that the DNA belonged to ancient microorganisms that invaded the bones. Another possibility is that the bones came from an ancient animal other than a dinosaur.   [Carlton E. Brett]

In WORLD BOOK, see DINOSAUR; PALEONTOLOGY.

The hottest race in cancer genetics ended in September 1994 with the announcement that a breast cancer gene called BRCA1 had been found by a group of researchers led by Mark Skolnick at the University of Utah in Salt Lake City. More than 100 researchers from around the world had been racing to find the gene ever since geneticist Mary-Claire King of the University of California at Berkeley published the approximate location of the gene in 1990.

Breast cancer gene. To find the gene, Skolnick's group tracked the inheritance of genetic markers in families with a high occurrence of breast cancer. Genetic markers are unique sequences of DNA (deoxyribonucleic acid, the molecule of which genes are made). The researchers looked for markers that were present in the women who developed breast cancer but not in their relatives without the cancer. The scientists reasoned that those markers must lie close to the breast cancer gene. After careful analysis of hundreds of markers and genes near those markers, Skolnick's group pinpointed BRCA1.

Experts said the discovery was a great step forward in understanding breast cancer. Unfortunately, the defective BRCA1 gene only accounts for an inherited form of the disease, which comprises about 5 to 10 percent of all cases of breast cancer. Most cases of breast cancer occur in a more sporadic fashion, the cause of which remains a mystery.

In addition, the BRCA1 gene does not account for all the inherited forms of the disease. At least one other gene, a newly discovered gene called BRCA2, appears to be as important as BRCA1. However, scientists believe that through further study of all the genes involved, researchers can begin to uncover the nature of the cancer. (In the Special Reports section, see HUNTING FOR CANCER GENES.)

Kidney disease gene. The identification of a gene responsible for the most common form of inherited kidney disease was announced in June 1994 by an international team of researchers led by Peter Harris of the Medical Research Council in Oxford, England. The team included scientists from Wales, Portugal, and the Netherlands.

The disease, which is called autoso-

Utah geneticists Mark Skolnick and Donna Shattuck-Eidens examine data they and their colleagues used to help track down the first known breast cancer gene. The group announced the finding in September 1994. The gene, called BRCA1, plays a role in the inherited form of the disease, which accounts for 5 to 10 percent of all cases of breast cancer.

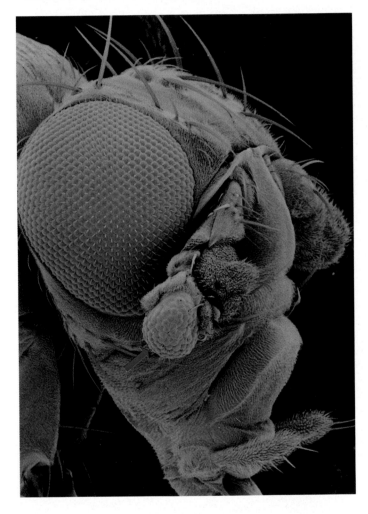

A fully formed eye grows on the antenna of a fruit fly after Swiss geneticists activated a single gene in antenna cells. According to their March 1995 report, the scientists also grew eyes on fruit fly legs and wings. The experiments suggest that the gene—called *eyeless* because flies born without it have no eyes—is the master control gene for eye development. In August 1994, the scientists had reported finding a similar gene in human beings and mice.

mal dominant polycystic kidney disease (ADPKD), produces fluid-filled cysts within the kidney that press on neighboring kidney tissue and inhibit the flow of blood to that tissue. Without adequate blood flow, the tissue dies, reducing the ability of the kidney to filter wastes out of the blood. In some cases, so much tissue dies that the kidney cannot function properly and the person must be put on a kidney dialysis machine, which filters the blood. Some ADPKD patients may require a kidney transplant.

Harris's team knew that the disease had a genetic component because of the way it runs in families. So they began their research by studying families afflicted with ADPKD. By following how the disease and certain genetic traits were passed from generation to generation, the scientists narrowed their search to one region of a chromosome. (Chromosomes are tiny, threadlike structures in cells that contain the genes.)

Using a genetic map, which shows the locations of known genes along a chromosome, the scientists determined that the gene linked to ADPKD was located in a region containing several unknown genes, any one of which could have been associated with the disease.

The final clue to locating the gene came with the discovery that in one of the families studied, members afflicted with ADPKD all carried two chromosomes that had swapped genetic material. The scientists theorized that the place where one of the swaps occurred contained the gene responsible for ADPKD. The researchers confirmed the theory by examining that gene in several hundred people with the disease. In most cases, a *mutation* (change or defect) was found in the gene.

Scientists say little is known about how the mutation causes the symptoms of ADPKD. But knowledge of the gene's location may help researchers design a test to determine who is likely to develop the disease. If physicians know who is predisposed to ADPKD, they may be able to prevent the development of harmful symptoms of the disease.

Obesity gene. The discovery of a gene responsible for obesity was reported in December 1994 by a group of researchers led by Jeffrey Friedman at the Howard Hughes Medical Institute

A laboratory mouse (right) that weighs up to three times as much as a normal mouse has a genetic defect that may play a key role in obesity. New York scientists reported in December 1994 that a strain of obese mice had inherited a defective form of a gene called *ob*, which appears to regulate body-fat storage. A similar gene was found in human beings.

of Rockefeller University in New York. Obesity, defined as weighing 20 percent or more than a person's ideal weight, is the most common nutritional disorder in Western societies. It can contribute to many medical problems, including high blood pressure and diabetes.

Friedman and his colleagues theorized that a defective gene caused the mice to weigh up to three times as much as normal mice. To find the gene, the scientists used a technique called *positional cloning*, in which they *clone* (produce identical copies of) genes from a small region of a chromosome and analyze the genes to determine if they are responsible for the trait.

Using this technique, the scientists found a gene that *codes for* (directs the production of) a protein found in fatty tissue. The researchers suspected that the protein played a role in regulating the amount of fatty tissue in the body. They named the gene *ob* for *obese*.

The scientists then confirmed that the ob gene was linked to obesity by showing that this gene was mutated in the overweight mice. They then

found a similar gene in human beings. Researchers say the discovery of the ob gene means it may one day be possible to treat obesity in some people by supplying them with the protein the normal gene produces. The protein would help the body properly control the storage of fat. Researchers caution, however, that other genes, diet, and other factors probably contribute to obesity. (See also NUTRITION.)

Plant "biological clock" gene. The discovery of a gene that controls a plant's "biological clock"—that is, how it responds to a typical cycle of daytime and nighttime hours—was announced in February 1995 by a research group led by Steve A. Kay at the University of Virginia in Charlottesville. The scientists found the gene using a novel approach that involved introducing a firefly gene into a plant to make it glow at certain times of the day.

Kay's group wanted to find out how plants control when certain functions occur and when they cease. To do so, they manipulated a gene called CAB, which is involved in *photosynthesis*

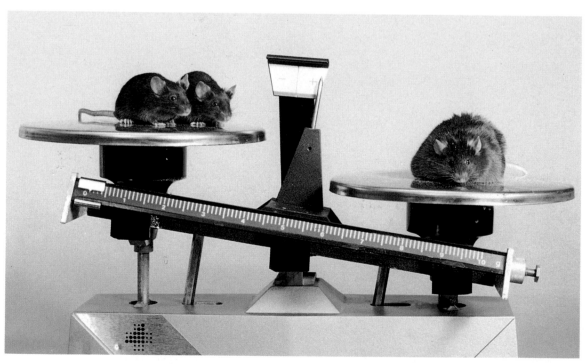

(the energy-capturing process of green plants) and is known to be active only during the day. To determine what factors control this activity, the researchers attached a firefly gene called luciferase to the CAB gene in mustard plant seedlings. The luciferase gene codes for a substance that causes a certain chemical in the firefly to glow. The scientists theorized that whenever the altered CAB gene was active in the presence of the chemical, the plant would glow.

As it turned out, most of the altered seedlings glowed only during the day, as expected, but some glowed at the wrong time. Kay's group found that such seedlings had a mutation in another gene. The researchers theorized that the second gene must control when the CAB gene is switched on and off. Scientists were optimistic that this novel approach can help researchers find other genes involved in driving a plant's internal clock.

Dwarfism genes. The discoveries of two genes responsible for two common forms of dwarfism were announced in 1994.

The location of the gene that causes the most common inherited form of dwarfism in the United States was reported in July 1994 by a group of scientists at the College of Medicine and the Human Genome Research Center at the University of California at Irvine. This type of dwarfism, called achondroplasia, affects about 1 in 26,000 people. It is characterized by an enlarged head, short limbs, and a normal torso.

The gene, called ACH, had been found in 1991. It was originally thought to be responsible for Huntington's disease, a severe disorder of the nervous system. ACH produces a protein called a growth factor receptor that signals cells to start or stop growing. A mutation in ACH affects the ability of the gene to produce the protein. Scientists said that the discovery of this gene will help in the creation of a prenatal test for detecting achondroplasia in a fetus.

The location of a gene responsible for the form of dwarfism known as DTD (diastrophic dysplasia) was announced by a research group led by Eric Lander of the Whitehead Institute for Biomedical Research in Cambridge, Mass., in September 1994. DTD is a disease of the skeletal system that can result in a number of abnormalities in bone and cartilage growth. It most commonly occurs among people of Finnish descent.

To find the gene, Lander's group used a method known as *fine structure linkage disequilibrium mapping*, in which a prediction of a gene location is made based on information obtained from a detailed genetic map. Such a map shows the known location of certain genes and genetic markers.

The researchers studied the genetic makeup of Finnish families in which at least one family member had the disease. By looking at the genetic differences between family members who inherited the disease and those who did not, the scientists were able to predict the exact location of the dwarfism gene.

An analysis of the gene they pinpointed this way showed its function was to help sulfate molecules move within the cells of cartilage and bone. When the flow of sulfate molecules is slowed or blocked, deformities may result.

Geneticists believe such predictions of gene locations will become more accurate as researchers develop improved genetic maps. Highly accurate maps are already being created as part of the international effort known as the Human Genome Project. The goal of this project is to learn the exact location and chemical makeup of all human genes.

New knock-out method. A method to "knock out" the function of a specific gene in just one type of cell in the body was announced in July 1994 by a group of scientists with the University of Cologne and the Max-Planck Institute in Germany and the University of British Columbia in Canada. Previously, it had only been possible to eliminate or alter the function of a gene in all cells of the organism, a process that sometimes killed the organism.

Using two sets of lab mice, the researchers set out to block the function of a gene in T cells, a type of white blood cell that plays an important role in the body's immune system. The targeted gene was the DNA polymerase B gene, which makes a protein needed for DNA replication during cell division.

One group of mice were *genetically engineered* (had genes altered or rearranged) to have special markers on both sides of the DNA polymerase B gene. These mice were then mated with a group of mice whose T cells contained a gene for a protein called *cre*. The function of the cre protein is to act as biochemical scissors to cut out the DNA between the special markers, if any are present in the cell.

Some of the offspring of the two sets of mice had both the cre-producing T cells and the markers flanking the DNA polymerase B gene. In those mice, the DNA polymerase B gene was naturally "knocked out" of the T cells.

Researchers believe the new procedure will help them investigate early stages of growth and development in organs and tissues. Being able to knock out specific genes should enable scientists to study how those genes are involved in the development process.

Gene therapy for clogged arteries. A new application of gene therapy to the treatment of heart disease was announced by a research team led by Gary and Elizabeth Nabel of the University of Michigan Medical Center in Ann Arbor. Gene therapy is a disease-fighting technique in which genes are introduced into body cells.

The researchers experimented on pigs that had undergone *balloon angioplasty*, a technique for opening up clogged arteries. After such a procedure, the walls of treated arteries often become thicker, creating blood flow problems. This thickening occurs because damage to the blood vessel causes certain muscle cells that line the artery to multiply.

The team used a respiratory virus to deliver a gene directly to the cells of the pigs' artery muscle. The gene codes for a protein called thymidine kinase (tk). Scientists had found that cells containing the tk protein did not divide in the presence of a drug called ganciclovir. By giving the pigs the tk gene along with doses of ganciclovir, the researchers were able to prevent the thickening of the pig's arterial walls. Researchers envision that such treatment in human beings could significantly reduce the thickening of arteries after balloon angioplasty.   [David S. Haymer]

In WORLD BOOK, see CELL; GENETICS.

Geology

At least four earthquakes of magnitude equal to or greater than 6.4 struck the area near New Madrid, Mo., before historical records were kept. According to the authors of a study reported in March 1995—seismologists Martitia P. Tuttle of the Lamont-Doherty Earth Observatory of Columbia University in New York City and Eugene P. Schweig of the U.S. Geological Survey—the area may produce strong earthquakes every few hundred years.

The report is significant in the aftermath of recent earthquakes, such as that in Kobe, Japan, on Jan. 17, 1995, and Northridge, Calif., on Jan. 17, 1994. The great damage that resulted from these quakes spurred interest in determining the frequency of major (magnitude 7 to 8) and great (above magnitude 8) earthquakes. (Higher magnitude numbers indicate more severe earthquakes. See also CLOSE-UP.)

New Madrid quakes. Historical records show that three large earthquakes with epicenters near New Madrid occurred in 1811 and 1812. Scientists estimate the magnitudes of the earthquakes

at more than 8. The quakes changed the landscape in ways that can still be seen today. Because the region was sparsely settled at the time, however, few people were killed.

To determine whether such large quakes had occurred before 1811, the researchers considered the phenomenon of ground liquefaction. When the ground shakes in a strong earthquake, the motion may cause soil to behave as a thick liquid. As the liquefaction occurs, buried layers of sand can erupt through the overlying soil, forming areas of displaced sand called sand-blow craters.

Geologists had identified several sand-blow craters in the New Madrid area, but had assumed they were formed during the 1811-1812 earthquakes. Tuttle and Schweig reexamined 14 sand-blow sites to determine the approximate date of their formation by calculating the age of materials found in them.

Two of the sites contained prehistoric Native American relics. The scientists determined the age of the artifacts by comparing them with similar relics whose ages were known. Another site

A freeway lies collapsed from the force of an earthquake that struck Kobe, Japan, on Jan. 17, 1995. The magnitude 6.8 quake killed more than 5,000 people, caused extensive damage, and underscored the difficulties of preparing for major earthquakes in densely populated areas.

contained pieces of wood that the scientists dated using radiocarbon dating. In this method, scientists analyze the amount of a radioactive form of carbon in wood, charcoal, and other remains of dead plants or animals. Because the amount of radioactive carbon in organic matter decays at a known rate after the plant or animal dies, the analysis allows scientists to determine the age of an object to within several hundred years.

On the basis of these techniques, the scientists concluded that there were at least four strong earthquakes in the New Madrid seismic zone between 4035 B.C. and A.D. 1811. Tuttle and Schweig concluded that the quakes must have been large, because previous studies had shown that soil liquefaction in the New Madrid area occurs only during earthquakes with a magnitude equal to or greater than 6.4.

Quake risk in Pacific Northwest. Another study reported evidence suggesting that the Pacific Northwest is at as much risk for a major earthquake as areas along the San Andreas Fault in California. Seismologists Kevin Copper-

smith and Robert Youngs of the engineering firm Geomatrix Consultants in San Francisco concluded that geological forces in the Washington-Oregon-Northern California coastal area could cause a series of earthquakes in the 8- to 8.5-magnitude range, or possibly one giant magnitude 9 quake.

The risk of earthquakes in the Pacific Northwest is due to motion of the Juan de Fuca Plate, one of Earth's large tectonic plates. According to the widely accepted theory of plate tectonics, the rigid rock of the plates moves about on top of more plastic, slowly flowing rock. Active earthquake zones occur where some tectonic plates collide and move over others.

The Juan de Fuca Plate is sliding eastward under the North American Plate at a relatively rapid rate of about 4.5 centimeters (1.8 inches) per year. Along the Pacific Northwest coast, however, seismic activity is much less than such a rate of convergence between two plates would normally produce. According to Coppersmith and Youngs, the lack of seismic activity is due to the fact that the

Beyond the Richter Scale

Since the 1850's, when geologists first attempted to compare the size of earthquakes, scientists have developed several methods of describing a quake's size, or magnitude. The Richter scale, a method developed in 1935 by seismologist Charles F. Richter at the California Institute of Technology in Pasadena, became a standard, and it is the scale that most nonscientists are familiar with.

But even though news reports often describe the strength of earthquakes in terms of the Richter scale, geologists actually use a newer measure of earthquake intensity called *moment magnitude*. Other scales used today are based on earthquake features called surface waves and body waves.

The search for better methods of calculating the strength of an earthquake began in the mid-1800's. At that time, geologists relied simply on visual analysis of an earthquake's effects on local landscape and buildings. But scientists soon learned that simple visual inspection of an earthquake's effects was not a good indication of an earthquake's true intensity. Too much depended on the observer's distance from the center of the earthquake, or *epicenter*, and the local geology. Seismologists soon learned that a better analysis involved studying the types of *seismic waves*—oscillating motions of the ground—produced by an earthquake.

Richter's method measured earthquakes based on the motion recorded by *seismographs* (instruments that measure seismic waves) in his laboratory. The Richter scale is based on a mathematical formula that takes into account an earthquake's maximum ground motion as measured by a seismograph, the earthquake wave's *period* (the time required for a wave to pass a given point), and the distance of the seismograph from the earthquake center.

The Richter scale is logarithmic, which means that a 10-fold increase in motion recorded by the seismograph corresponds to a 1-point increase on the scale. A 100-fold increase in motion corresponds to a 2-point increase.

Readings on the Richter scale range from negative numbers for quakes with very low magnitudes to an indefinite upper limit. A quake must exceed about 5.5 on the scale in order to produce significant damage near the epicenter. Although there is no theoretical upper limit to Richter magnitudes, no rocks could withstand the force released by an earthquake greater than Richter magnitude

9, and if the rocks disintegrated, there could be no seismograph reading.

Although Richter magnitudes measure the motion caused by an earthquake, they do not directly measure the energy released by a quake. A 1-point jump in Richter magnitude represents about a 32-fold increase in energy released. Thus an earthquake of Richter magnitude 7 releases about 32 times more energy than a magnitude 6 quake, and a magnitude 8 quake releases about 32 times more energy than does a magnitude 7.

Unfortunately, the Richter scale turned out to be an uncertain description of earthquakes, because it was simply based on the largest motion of the ground recorded by the seismograph and did not take into account the fact that deep earthquakes produce different motions than shallow ones. Richter's seismographs clearly picked up seismic waves only from relatively nearby, shallow earthquakes. The machines failed to detect seismic waves from quakes that occurred more than about 32 kilometers (20 miles) below Earth's surface and were incapable of accurately recording seismic waves from shallow quakes that originated more than about 600 kilometers (370 miles) away.

In the 1950's and 1960's, seismologists developed more sophisticated seismographs and modified the original Richter magnitudes to allow readings of more distant and deeper earthquakes. The modifications relied on the detection of two types of seismic waves—body waves and surface waves.

Body waves travel deep through Earth's interior (its body). There are two types of body waves—primary waves, called *P waves*, and secondary waves, called *S waves*. Primary waves are pressure waves—alternating compressions and expansions of the ground. They are the fastest waves and always arrive first at the seismograph. A determination of an earthquake's magnitude based only on P waves yields a value known as the *wave magnitude*, which is abbreviated m_b. Geologists use P waves to determine the magnitude of deep quakes, because the primary waves are not affected by the depth of the quake.

The other type of body wave, called secondary or S waves, shear rock with a crosswise motion. Secondary waves that travel no deeper than about 15 kilometers (9 miles) below Earth's surface are called surface waves. Surface waves also come in two types—Love waves and Rayleigh waves. Love waves move the ground from side to side. Rayleigh waves make Earth's surface roll like water waves. Typical Love waves travel at 4.4 kilometers (2.75 miles) per second, and Rayleigh waves, the slowest of the seismic waves, move at about 3.7 kilometers (2.3 miles) per second.

A magnitude reading based on surface waves is dubbed the M_s reading. Seismologists usually base

Four ways to measure earthquakes

Local magnitude: The original measurement devised by Charles Richter in 1935 to determine the relative size of earthquakes. Local magnitude represents how hard an earthquake shakes the ground as measured by a seismograph's reading of the largest of several types of seismic waves. The type of seismograph in use in 1935 did not accurately record earthquakes more than about 600 kilometers (370 miles) away, and for this reason, local magnitude is rarely used to measure the relative force of earthquakes.

Surface-wave magnitude: How hard an earthquake shakes the ground as measured by the size of particular types of seismic waves called surface waves. This measurement best describes shallow earthquakes (within about 32 kilometers [20 miles] of the surface).

Body-wave magnitude: Measurement of seismic waves called body waves, which are produced by earthquakes at any depth. The measurement is most useful for earthquakes deeper than 32 kilometers.

Moment magnitude: Geologists' preferred method of measuring earthquakes, sometimes erroneously described as based on the Richter scale. Moment magnitude measures the total energy of an earthquake rather than just the energy that shakes the surface. Moment magnitude encompasses many aspects of an earthquake, including the entire length over which the fault slips, the depth and angle of a fault, and the rigidity of the rock along the fault.

How recent earthquakes stack up

Quake	Surface-wave magnitude	Body-wave magnitude	Moment magnitude
Kobe, Japan (1995)	6.8	6.4	6.8
Northridge, California (1994)	6.8	6.4	6.7
Loma Prieta-San Francisco (1989)	7.1	6.5	7.2

Source: United States Geological Survey.

the M_s value on Rayleigh waves, because these waves travel farther than Love waves and can give a more accurate picture of the power of a distant quake.

Both the m_b and M_s magnitude scales are calculated in the same way as the Richter scale, and the values are roughly comparable. They can produce different readings for the same quake, however. Seismologists have determined that a March 28, 1964, earthquake in southern Alaska, for instance, had a 6.2 surface-wave magnitude but only a 5.5 body-wave magnitude.

Despite having three different ways to measure earthquakes, seismologists by the 1970's had found that their readings underestimated the magnitude of very large quakes. To overcome that problem, seismologists developed the moment magnitude scale, which attempts to calculate the total energy released by an earthquake.

The term *moment* in the name comes from the term used in physics to describe the work performed by forces acting in different directions. In geology, the seismic moment is the work performed by an earthquake as the two sides of a fault apply force over a distance. Most calculations of moment magnitude (abbreviated M_w) factor in the length of the surface that slipped during the quake, the distance the rock on one side moved relative to the rocks on the other side, and the rigidity of the rock along the fault.

Like the other methods of describing earthquakes, the values for moment magnitude roughly correspond to Richter-scale numbers. The largest earthquake ever recorded using the moment magnitude scale measured 9.5. It occurred along the Pacific coast of Chile in South America in 1960.

Scientists did not adopt the moment magnitude scale widely until the late 1970's, but today it is the preferred measurement because it describes the power of earthquakes more comprehensively than other methods. By the mid-1990's, it was possible to determine moment magnitude in many earthquake-prone areas, using seismographs that respond to a wide range of frequencies of earthquake waves. (A wave's frequency is the number of waves that pass a given point each second.)

With such a variety of ways to describe earthquake magnitudes, it's no wonder that the terms get confusing. Because moment magnitude requires two hours to calculate, geologists may substitute other readings just after big quakes to meet public demand for knowledge. That, too, adds to the confusion. Yet one thing is clear—the Richter scale is out of date.   [William W. Hay]

Volcanoes mapped with radar

Microwave radar images taken with the space shuttle Endeavour and published in late 1994 illuminate volcanoes in Russia, the Philippines, and Africa. In one of the most active volcanic regions on Earth, *above,* the erupting Kliuchevskoi volcano on Russia's Kamchatka Peninsula is visible as a large white peak near the center of the false-color image. A large lake nearly fills the *caldera* (collapsed crater) of the Taal volcano near Manila on the Philippine island of Luzon, *right.* The Virunga volcano chain, *below,* borders Rwanda, Zaire, and Uganda. Geologists plan to study these and other radar images to learn more about the geology of the areas and to better understand volcanic processes.

two plates are locked together in that area.

Based on evidence of prehistoric earthquakes, Coppersmith and Youngs believe that within the next few hundred years, the locked zone will break in two segments, causing two magnitude 8.5 earthquakes, or in four pieces, creating four magnitude 8 earthquakes. A 5 percent chance of a magnitude 9 quake exists, they said.

Rapid sea-level rise. Contrary to the belief of many scientists, sea levels may have risen in three quick bursts after the last Ice Age. At the height of the last Ice Age, sea level was about 130 meters (430 feet) lower than it is today. Scientists had long speculated that the sea level then rose at a slow, uneven rate as the ice sheets melted.

Two Canadian scientists reported in January 1995 that there may have been three episodes of very rapid sea-level rise much greater than had been previously suggested. Geologist Paul Blanchon and geographer John Shaw of the University of Alberta in Edmonton, Canada, based their conclusion on studies of a particu-

lar type of shallow-water coral common in the Caribbean Sea.

Shaw and Blanchon relied mainly on studies of the moose-horn coral *Acropora palmata*, the most prominent coral on the crest of shallow Caribbean reefs. *A. palmata* grows no deeper than 10 meters (33 feet), and it dies if sea levels rise more rapidly than 14 millimeters (0.6 inch) per year. Such changes bring reduced sunlight, which causes the death of the coral.

Blanchon and Shaw found a number of sites where *A. palmata* appeared to have died suddenly or been replaced by other corals. The researchers speculated that the evidence of death and replacement indicates instances where sea level rose more than 14 millimeters a year.

Blanchon and Shaw suggested that surges of ice sheets in North America caused the first two rapid sea level rises. Surges occur as ice sheets warm and begin to flow into the sea. A surging of the west Antarctic ice sheet caused the third rapid sea-level rise, they said.

Wandering continents. Antarctica and North America may once have

Scientists prepare a robot to venture into the crater of an active volcano in Alaska in August 1994. The robot, named Dante II, was designed by researchers at Carnegie Mellon University in Pittsburgh with assistance from the National Aeronautics and Space Administration. Using a remote-control hookup, scientists helped Dante maneuver into the dangerous depths of Mount Spurr. There, Dante mapped the surface and analyzed volcanic gases. The mission was brought to an end when the robot toppled over on a steep slope.

Geology continued

been neighbors. That was the conclusion of an investigation reported by geologist Ian Dalziel of the Institute of Geophysics of the University of Texas at Austin in January 1995.

Scientists have long accepted the idea that all of Earth's major continents were assembled into a giant landmass called Pangaea at the end of the Paleozoic Era, about 245 million years ago. But some scientists believe that Pangaea was formed through the collision of even older continents during the Paleozoic Era (570 million to 240 million years ago). Many geologists also believe that the older continents formed as the result of a breakup of a more ancient giant landmass, called Rodinia, but little is known of their arrangement in that supercontinent.

Working with geophysicist Lisa M. Gahagan at the University of Texas and using a computer program that simulates the movement of tectonic plates on a globe, Dalziel found that Antarctica's shape fits well against the western edge of North America in the area of the Southwestern United States. Partly

as a result of this realization, Dalziel theorized that the two continents may have been in contact 750 million years ago in the late Proterozoic Era (270 million to 750 million years ago).

Similarities between volcanic rocks found in east Antarctica and the Southwestern United States bolstered Dalziel's theory. When lava is hot and liquid, magnetic minerals in it align themselves freely with Earth's magnetic field, like tiny compass needles. Once the lava cools and solidifies, however, the magnetic particles are trapped and can no longer move, even if the rock changes its position in relation to Earth's magnetic field because of the motion of the continents.

Dalziel reported that a preliminary analysis of volcanic rocks collected in southern North America and East Antarctica shows that they have magnetic particles pointing in the same direction. This finding may indicate that the two plates on which North America and Antarctica rest may have once been side by side. [William W. Hay]

In WORLD BOOK, see GEOLOGY.

Medical Research

Encouraging research on Alzheimer's disease emerged in 1994 and 1995, including a possible test to help physicians diagnose the disorder and the creation of a genetically altered mouse that will help investigators study the disease and test new drugs. Alzheimer's, a disorder that typically strikes people over the age of 60, involves a gradual deterioration of brain cells that leads to a severe loss of mental ability.

Alzheimer's test. In November 1994, researchers at Harvard Medical School in Boston announced a quick, simple test to help diagnose Alzheimer's disease in living patients. Doctors traditionally depend upon a costly combination of neurological and psychological tests to diagnose the disorder. But the only way to confirm the diagnosis is to autopsy brain tissue after death for such features as *neuritic plaques,* deposits of sticky protein surrounded by debris from deteriorating nerve cells, and twisted protein fibers called *neurofibrillary tangles.*

The new test was based on the discovery that the eyes of Alzheimer's patients are highly sensitive to a drug called

tropicamide, which is used to *dilate* (widen) the pupils of the eyes during an eye exam. Pupils of patients with the disease dilated in response to an extremely dilute concentration of tropicamide, while those of healthy people showed a much smaller response.

The researchers suggested that using tropicamide to test for Alzheimer's may some day help predict which individuals will develop the disease before any symptoms have occurred. If so, the test could open the door to new treatments aimed at halting the progression of the disease before it has a chance to cause extensive brain damage.

Model mice. The creation of a strain of genetically altered mice that suffer from the type of brain deterioration seen in people with Alzheimer's disease was announced in February 1995 by scientists at Athena Neurosciences, a company in South San Francisco, Calif., and Eli Lilly & Company, a pharmaceutical firm in Indianapolis. The scientists gave the mice a *mutated* (altered) human gene that has been linked to Alzheimer's disease in some families. The muta-

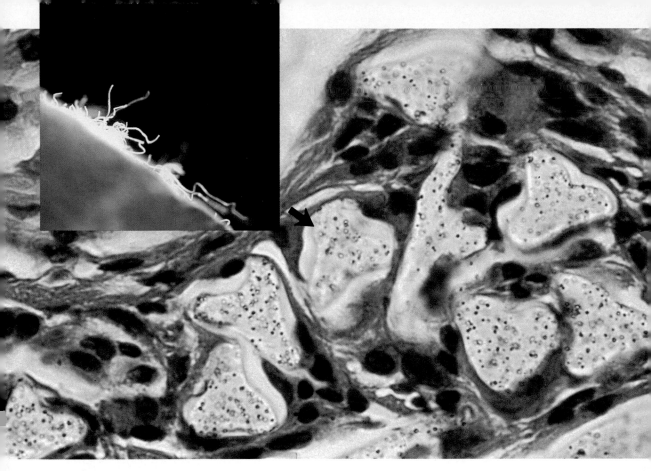

Cigarette fiber threat?

Tiny fibers from cigarette filters, *inset*, can be inhaled while smoking and become imbedded in the lung tissue, according to a January 1995 report. Immunologist John Pauly of the Roswell Park Cancer Institute in Buffalo, N.Y., led researchers who found cigarette fibers in the lung tissue of human smokers. The scientists also implanted fibers from popular cigarette brands into laboratory mice. Six months later, they found the fibers still imbedded in the lung tissue, *above* (arrow). The health effects of the imbedded fibers were under study.

tion results in an altered form of a common brain protein, called amyloid precursor protein (APP). When APP breaks down, one of its fragments is amyloid, the abnormal protein found in the plaque seen in the brains of Alzheimer's patients. The researchers also linked the inserted gene to a bit of genetic material that instructs brain cells to churn out large quantities of the altered APP.

As the mice reached middle age, they developed many of the hallmarks of the disease. These included deteriorating nerve cells, loss of *synapses* (connections) between brain cells, and numerous amyloid plaques, particularly in the areas of the brain used for learning and memory. The investigators planned to test whether the mice showed impaired memory as Alzheimer's patients do.

The researchers said that their work supports the theory that APP and amyloid play a role in the development of Alzheimer's disease. Furthermore, the genetically altered mice are expected to greatly aid future research on Alzheimer's disease and the testing of drugs to treat the disease.

Malnutrition and infection. The first direct evidence that a virus can mutate and become more dangerous because its host has a nutritional deficiency was reported in May 1995. Scientists with the University of North Carolina at Chapel Hill and the United States Department of Agriculture in Beltsville, Md., reported on their study of mice fed a diet deficient in a trace mineral called selenium.

The researchers studied a human virus called Coxsackie B3 that had been linked to a heart condition called Keshan disease. This ailment, once common in China among people whose diets were deficient in selenium, largely disappeared through use of dietary supplements that included the mineral.

In the study, mice were fed either a normal diet or a selenium-deficient one. After four weeks, both groups were injected with Coxsackie B3. Although the virus had no effect on the mice that ate the normal diet, it caused severe heart damage 7 to 10 days later in those deprived of selenium.

When the researchers isolated the

virus infecting the selenium-deprived mice and injected it into the mice that had been eating the nutritionally balanced diet, the previously healthy animals then developed heart damage. This finding, the researchers said, indicates that the virus infecting the selenium-deficient animals had mutated into a more virulent form, one that could harm even those that had received adequate amounts of selenium.

The researchers then analyzed the genetic structure of the virulent virus recovered from four of the selenium-deficient mice and compared it with the genetic makeup of the original form of the microbe. They discovered that the virus had undergone six changes in its genetic structure.

The researchers speculated that the immune systems of nutritionally deficient mice responded more weakly to infection, permitting the Coxsackie virus to grow in greater numbers, thus increasing the likelihood that a mutation would occur. Another possibility was that the lack of selenium helped foster some mutations.

The finding that the mutated viruses remained virulent even when they were injected into well-nourished mice might have implications beyond nutritionally deprived people. In theory, the investigators noted, "only one [selenium-]deficient person would be needed to give rise to a new family of virus mutants with unpredictable properties." If viruses other than Coxsackie B3 react to nutritional deficiencies in a similar manner, that might explain, for example, why new strains of influenza virus emerge regularly from China, which has had extensive selenium-deficient areas.

Cross-species transplants. A major step in the quest to transplant animal organs into human beings was reported in May 1995 by a research team from Duke University Medical Center in Durham, N.C., and Nextram, a biotechnology firm in Princeton, N.J. The team succeeded in implanting genetically altered pig hearts into baboons, without causing the baboons' immune systems to mount a fierce attack on the hearts.

Since the 1960's, scientists have researched the transplantation of animal organs into people because the number of people who needed transplants exceeded the supply of human organs. But researchers needed to find a way to make the animals' tissues compatible with the recipients' immune systems. Experiments with species-to-species transplants had found that implanted organs became the target of *hyperacute rejection,* in which the recipient's immune system abruptly rejects the foreign tissue, sometimes within minutes of transplantation.

An element of immune defenses called the complement protein system is key to hyperacute rejection. Normally, the body produces the proteins in this system to defend itself when foreign organisms such as disease-causing bacteria are detected. The body also makes biochemicals called complement regulatory proteins that help control the complement system and prevent an attack on the body's own tissues.

When a human being receives an organ from another species, the organ usually lacks the protective regulatory proteins needed to suppress the human complement system. Without such proteins, the foreign organ faces an attack that quickly destroys the transplant.

In the new study, the researchers looked for a way to protect the transplanted pig hearts without impairing the immune system's ability to fight off harmful microbes. To do this, they created a special strain of pigs by giving pig embryos genes that would cause the animals to make human complement regulatory proteins. Because human and baboon regulatory genes resemble each other, either was expected to have the same effect.

After the pigs reached adulthood, the researchers connected the hearts of three of them to major blood vessels of three baboons. The baboon hearts were not removed, to ensure that the surgery itself would not cause the baboons to die. This arrangement allowed the baboons' blood to circulate through the pigs' hearts, where rejection would quickly follow without the protective human regulatory genes.

The pig hearts continued to beat 4 to 30 hours after the surgery, considerably longer than the survival times of an hour or less seen in previous cross-species transplant studies. The researchers then examined the heart tissue for signs of hyperacute rejection and found only minimal damage, indicating that the hearts had resisted as-

Tracking a killer of horses and humans

Investigators with the Australian Animal Health Laboratory, *above right*, wear special gear to avoid infection as they prepare to test tissue samples from horses struck down by a mysterious illness. The disease killed 14 racehorses and a horse trainer by late September 1994. Within two weeks, scientists had identified a new virus as the cause of the illness. The microbe, named equine morbillivirus, *above*, is in the same family as the viruses that cause measles and canine distemper.

sault by the baboons' immune systems.

The experiment was a step toward solving the problem of thousands of people with diseased organs who die because there are not enough human organs available for transplant. However, experts cautioned that other immune response difficulties must be solved before cross-species transplants would be feasible.

Mysterious new virus. Just 12 days after an outbreak of a mysterious ailment on a farm near Brisbane, Australia, left 1 man and 14 racehorses dead in late September 1994, Australian researchers identified the virus that caused it. The previously unknown virus belonged to the morbilliform family, a group that includes the viruses that cause measles in humans and canine distemper in dogs.

The new virus, named equine morbillivirus (EM), was the first new virus in the morbilliform family found to attack humans since measles was first described in the 900's. The EM infection is characterized by high fever and breathing difficulty caused by a rapid accumulation of fluid in the lungs.

Eleven horses had died from the unknown disease and their trainer was seriously ill when health authorities were called in to investigate the outbreak. Worried that the deadly illness could sweep across Australia, investigators sprang into action to identify its cause.

First, the researchers analyzed tissue samples from the dead horses to rule out various disease agents known to cause serious respiratory illnesses. Within several days, the investigators became aware of an unknown virus growing in tissue cultures. They examined the virus under an electron microscope and saw that it had the characteristic shape of a family of viruses that includes the morbilliviruses.

The investigators found the virus in the lungs of the dead horses but not in healthy horses. They also found the virus in tissue samples from the trainer, who died. Furthermore, healthy horses injected with biological material from a sick animal or with purified EM came down with the disease, confirming the virus's role in the ailment.

Within a week, the researchers had

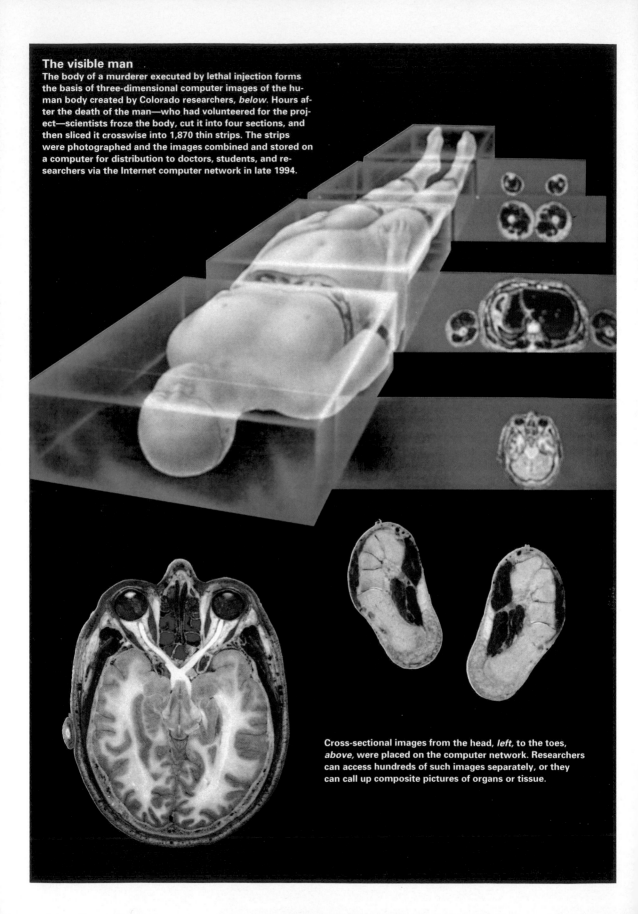

The visible man
The body of a murderer executed by lethal injection forms the basis of three-dimensional computer images of the human body created by Colorado researchers, *below*. Hours after the death of the man—who had volunteered for the project—scientists froze the body, cut it into four sections, and then sliced it crosswise into 1,870 thin strips. The strips were photographed and the images combined and stored on a computer for distribution to doctors, students, and researchers via the Internet computer network in late 1994.

Cross-sectional images from the head, *left*, to the toes, *above*, were placed on the computer network. Researchers can access hundreds of such images separately, or they can call up composite pictures of organs or tissue.

developed a test to determine if people or horses had been infected by the virus. Testing about 1,600 horses and 90 people who worked or lived near the outbreak showed that none of them were infected, indicating that the disease had not spread.

By the end of the outbreak, seven infected horses and one infected man, a 40-year-old stable hand, had survived the illness. No further cases were seen after the initial outbreak.

Fetal cells ease Parkinson's. Fetal tissue transplanted into the brain of a patient with Parkinson's disease grew and supplied the brain with new nerve connections, a group of researchers from Chicago, New York, and Florida reported in April 1995. Although previous studies of fetal cell transplants in such patients had suggested that the procedure could be beneficial, proof that the cells actually grew new connections in the recipients' brains had been lacking.

Parkinson's disease, which affects an estimated 500,000 to 600,000 Americans, is a chronic brain disorder characterized by muscle rigidity and tremors that interfere with normal movement. These symptoms are the result of the destruction of specialized brain cells that produce a brain chemical called dopamine, which plays a key role in regulating movement.

During early stages of the disease, patients respond to a drug called L-dopa, which replaces the missing dopamine. After 5 to 10 years, however, the drug usually starts to lose effectiveness, and patients become increasingly disabled.

In the late 1980's, researchers seeking to help such patients began experimenting with a procedure that involved implanting dopamine-secreting nerve cells taken from the brain tissues of aborted fetuses. Some investigators reported that many patients benefited from the treatment, and brain scans showed that dopamine was being released in the transplant areas. But results were mixed, perhaps because the implanted cells survived in some patients but not in others.

In the new study, the sudden death of a patient with Parkinson's disease who had undergone the fetal cell operation 18 months earlier gave the researchers an opportunity to see how the transplanted cells had fared. The 59-year-old man, who had improved dramatically

after undergoing the transplant procedure, had died of unrelated causes.

The researchers found that large numbers of fetal nerve cells had survived, grown, and sent out long, fiberlike extensions that released dopamine. These new findings, they said, prove that fetal cell transplantation is an effective treatment for the disease. To verify the results, the National Institute of Neurological and Communicative Disorders and Stroke in Bethesda, Md., launched a two-year fetal cell transplant study involving 36 patients with Parkinson's disease.

Diagnosing back pain. The use of magnetic resonance imaging (MRI) to diagnose certain back problems could be a waste of money and invite unnecessary treatment, according to a July 1994 report in *The New England Journal of Medicine* by a team of researchers from California and Ohio. MRI is a technique used to produce images of body tissues.

In recent years, physicians have increasingly used MRI or other scanning techniques to examine the spines of patients with lower-back pain, particularly to determine if the patients had disk problems. (Disks are the elastic pads of tissue that separate the vertebrae and act as shock absorbers.) When disks are injured, they can bulge or herniate—that is, protrude asymmetrically beyond the vertebrae.

But the new study revealed that even people without backaches often have such disk abnormalities. The scientists scanned the spines of 98 people with no back pain and found that over half had bulging disks, and over one-fourth had herniated ones. The researchers concluded that the high rate of disk abnormalities seen in people without symptoms suggests that finding disk bulges or protrusions in people with low back pain may often be a coincidence.

Experts suggested that imaging techniques such as MRI should be used only for people with certain types of back pain. These people include those who have other signs of an underlying disorder, such as cancer, or those who are considering surgery after failing to improve with four to six weeks of conservative treatment, such as exercise and physical therapy.   [Joan Stephenson]

In WORLD BOOK, see ALZHEIMER'S DISEASE; IMMUNE SYSTEM; VIRUS.

Meteorology
See Atmospheric Science

Neuroscience
See Biology; Medical Research

Dieters received good news and bad news in 1994 and 1995. The good news: The discovery of a gene for obesity may help explain the causes of overweight. The bad news: A new study indicates that weight loss causes the body to burn calories at a slower rate.

Obesity gene. The discovery of a gene that may be responsible for obesity in mice provides new evidence that body weight is physically regulated, according to a December 1994 report by a team of researchers led by geneticist Jeffrey Friedman at Rockefeller University in New York City. Genes, the units of heredity, control the structure and function of all living things.

About 30 percent of people in the United States are *clinically obese*—weighing at least 20 percent more than their ideal body weight. In human beings, obesity is linked to diabetes, heart disease, and many other health problems.

To find the obesity gene, the researchers studied a specially bred strain of mice that reaches three times the normal body weight. The investigators identified an abnormal gene in the obese mice that appeared to cause fat cells to release smaller than normal amounts of a hormone into the bloodstream. The function of that hormone, the scientists theorized, was to cause the brain to register a feeling of fullness after eating. Mice with abnormal versions of the gene would eventually become obese, because the brain would not get the normal chemical messages to stop eating.

After discovering the mice obesity gene, called *ob*, the researchers examined human genetic material to look for an equivalent gene. They found a corresponding human gene that was 84 percent chemically identical to the mouse gene. Although other factors, including other genes, are probably involved in most cases of obesity, experts said the ob gene discovery could possibly lead to the development of new weight-control drugs or other treatments. (See also GENETICS.)

Metabolism and weight loss. The most difficult aspect of weight control for many dieters is keeping the pounds off once they have been lost. Research reported in March 1995 indicates that the problem may be that the body responds to weight loss by burning calories at a lower than normal rate. The new study supports the theory that an internal control mechanism tries to keep body fat at a constant level by adjusting the *metabolic rate* (the rate at which the body uses food energy) in response to weight loss and gain.

In the study, physician Rudolph Leibel and his colleagues at Rockefeller University monitored the rate of metabolism in 18 obese volunteers and 23 volunteers who had never been significantly overweight. The scientists examined the volunteers once before the subjects began a calorie-restricted diet, once after they lost 10 to 20 percent of their body weight, and once after they had regained 10 percent of their body weight by overfeeding.

Both the obese and lean subjects responded to weight changes in the same way. After the subjects lost 10 percent of their body weight, they burned 15 percent fewer calories than normal. When the subjects increased their weight by 10 percent, they burned 15 percent more calories than normal.

Normally, about 60 percent of the body's food energy is devoted to the *resting metabolism*, the energy requirements of vital involuntary activities such as breathing and the pumping of the heart. Another 10 percent is used for the digestion and utilization of food. The remaining 30 percent is burned up in voluntary physical activities such as working or exercising.

The New York researchers found that after the subjects gained weight, they burned up more calories during physical activity than would be expected, but their resting metabolic rate did not change. After the subjects lost weight, however, both the resting metabolic rate and the energy required for physical activity decreased.

The results thus support the notion that after weight gain or weight loss, the body tries to return to a particular weight level, called a *set point*. Scientists still do not know how a person's weight level is set, however.

Breast cancer risk and diet. A study of more than 2,000 Greek women suggested that consuming olive oil may be associated with a reduced risk of breast cancer, according to a January 1995 report. Scientists had known that the rate of breast cancer among women in the

Mediterranean region, where olive oil is an important component of the diet, was about half that of women in the United States. In addition, experiments on animals had suggested that olive oil did not promote breast tumors as other dietary fats have been seen to do.

Nutrition professor Antonia Trichopoulou and colleagues at the Harvard School of Public Health in Boston examined the diets of 820 Greek women with breast cancer and 1,548 women without breast cancer. The women with breast cancer were newly diagnosed patients admitted to hospitals in the Athens, Greece, area during the period of 1989 to 1991. The other subjects were women from the same area.

All were interviewed and given a questionnaire about their dietary habits during the year before the onset of the cancer or before the interview. The researchers used the information to look for relationships between the women's health and their frequency of consumption of certain foods and nonalcoholic beverages.

The data showed that frequent consumption of vegetables and fruit was associated with significant reductions of breast cancer risk. The risk dropped by as much as 8 percent for women who consumed fruits frequently and as much as 12 percent for those who ate frequent servings of vegetables.

The only other foods significantly related to the risk of breast cancer in the study were fats. Women who consumed olive oil more than once a day had a 25 percent lower risk of breast cancer than women who consumed olive oil only once a day.

The researchers found that the relationship of increased olive oil consumption and lowered breast cancer risk was particularly significant among women who had passed menopause, the time of life when menstruation ceases. The scientists also reported that the women who had breast cancer were more likely to have consumed margarine more than four times a month than the women who did not have the disease.

[Phylis B. Moser-Veillon]
In WORLD BOOK, see NUTRITION.

Oceanography

The phenomenon known as El Niño can create a pool of warm water that lasts up to 12 years in the Pacific Ocean, an effect lasting far longer than scientists had believed possible. That was the conclusion of a study reported by oceanographer Gregg Jacobs of the Naval Research Laboratory at the John C. Stennis Space Center near Bay St. Louis, Miss., in August 1994. El Niño is a complex change in ocean circulation and winds in the tropical Pacific Ocean that disrupts temperature and rainfall patterns around the world. El Niños occur every three to seven years. The most intense El Niño on record occurred in 1982-1983.

The telltale sign of an El Niño is the eastward movement of an abnormally warm body of water about the size of the United States across the tropical Pacific Ocean toward South America. Normally, the pool of warm water disperses soon after reaching South America. But Jacobs claimed to have found remnants of the 1982-1983 El Niño as late as 1995 in the form of a wave of warm water that had rebounded off the coast of

South America and moved back across the Pacific, where it extended from northern Japan to Alaska.

Jacobs used computer simulations and satellite measurements of changing sea-surface heights to study the pool. Because seawater expands when it is warm, the pool was 20 centimeters (8 inches) higher than the surrounding water. That feature allowed satellites to track the pool's movement. The satellite measurements showed that, by early 1995, the pool had pushed the Kuroshio current off the coast of Japan 320 kilometers (200 miles) northward before finally fading away in the Bering Sea.

Tropical seas and global warming. The tropical Pacific Ocean not only sets off El Niños, but it may also help accelerate the pace of global warming, according to a February 1995 report by Nicholas Graham, a research meteorologist at Scripps Institution of Oceanography in La Jolla, Calif. Graham's computer simulation of the atmosphere closely reproduced actual temperatures based solely on increases in the temperature of tropical sea surfaces.

Record growth at deep ocean vents

Only 21 months after the first signs of life are visible at a new-ly formed deep-sea volcanic vent, *below,* the vent is covered with giant tube worms nearly 1.5 meters (5 feet) tall, *bottom.* According to an October 1994 report on life at the Pacific Ocean vents, giant tube worms appear to grow faster than any other marine *invertebrates* (animals without backbones).

Global warming describes a predicted rise in Earth's average surface tempera-ture, mainly due to the emission of heat-trapping gases into the atmosphere. The heat-trapping gases are called green-house gases, because they behave some-what like the glass in a greenhouse—allowing visible light from the sun to reach Earth's surface and at the same time absorbing *infrared* (heat) energy emitted by Earth. Burning *fossil fuels* (coal, oil, and natural gas) produce one of the most important greenhouse gas-es, carbon dioxide. Levels of carbon dioxide in the atmosphere have in-creased by about 25 percent since 1870.

The prospect of global warming has alarmed many scientists. They believe that global warming could begin to melt the polar ice caps, increase the frequen-cy of major storms, cause widespread drought, and flood low-lying islands and coastal areas.

Some scientists point to rising global temperatures as evidence that a global warming may have already started. Stud-ies show that the average world air tem-perature has risen 0.5 Celsius degrees (0.9 Fahrenheit degrees) during the 1900's, with 0.4 Celsius degrees (0.7 Fahrenheit degrees) of that rise coming since the mid-1970's.

Graham's computer simulation was unusual because it reproduced the re-cent rise in Earth's average surface tem-perature without considering atmo-spheric carbon dioxide levels. Graham's simulation instead emphasized only the actual sea-surface warming in the Pacif-ic, tropical Atlantic, and Indian Oceans.

According to Graham, warmer sea-surface temperatures lead to higher air temperatures because they increase the evaporation of sea water. Large amounts of heat energy are required to convert liquid water to vapor, and warm ocean water can provide that heat. As the evap-orated water rises in the air, it cools and condenses, producing clouds and rain. During condensation, heat is released to the air. Winds transport the heated air, resulting in higher atmospheric temper-atures around the world.

But why the tropical oceans, particu-larly the Pacific, should be warming is unknown, Graham said. It could be part of a natural trend, or rising levels of car-bon dioxide in the atmosphere might be involved.

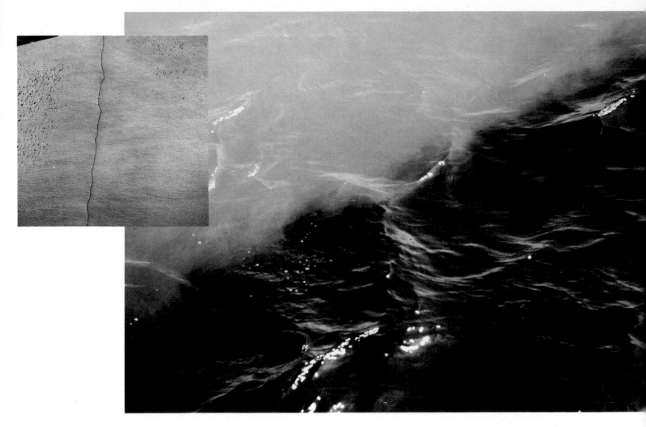

A crack in the sea?

In a photograph taken from the space shuttle Atlantis, a 57-kilometer (35-mile) dark line zig-zags across the tropical Pacific Ocean, *inset*. The line, which appears between warm and cold masses of water, is equally dramatic in a photograph taken from a research vessel, *above right*. In October 1994, oceanographers reported that the line forms when nutrients well up from cold deep water and increase the growth of *diatoms* (microscopic, single-celled organisms), turning the water greener than usual. Waves from the mixing of cold and warm currents enhance the boundary's visibility, according to scientists.

Warm water depletes zooplankton. Researchers also reported evidence in 1995 of warming in nontropical oceans, a change that threatens large numbers of marine life by killing zooplankton. In March 1995, oceanographers Dean Roemmich and John McGowan of Scripps Institution of Oceanography released findings of a study showing a 70 percent decline in the volume of zooplankton off southern California since 1951. Zooplankton are microscopic marine animals that float with the currents and provide food for many other types of marine life.

The two researchers said that warmer surface waters had probably caused the zooplankton decline. They had reported in 1992 that since 1950, waters in the upper 100 meters (330 feet) off southern California had warmed an average of 0.8 Celsius degrees (1.4 Fahrenheit degrees) and that significant warming had reached depths of 300 meters (1,000 feet).

Roemmich and McGowan concluded that the warming reduced the mass of the zooplankton by upsetting the supply

of nutrients coming from cold deep waters. The nutrients rise to the surface when prevailing winds push the surface waters away from the California coast. Warmer surface waters increase the differences in density between the upper and deeper layers. These differences inhibit exchanges between the layers of ocean water and the the upwelling of nutrient-rich deep waters.

First look at sea-floor spreading. In January 1995, scientists reported the use of undersea military sensing technology to detect and monitor for the first time the formation of new sea floor from fresh lava flows. Geophysicist Christopher G. Fox of the Hatfield Marine Science Center in Newport, Ore., and his colleagues reported their discoveries from observations of a swarm of submarine earthquakes some 450 kilometers (280 miles) off the Oregon-Washington coast.

The earthquakes began in the deep ocean on June 26, 1993. They occurred near the Juan de Fuca Ridge, an area where two of Earth's *tectonic plates* (huge pieces of crust that move about on top of molten rock) move against each other. The earthquakes parted the plates, allowing lava to reach the surface and harden into new oceanic crust. Nearly 700 weak quakes occurred within a three-week span.

Previous attempts to closely monitor submarine seismic activities had been hampered by the limitations of the recording instruments. Those instruments are generally moored on the sea floor for extended periods and are unable to transmit data as it happens. Scientists must retrieve the instruments in order to analyze the data they record.

But the U.S. Navy allowed the Oregon scientists to use its Sound Surveillance System (SOSUS) installed in Puget Sound, north of Seattle, which almost immediately relayed information to science labs. A SOSUS detects certain types of seismic waves that can travel through water and that are too small for land-based seismic monitors to pick up.

The SOSUS system detected the submarine earthquakes as they began. Research vessels quickly responded, and for the first time, scientists watched new

sea floor form from lava. Oceanographers aboard the research ships found at least three very large *hydrothermal plumes* (areas where water superheated by lava escapes through small openings, or vents, in the sea floor) over the Juan de Fuca Ridge. Each plume occupied volumes of 10 billion to 40 billion cubic meters (13 billion to 52 billion cubic yards). Researchers photographed the sea floor using a remotely-operated, towed vehicle in order to firmly establish the connection between plume development and the expulsion of lava from the sea floor.

Scientists aboard the submersible research vessel *Alvin* determined that the new crust was highly magnetized and that the magnetic strength appeared to be weakening at a rate of about 10 percent per year, much faster than had been expected. Finally, scientists found that deposits of bacteria and of minerals, mainly iron and silica, covered 7 to 14 percent of the area of the new lava flow.   [Ray G. Peterson]

See also ATMOSPHERIC SCIENCE; GEOLOGY. In WORLD BOOK, see OCEAN.

Physics

The biggest news in physics in 1995 was an announcement on March 2 confirming that the long-sought top quark, an elementary building block of matter, had been discovered. The quark was found by two teams of researchers at the Fermi National Accelerator Laboratory (Fermilab) near Batavia, Ill. The top quark is the 12th and almost certainly the last fundamental building block of matter to be found. After its discovery, particle physicists, who study nature at its smallest scales, planned to turn their attention to other mysteries of matter. The foremost question to be answered is why matter has mass, the property that gives an object weight and resistance to motion. (In the Special Reports section, see FOUND—THE TOP QUARK.)

A new accelerator for Europe. Particle physicists hoping to investigate the origin of mass got good news in December 1994, when the governing council of the European Laboratory for Particle Physics (CERN) approved construction of a particle accelerator more powerful than the Fermilab machine, known as the Tevatron. The CERN accelerator

will be known as the Large Hadron Collider (LHC). Hadrons are subatomic particles made of quarks.

A particle accelerator is a huge machine that uses electrical forces to boost beams of subatomic particles to immense speeds. The particle beams are crashed together or into stationary targets, resulting in tiny explosions of energy that "condense" into swarms of short-lived particles. Researchers study this subatomic debris to learn how atoms are constructed.

The LHC will be constructed in an existing circular tunnel 27 kilometers (17 miles) in circumference on the French-Swiss border near Geneva, Switzerland. The tunnel was originally built to house a less powerful particle accelerator that will be decommissioned when the LHC goes into operation soon after the year 2000.

The LHC will ultimately generate beam energies of 7 trillion electronvolts (TeV), more than 7 times the energy of the Tevatron. (An electronvolt is the amount of energy acquired by a single electron as it passes through a one-volt

A magnetic field (rainbow colors) is visible in a computer-enhanced image of a circular zone of a superconducting crystal made by IBM researchers. Superconductors are materials that conduct electricity with no resistance. Physicists think an electric current in a superconductor consists of electrons moving in pairs. The characteristics of the magnetic field detected in the IBM experiment supports a theory that some materials are superconducting at relatively high temperatures because they cause electrons to pair up through the formation of magnetic bonds.

battery. By way of comparison, most flashlight batteries are 1.5 volts.)

The particle beams generated by the LHC will circulate in vacuum pipes in opposite directions within the tunnel. The beams will be held on course by more than 1,200 powerful superconducting electromagnets. In a superconductor, electricity flows without encountering resistance or generating heat. Once started, a current in a superconductor can flow forever without any external power source. Superconducting magnets significantly reduce the amount of electric power that an accelerator consumes.

At four points along the circular route, the LHC's particle beams will cross and be brought to a sharp focus inside huge arrays of electronic particle detectors. Each time the beams converge, a few particles will collide head-on, and the detectors will track the many new particles that emerge from the collisions.

Most of the time, the LHC will circulate beams of protons, the positively charged particles that, together with un-

charged neutrons, make up the atomic nucleus. But the LHC will also be able to accelerate complete atomic nuclei. Two of the detectors planned for the machine are designed to study proton-proton collisions; the other two are tailored for collisions of nuclei.

The design of the LHC is similar to that of the ill-fated Superconducting Super Collider (SSC), which had been under construction in Texas until being canceled by the United States Congress in October 1993. The SSC would have been three times more powerful than the LHC. The project was terminated because its projected cost of at least $11 billion was deemed too high in an era of persistent U.S. government budget deficits.

The construction schedule approved by the CERN council calls for the LHC to begin operating in 2004 at two-thirds power. This will be accomplished by leaving out one-third of the magnets that guide the beam. The upgrade to full 7 TeV beams is expected by the year 2008.

This two-stage program was adopted

primarily to ease the financial burden of construction, which will be shared by the 19 nations that support the CERN laboratory, with extra contributions from France and Switzerland as the host nations. The CERN members are hoping the United States will join the LHC project. American support might make it possible to speed up the installation of the full set of magnets.

The missing-magnet design will probably make it impossible for the LHC to achieve its primary scientific goal, the discovery of the Higgs boson, until after the year 2008. The Higgs boson is a particle that, according to theory, imparts mass to matter. Most theorists agree that while there is some chance that 7 TeV beams will generate enough Higgs bosons to confirm the particle's existence, an energy output of only two-thirds that level will almost certainly not be enough.

Approval of the LHC came on the CERN laboratory's 40th birthday. The impending construction of the new accelerator seemed likely to ensure that CERN will be the world's leading center for particle physics research well into the 21st century.

Two new heavy elements. The synthesis of two new laboratory-made elements—numbers 110 and 111 in the periodic table of the elements—was announced in late 1994 by an international team of scientists at the Society for Heavy Ion Research (GSI) laboratory in Darmstadt, Germany. The investigators reported the creation of element 110 in November 1994, and they followed that up the next month with the announcement of element 111. The same research team had previously synthesized elements 107, 108, and 109 for the first time.

The scientists created element 110 by accelerating the nuclei of nickel atoms in a particle accelerator and guiding them into a stationary target of lead. One nickel nucleus fused with a lead nucleus to form a giant nucleus containing 110 protons and 160 neutrons. A neutron in the newly created nucleus quickly broke free, leaving a nucleus with a *mass number* (number of protons and neutrons) of 269 and an *atomic number* (number of protons) of 110. (Atoms with the same atomic number are the same element, but if their mass numbers differ, the atoms are said to be different isotopes.)

Element 111 was formed in a similar reaction, combining the nuclei of nickel and bismuth atoms. The researchers produced an isotope of element 111 with a mass number of 272.

Making the new elements required considerable finesse. The collisions in the GSI accelerator, unlike the violent head-on collisions studied in particle physics, were carefully tuned to be as gentle as possible. This allowed two nuclei to merge rather than to smash each other to pieces.

This kind of collision is much like one automobile gently touching bumpers with another as it comes to a stop. But whereas the auto bumpers absorb the energy of the slow collision, keeping the cars intact, the situation is different at the atomic level. In this case, the excess energy imparted to the nucleus must be gotten rid of in order to satisfy the laws of momentum and energy conservation. This is done by expelling at least one particle from the nucleus. The particle (or particles) carries away exactly the required amount of energy.

Even after expelling a particle, the massiveness of the nuclei makes them terribly unstable, and they exist less than a millisecond (0.001 second) before breaking apart. The researchers thus found it impossible to identify either of the new elements by chemical tests. Instead, the nuclei emerging from the collision target were sorted with the aid of a device that determined whether they were moving at the expected speed when they were created. The instrument also measured the energy released when the nuclei broke up.

The breakup process is called alpha decay, because the nucleus emits an *alpha particle,* which consists of two protons and two neutrons. After the emission, the nucleus is a lighter element, with an atomic number that has decreased by two and a mass number that has decreased by four. If the new nucleus is also unstable, it may emit another alpha particle. The decay process may continue in this fashion until a stable isotope is formed.

Element 110 was identified by a chain of four alpha decays, leading to known isotopes of elements 108, 106, 104, and 102 in sequence. Element 111 went through a similar decay chain, but in this case the first two steps led to previously unknown isotopes of elements 109 and 107, which counted as additional discoveries for the team.

The experimenters also produced nuclei of an isotope of element 110 with a mass number of 271. From a scientific standpoint, the creation of this isotope may have been the scientists' most significant accomplishment. With 161 neutrons, this isotope is close to a theoretical "rock of stability" for very heavy nuclei. Physicists' calculations suggest that nuclei containing exactly 162 neutrons should be exceptionally stable. One sign that this may be true is that the 271-isotope of element 110 existed without breaking apart about eight times longer than an isotope with two fewer neutrons.

For the time being, elements 110 and 111 will remain officially nameless—as are all the elements beyond number 103, Lawrencium. The discoverers of a new element normally have the right to name the element, but competing research teams disagree over who first discovered each of the heavier elements. An additional dispute has arisen over whether an element may be named in honor of a scientist who is still living. The International Union of Pure and Applied Chemistry is waiting for these disputes to be settled before it certifies names for any new elements.

New magnet lab opens. On October 1, 1994, Vice President Albert Gore officially dedicated the National High Magnetic Field Laboratory (NHMFL) at Florida State University (FSU) in Tallahassee. This laboratory, which is sponsored by the National Science Foundation (NSF), is destined to be the preeminent research center in the United States for the study of magnetism. Additional facilities will be located in branch laboratories at the University of Florida in Gainesville and in Los Alamos, N.Mex.

Since 1960, the U.S. leader in magnetism research has been the Francis Bitter National Magnet Laboratory at the Massachusetts Institute of Technology (MIT) in Cambridge. MIT competed for the new laboratory but lost out when Florida offered a more generous financial package.

The centerpiece of the NHMFL will be an electromagnet that produces a magnetic field of 45 teslas in a metal cylinder just 32 millimeters (1.3 inches) in diameter. (A tesla is a unit of magnetic field strength.) The strength of the Florida magnet will surpass that of the long-time world recordholder, a 38.7-tesla magnet at the Bitter laboratory.

In comparison, the powerful superconducting electromagnets built for particle accelerators achieve fields of 6 to 8 teslas in a much larger volume. High-quality permanent magnets are generally around 0.5 tesla, and Earth's magnetic field is less than 0.0001 tesla.

The 45-tesla magnet will be a "hybrid" design incorporating both superconductors and ordinary conductors. It is being designed and built as a joint effort of MIT, FSU, and 17 industrial firms. Magnets built exclusively with superconductors are limited to fields of about 20 teslas.

While waiting for the 45-tesla magnet, researchers at NHMFL will not be idle: The laboratory already has a 27-tesla and two 20-tesla magnets in operation. The Gainesville laboratory is also developing a 20-tesla magnet with a refrigerator that will permit studies of magnetic properties at temperatures as low as one two-thousandth of a degree above *absolute zero*, the lowest possible temperature that anything can be. Absolute zero is -273.2 °C on the Celsius scale (-459.7 °F on the Fahrenheit scale).

All of these magnets generate steady magnetic fields. Even stronger magnetic fields can be generated in short bursts at the NHMFL's Los Alamos site. The Los Alamos magnets generate fields of up to 220 teslas for a few microseconds (millionths of a second), or 75 teslas for a few milliseconds.

Very strong magnetic fields alter the motions of electrons in atoms and molecules, changing their chemical properties and the way they emit and absorb radiation. Magnetic fields also affect the orientation of spinning atomic nuclei.

Studies of magnetism and its subatomic effects can lead to the development of useful new materials for industry. At the level of basic understanding, such research can provide clues to the structure of crystals and large molecules and help unravel the complex chemical reactions that take place in living cells.

New X-Ray Sources Open a World of Discovery

A century after Wilhelm Conrad Roentgen discovered X rays in 1895, two new facilities switched on the most intense X-ray beams ever created, giving scientists powerful new tools for probing matter at the atomic level. The first new facility was the European Synchrotron Radiation Facility (ESRF) in Grenoble, France, which opened in September 1994. The second, the Advanced Photon Source (APS) at the Argonne National Laboratory near Chicago, was expected to begin operations in August 1995.

Both new facilities contain a type of particle accelerator called a *synchrotron*. By setting subatomic particles whizzing around huge rings at nearly the speed of light, the new synchrotrons produce *synchrotron radiation*, intense X-ray beams tens of thousands of times more powerful than those produced by conventional X-ray tubes.

Physicists once considered synchrotron radiation an annoying source of energy loss in particle accelerators. Soon, they realized the X rays were useful for investigating matter at the atomic level. X rays, like radio waves, visible light, and other forms of electromagnetic radiation, are characterized by their *wavelength*, the distance between the peaks of two successive waves. The ESRF and the APS can produce X rays with wavelengths comparable to the diameter of an atom or smaller. Such rays have tremendous energy and penetrating power. Just as an ordinary microscope uses waves of visible light to create magnified images of objects the size of a few cells, the ESRF and APS can be thought of as "X-ray microscopes" that allow

France's European Synchrotron Radiation Facility was completed in September 1994.

scientists to view much smaller structures, including viruses or biological molecules.

Synchrotrons create X-ray beams by accelerating negatively charged particles called electrons or their positively charged counterparts, called positrons, through an electric field. Once the particles reach a velocity close to the speed of light—299,792 kilometers (186,282 miles) per second—they are injected into a huge storage ring. Inside the ring is a long vacuum chamber within a series of magnets called *bending magnets*. The bending magnets produce a magnetic field that bends the straight path of the particle into a circular orbit. As the particles are forced into a circular orbit, they give off X rays. The X rays are then funneled to stations where scientists use the radiation to probe the structure of matter.

What sets the ESRF and APS apart from other synchrotrons is their ability to produce X-ray beams of even greater intensity. The more intense beams are produced by magnetic devices called *wigglers* and *undulators*. Each consists of a series of magnets with alternating magnetic fields that cause the particle beam to wiggle and emit a pencil-sharp beam of X rays with high intensity.

The APS will be the largest and most powerful synchrotron in operation. It has a storage ring measuring 1,104 meters (3,622 feet) around and can accelerate particles to energies reaching 7 billion electronvolts (7 GeV). (An electronvolt is the energy gained by an electron moving through a potential difference of 1 volt. A flashlight battery is 1.5 volts.) Up to 70 separate experiments will be conducted using the APS at one time. The ESRF has a ring measuring 844 meters (2,769 feet) in circumference and can accelerate particles to 6 GeV. By the late 1990's, up to 40 experiments will be run at a time. Japan has plans to start up an even more powerful synchrotron, an 8-GeV machine called SPring-8 in 1998.

Physicists hope that the synchrotron radiation produced at all three sites will lead to an avalanche of breakthroughs. Researchers at ESRF say they are already able to achieve a level of detail in visualizing proteins that had been impossible with other X-ray sources. And because the beams are intense, the time required to expose a sample is very brief—less than a billionth of a second for the APS and the ESRF. The rapid exposure will allow scientists to take "snapshots" of molecules during very fast chemical reactions and to see how individual atoms combine to form complex molecules. And, in addition to the discoveries they bring, the new synchrotrons foster a new type of multidisciplinary scientific enterprise, in which physicists, biologists, geologists, chemists, material scientists, and other experts work side by side to make the most of a powerful new tool.

[Alexander Hellemans]

Physics continued

Thus, experimentation with powerful magnetic fields contributes to both basic and applied science.

One of the better-known applications of this field of research is nuclear magnetic resonance (NMR) imaging, which uses magnetic fields to produce images of structures in the body. The stronger the magnetic field that is used, the sharper the images that result. The Gainesville facility will include a 12-tesla experimental NMR machine large enough for the study of small animals.

The laboratory has already attracted distinguished senior staff members from the United States and abroad. The NHMFL's chief scientist, John Robert Schrieffer, formerly of the University of California at Santa Barbara, was coauthor of the first successful theory of superconductivity and shared the 1972 Nobel Prize for physics. Another eminent researcher lured to the laboratory is Lev Gorkov, founder of Russia's most distinguished theoretical physics center, the Landau Institute in Moscow.

In addition to serving as a leading science center, the NHMFL will be a test of a new kind of relationship between federal and state governments, universities, and private industry. Previous national laboratories were funded almost entirely by the federal government, but from the outset NHMFL has been a partnership between the NSF and the state of Florida, with some additional contributions from the private sector.

Florida bore most of the $75-million cost of constructing the facility and equipping it with instruments. The NSF will provide about 60 percent of the projected operating budget of $20 million a year. Private industrial firms contributed several million dollars worth of magnets and other instruments to the laboratory.

About 400 scientists, mainly from the fields of biophysics, chemistry, solid state physics, and materials science, will work at the laboratory each year. Researchers will come from universities throughout the United States, from foreign countries, and from industry.

[Robert H. March]

In WORLD BOOK, see MAGNET AND MAGNETISM; QUARK; PARTICLE ACCELERATOR.

Psychology

Illicit drug use among 8th, 10th, and 12th graders increased an average of 4.3 percent in 1994, according to data from a national survey of students released in December 1994 by the National Institute on Drug Abuse (NIDA). The increase had begun three years before. Drug abuse among junior high and high school students was more prevalent in the early 1990's than in the late 1980's but still not as common as in the peak years, 1978 and 1979.

Teen drug abuse on the rise. Among the illegal drugs that adolescents use most frequently, marijuana showed the greatest increase. "The discovery of increasing marijuana use is an early warning sign," cautioned Alan I. Leshner, director of NIDA. According to Leshner, rising marijuana use was an indicator of an "erosion of antidrug attitudes" among teen-agers. In Leshner's view, there is a sequence in an adolescent's behavior that begins with a reduced appreciation of a drug's danger, then moves to an acceptance of peers' use of the drug, and finally, to the adolescent's own use of the drug.

In response to the upward trend in marijuana use, NIDA announced plans to launch a program aimed at adolescents that would publicize facts about how marijuana and other drugs affect the brain. Marijuana, for example, interferes with motivation and impairs thinking, communication, problem solving, and memory. In a number of studies, students under the influence of the drug show difficulty learning and retaining information. The NIDA prevention program also planned to use sports stars and other role models to promote the message that illicit drugs are neither "cool" nor "trendy."

The brain's emotion detector. People can understand the intentions and moods of others because of the functioning of the amygdalae, two almond-shaped structures that lie deep within the brain. That was the finding of a pair of studies reported in December 1994 and February 1995. Both studies involved patients who suffered damage to the amygdalae.

The first report was the work of researchers at the University of Iowa College of Medicine, in Iowa City, who studied the case of S. M., a 30-year-old woman whose amygdalae were destroyed by a disease that left her otherwise normal. Led by neuroscientist Antonio Damasio, the group examined S. M.'s ability to sense others' emotions based on her response to photographs of the faces of sad, angry, happy, or surprised men and women. The researchers then compared her responses to those of 12 people with other types of brain damage, and to the responses of 7 normal subjects.

S. M. could recognize familiar faces. But, unlike the other subjects, she could not assign the proper intensity levels to the fearful expressions in the photographs she was shown. She also had difficulty perceiving similarities among pictured emotions. For example, she did not realize that the photographs of surprised faces and happy faces looked more alike than did the photos of sad faces and happy ones. The other subjects in the study were able to grasp these distinctions.

The second report was the result of research on another patient who had damaged amygdalae. Psychology professor Andy Young and his associates at the University of Cambridge in England reported that amygdalae damage prevented this patient from knowing when people were looking at her or away from her. In addition, Young's patient could not identify a number of emotional expressions on the faces of others. Experts said that the two studies of patients with damaged amygdalae suggest that mental conditions involving extreme trouble with interpersonal skills—such as autism—may be associated with problems in the amygdala.

Sleeping brains process memory. The brain seems to learn as it sleeps, according to the findings of two experiments reported in July 1994. The new research supports scientists' thinking about how the brain forms memories.

In one study, psychology professors Matthew Wilson and Bruce McNaughton at the University of Arizona in Tucson implanted tiny electrodes into the hippocampal region of rats' brains, an area known to be involved in processing and retaining spatial memories. The rats were then taught to navigate a maze. During the process, the researchers used the electrodes to monitor the rats'

brain activity. As a rat moved through different parts of the maze, the researchers saw changes in the brain's pattern of electrical activity. Later, the scientists monitored brain activity as the rats slept. For several nights, activity in the hippocampal region was similar to the daytime pattern detected when the rats were learning the maze.

That finding indicated to the scientists that the sleeping rats' brains were repeating and reviewing the information received during the learning process. The rate of the nighttime brain activity was faster, however, suggesting that the brain may play back information at a quicker, more efficient rate for review during sleep.

In the second study, at the Weizmann Institute of Science in Rehovot, Israel, a group led by neurologist Avi Karni taught human subjects a procedural task. During the night, the subjects were awakened at various stages of sleep. The researchers found that subjects performed the task better the next day if they had not been deprived of REM (*r*apid *e*ye *m*ovement) sleep, the stage during which dreams occur. The finding suggested that the human brain reviews certain learned tasks during REM sleep.

Social phobia. Social phobia, an anxiety disorder first recognized in the late 1970's, drew increasing attention in 1994 and 1995. In 1994, the National Comorbidity Survey, published by sociologists with the University of Michigan in Ann Arbor, showed that social phobia was far more common in the United States—and more treatable—than previously thought. People with social phobia are persistently afraid of being in situations in which they are exposed to unfamiliar people or to the scrutiny of others. The sufferers fear that they will act in a way, or show anxiety in a way, that will deeply humiliate them. Children and adolescents can also suffer from social phobia.

Two studies completed in the mid-1980's had shown that up to 2 percent of the U.S. population was suffering at the time from some form of social phobia. The National Comorbidity Survey gathered data on the number of Americans who suffered from this condition at any time over the course of their entire lives. The researchers found that social phobia had affected about 13 percent of the population. With that prevalence, social phobia ranks as the third most common mental disorder, behind depression and alcoholism.

Without treatment, adults with social phobia tend to panic or behave nervously when they are in a feared situation, and socially phobic children may shrink and withdraw, freeze, cry, or have tantrums. The sufferers anxiously anticipate social situations or avoid them entirely. In either case, social phobia interferes significantly with normal routines and functioning at school, at work, or in relationships.

Psychiatrists and psychologists treat social phobia with medications, psychotherapy or, most commonly, a combination of both. Medications to treat social phobia include three types of drugs commonly prescribed for depression. The classes of drugs are monoamine oxide inhibitors (MAOI's), benzodiazepine tranquilizers, or selective serotonin reuptake inhibitors (SSRI's). Each medication has limitations, however. MAOI's require diets prohibiting certain foods. Benzodiazepines may have only a temporary affect on social phobia, with symptoms returning as soon as patients stop using the drug. In some instances, benzodiazepines lead to habitual use or addiction. Experts say the most promising medications for social phobia seem to be SSRI's, the most well known of which is Prozac, but their effectiveness has not been thoroughly tested. SSRI's are not currently recommended for children, because they have not been sufficiently studied among this age group.

Therapists can help social phobia patients learn to face feared situations, using a treatment called cognitive behavioral therapy. In this approach, patients are helped to conquer mildly feared situations and then to face more strongly feared ones. When medication and behavior therapy are combined with psychotherapy geared toward understanding why the person holds the fears, a great percentage of patients with social phobia markedly improve.

[Lenore C. Terr]
In WORLD BOOK, see PSYCHOLOGY.

Public Health

One of the deadliest known infectious agents, the Ebola virus, inspired mass fear in April 1995, when an Ebola outbreak struck the African nation of Zaire. By mid-June, more than 220 people had died of the disease.

Ebola outbreak. Ebola, first noted in 1976, causes severe hemorrhaging and kills up to 90 percent of its victims, usually within a week. The 1995 outbreak began with a clinic patient in Kikwit, a city of 150,000. Several health care workers contracted the disease, which is transmitted through body fluids. Unsanitary conditions helped it spread.

The Zaire government quarantined Kikwit in the hope of preventing the spread of the disease to nearby Kinshasha, Zaire's capital. As public health workers monitored the epidemic, which appeared to have peaked by late May, medical researchers sought to determine which animal species are natural carriers of the Ebola virus, and what factors cause it to infect human beings.

Diphtheria epidemic. After nearly 30 years of control by childhood vaccinations, epidemic diphtheria emerged again in the former Soviet Union in 1994. Diphtheria is a potentially fatal contagious infection of the upper respiratory system or the skin. The World Health Organization (WHO) reported in early 1995 that diphtheria cases in the former Soviet Union had increased from 840 in 1989 to 47,800 in 1994. About 70 percent of cases occurred in children under 16.

The WHO called the rapidly expanding epidemic an international public health emergency. At least 20 diphtheria cases occurred in the neighboring countries of Bulgaria, Finland, Germany, Norway, and Poland. Reasons for the epidemic were not clear, but experts blamed crowding, migration, and low levels of vaccination among children.

Plague struck the western Indian state of Maharashtra in August 1994. In September, cases of pneumonic plague, a more contagious and deadly form, were reported in Surat, in the state of Gujarat. Despite fears that the disease would spread, public health workers brought it under control by December, after more than 50 people died.

Public Health continued

Women in Surat, India, *below,* burn roadside garbage in hopes of killing plague-bearing fleas during a panic that hit the nation in September 1994. As the number of reported plague cases mounted, many people fled the affected areas, and travelers avoided India. Although nearly 6,000 cases of illness were reported as plague, the World Health Organization verified only two limited outbreaks in the Bid District of the state of Maharashtra and in Surat, *bottom.*

Health of women and minorities. Minorities and women in the United States were reported in 1995 to have been hard hit by two of the deadliest known diseases: cancer and AIDS.

An American Cancer Society report on cancer deaths released in early 1995 for the first time calculated deaths among ethnic minorities separately from deaths of white Americans. The statistics showed that African Americans have a 35 percent greater chance of dying of cancer than white Americans do.

In February 1995, the Centers for Disease Control and Prevention (CDC) in Atlanta reported that in 1994 AIDS became the fourth leading cause of death among women aged 25 to 44. Since 1992, the number of AIDS cases among women had increased about 17 percent each year. About 77 percent of those cases occurred among minority women. Women at greatest risk for AIDS are those who injected illicit drugs or have sexual partners who did.

Preventing AIDS in infants. The CDC in February 1995 began urging that all pregnant women be tested for the human immunodeficiency virus (HIV), which causes AIDS. The CDC made its recommendation after studies found that pregnant, HIV-infected women who used the AIDS drug zidovudine (AZT) reduced the risk of passing the infection to their infants.

A key study, which was reported in November 1994 by the National Institutes of Health in Bethesda, Md., followed 180 infants born to AZT-treated mothers. The infants had an 8-percent infection rate compared with a 25-percent infection rate among infants of untreated mothers. The transmission of HIV from mother to baby during pregnancy and childbirth accounts for most childhood AIDS cases.

Premature birth, premature death. The baby born too soon—not the one born too small—is at greater risk of dying during the first 27 days of life, according to a report in March 1995 by researchers in the United States and Norway. Their findings challenged a belief that a baby's low weight, rather than early birth, was the root cause of infant mortality. Health policies that attempt to increase birthweights, the researchers stated, may be misdirected. Instead, efforts should be directed toward the prevention of preterm deliveries.

The study compared almost 7.5 million births in the United States with 100,000 births in Norway, which has lower rates of infant death soon after birth. At all birthweights, infants in both countries had similar rates of survival, the study found. The higher mortality rates seen among the American infants appeared entirely due to the greater number of preterm deliveries in the United States.

College binge drinkers. Although overall drinking has declined in the United States, college campuses may perpetuate problem drinking, according to a study reported in December 1994. Behavior that elsewhere is considered alcohol abuse was found to be prevalent and even socially acceptable on some campuses.

Almost half of about 17,500 college students surveyed by researchers at the Harvard School of Public Health in Boston reported having engaged in binge drinking—drinking four (for women) or five (for men) or more alcoholic beverages in a row—in the previous two weeks. Nearly one-fifth had binged three or more times during the two weeks.

Students who binged frequently were 7 to 10 times more likely to undertake other risky behaviors: having unprotected or unplanned sex, encountering trouble with campus police, damaging property, or becoming injured. They were also more likely to drive after drinking.

Fatter Americans. More than 30 percent of Americans were overweight in the early 1990's, compared to 25 percent in the late 1970's, reported the National Center of Health Statistics in December 1994. Overweight was defined as weighing at least 20 percent more than one's ideal body weight.

The next generation may be even heftier, the public health experts worried. Only 15 percent of adolescents were overweight in the 1970's, but in 1994 more than 20 percent were, according to the report.

[Richard A. Goodman
and Deborah Kowal]
In WORLD BOOK, see PUBLIC HEALTH.

Science and Society

Advances in biotechnology and growth in electronic communications brought the ethical and social dimensions of science and technology into sharp focus in 1994 and 1995. At the same time, national policy changes resulting from the end of the Cold War kept such issues as government secrecy and the future of nuclear weapons laboratories high on the agenda of national policymakers.

"Net" scams. Kevin D. Mitnick, one of the world's most wanted computer criminals, was captured by Federal Bureau of Investigation (FBI) agents on Feb. 15, 1995, near Raleigh, N.C. Mitnick was alleged to have broken into numerous computer systems using telephone systems and the global computer network known as the Internet. Mitnick was accused of vandalizing computer systems and stealing data files, including software and thousands of credit card numbers. Authorities charged him with illegal use of a telephone access device and computer fraud.

FBI agents, aided by computer expert Tsutomu Shimomura, had tracked Mitnick all the way from California, where he was wanted for parole violation associated with an earlier conviction for computer crimes. Mitnick had been on the run from federal agents since 1992.

Within days of Mitnick's arrest, police in Helsinki, Finland, raided the apartment of Johan Helsingius, a service provider on the Internet, and seized information from his computer database. Helsingius had operated an "anonymous remailer" service that strips electronic mail of its return address and forwards the mail anonymously. The police searched Helsingius's database and obtained the name of a person who had used the remailer to anonymously post on the Internet a file stolen from a computer at the Church of Scientology. The Church claimed this posting constituted breach of copyright.

Internet dilemmas. The Mitnick case and the anonymous remailer incident highlight some of the troubling ethical and legal issues that have evolved with the growth of the Internet, which by mid-1994, reportedly serviced over 20 million people worldwide. Experts say the number of Internet users and the types of services found on the Internet continue to grow. Today, the Internet serves as a vehicle for commerce, entertainment, and information services.

With the growth of the Internet has come a host of new social and economic issues related directly to its use. One unresolved issue is determining who is responsible for the content of material on the Internet.

Other issues concern privacy and security on the Internet. Some experts think the government should be allowed to eavesdrop on Internet communications so that it can track potential criminals. Others believe that maintaining the privacy of communications for all citizens is more important. Observers also wonder if methods can be developed to prevent unauthorized access to computer networks by *hackers*—who break into computers for the fun of it— and *crackers*—who break into computers for such malicious purposes as computer theft—without impeding the flow of information. Finally, social scientists question whether the growth of electronic communications will widen the existing social and economic gap between those who can afford access to the Internet and those who cannot.

Topics like these were the subject of heated discussion among computer experts, scholars, lawyers, ethicists, and policymakers in 1994 and 1995. In most cases, the answers to these questions were not yet clear. The results of their debate are likely to influence the shape of communications in the next century.

Guidelines for embryo research. Guidelines for research on human embryos were approved by a high-level advisory committee at the National Institutes of Health (NIH) on Dec. 2, 1994, ending a 13-year ban on government funding of embryo research. Scientists believe such research could yield tremendous insights into the nature of genetic diseases, cancer, infertility, and other medical problems. Opponents of embryo research argue that embryos deserve the same treatment as unborn fetuses and should not be subject to scientific experimentation.

The advisory panel developed the guidelines after consulting with doctors, researchers, ethicists, a social scientist, and a lawyer. Among the issues under discussion were: (1) under what condi-

tions may embryos be used in research; (2) at what stage of development is the use of the embryo no longer acceptable; and (3) under what conditions are the donation or sale of embryos acceptable.

After deliberating for nearly a year, the panel limited the use of embryos to studies with goals that cannot be achieved using animals or *gametes* (unfertilized eggs or sperm). It also specified that embryos used in research must be less than 14 days old. That is the point at which the *primitive streak*—the first trace of a nervous system—appears. Embryos at this early stage of development are made up of only a few dozen cells and are no bigger than the period at the end of this sentence.

The panel also decided that embryos produced in private fertility clinics through a technique called *in vitro fertilization* can be used in research. In this technique, the mother's eggs are fertilized by the father's sperm in a laboratory dish and then implanted into the mother's uterus, where one or more of the eggs may develop into a normal fetus. The in vitro fertilization process often produces extra embryos, and these embryos, the panel decided, could be used for research. The panel also approved the donation of embryos from women undergoing pelvic surgery.

The panel's most controversial recommendation was to allow the creation of embryos specifically for research under certain conditions. President Bill Clinton, anticipating many objections to this provision, overruled it just hours after the guidelines were announced.

Struggles with Cold War legacies. The future of the nation's large nuclear weapons laboratories was called into question after a commission headed by Robert Galvin, former chairman of Motorola Corporation, recommended on Feb. 1, 1995, that the labs be streamlined and operated under a semipublic corporation. Such restructuring would require that the government only partially fund the labs while a private enterprise ran them like a business. The laboratories include the Los Alamos National Laboratory in Los Alamos, N. Mex.; Argonne National Laboratory near Chicago; and Brookhaven National Laboratory on Long Island, N.Y.

Some of the labs were founded during World War II (1939-1945) to produce the first atomic bombs. During the Cold War that followed, several of the labs worked on weapons projects aimed at keeping the United States ahead of the former Soviet Union militarily.

Since the 1980's, the labs have been the subject of vigorous debate in the government and in the scientific community. Critics argue that the labs have outlived their purpose and that some should be closed and the remainder reduced in size. They contend that money spent on the labs would be better used for research in universities and industry or for reducing the federal deficit.

But others regard the labs as precious national resources, with unique facilities and equipment, highly qualified staff, and a proven capability to conduct large-scale team research on important national problems. The labs' supporters suggested that the labs focus on such pressing national problems as ensuring the long-term availability of energy supplies, protecting the environment, and supporting industry's efforts to become more competitive internationally.

Members of Congress in whose districts and states the labs are located are likely to oppose cutbacks in the labs because all of the labs are major employers. A lab closure or staff reduction would have a significant economic impact on the local community. However, despite this political support for the labs, experts say the nation is likely to see significant changes in the structure of the laboratories in the near future.

Science and secrecy. The signing of an executive order declassifying more than 800,000 previously secret satellite photographs was announced on Feb. 24, 1995, by Vice President Albert Gore. The photographs date from the 1960's and the 1970's and include pictures of Soviet air and missile bases as well as many geographical features around the world. Public release of the photographs is part of a growing trend toward declassifying materials that the federal government has kept secret for decades.

During World War II and the Cold War that followed, millions of scientific reports and documents were stamped "secret" by federal government officials to keep them from falling into the hands of potential enemies. Many scientists criticized this system of classified information. They claimed that it slowed

scientific progress by preventing scientists from gaining access to information that could help their research. Others suggested that the system had often been used to cover up the misdeeds of the government and government workers rather than to protect national security. Reports indicated, for example, that the human radiation experiments that were widely publicized in the early 1990's had been kept secret for years mainly because government officials wanted to avoid lawsuits and bad press.

Once the Cold War was over, scientists and others began to say it was no longer really necessary to keep much of this material secret. Deciding what should be declassified, however, is a costly and time-consuming endeavor.

To short-cut the process, President Clinton in November 1994 signed an order declassifying, without detailed review, nearly 44 million pages of classified files, about half of which date from after World War II. Although this was the largest declassifying action ever, the nearly 23 million pages of post-1945 materials represent only about 1 percent of all classified Cold War files.

To further reduce the amount of secret material, President Clinton signed an executive order on April 17, 1995, that automatically declassified all existing documents more than 25 years old and that called for the declassification of most future documents after 10 years. The order further stipulated that any future classifying must be supported by sound documentation.

Science standards drafted. A draft of the nation's first voluntary science standards was unveiled by the National Academy of Sciences (NAS) on Dec. 1, 1994. The purpose of the standards is to promote science literacy among elementary and high school students.

The draft spells out the content of science curricula and also seeks to integrate lesson content with teaching and testing methods that encourage students to ask questions, think critically, and relate science to real-world circumstances rather than just asking students to memorize facts and terms. The draft also provides states and local school districts with guidelines on how to develop a curriculum that will fulfill the science goals. The final form of the guidelines was due by late 1995. [Albert H. Teich]

Science Student Awards

See Awards and Prizes

The United States and Russia began moving rapidly in 1995 to merge much of their human spaceflight programs. In February, the U.S. space shuttle Discovery, with a Russian cosmonaut among the crew, flew a dramatic close rendezvous with Russia's Mir space station. And in March, a U.S. astronaut and medical doctor, Norman E. Thagard, flew with two Russians on a Soyuz spacecraft to Mir, where he remained for several months.

The missions were aimed at paving the way for a series of joint U.S.-Russian spaceflights. Those missions, scheduled to begin later in the year, were to include flights of American space shuttles to Mir and, later, the construction of a new international space station. (See CLOSE-UP.)

Spaceflight record. One of the Mir crew who greeted Thagard was also a physician—cosmonaut Valery Polyakov. He had already set a new space endurance record. When he finally returned to Earth from Mir on March 22, Polyakov had spent 439 days in orbit. The old record, set in 1988 by cosmonauts Musa Manarov and Vladimir Titov, was 366 days.

Summer shuttle flights. In July 1994, the U.S. space shuttle Columbia flew for two weeks to conduct the second International Microgravity Laboratory mission. The crew of seven included the first Japanese woman in space, Tokyo heart surgeon Chiaki Naito-Mukai.

Working in the Spacelab module, which was carried in the shuttle's cargo bay, the Columbia astronauts conducted more than 80 biological and materials-science experiments that had been planned by researchers in the United States, Canada, Europe, and Japan. The crew divided into two shifts, so work could go on around the clock. The gravity-free environment of the shuttle allows scientists to see new phenomena or processes that are masked by gravity on Earth.

In September, six astronauts aboard the shuttle Discovery spent 11 days in orbit testing a laser system called a lidar to study the atmosphere. Lidar, short for *light detection and ranging*, is like radar except that it uses light waves instead of radio waves. The system sends pulses of low-energy laser light into the atmosphere, and an instrument connected to a telescope records the reflections that are bounced back.

The system provides information about pollutants and other particles and chemicals in the atmosphere. The purpose of the test, which was judged a success, was to show that a lidar system in space is feasible and would be a valuable tool for analyzing the atmosphere.

Near the end of the flight, two astronauts donned space suits and tested a new "self-rescue" device on a spacewalk. The device is a small jet pack that attaches to the bottom of a space suit's backpack, which contains the astronaut's life-support system.

Previously, astronauts working outside a spacecraft always had to make sure they were tethered to it in case they lost their grip and started floating away. Without a tether, an astronaut who did float away could not get back to the ship on his or her own.

That is not a big concern on shuttle missions, because the shuttle pilot can simply maneuver the craft until the astronaut can grab hold. But on a space station, a shuttle might have to undock first, and by that time the astronaut might be far away. The jet pack will allow an astronaut who floats away from a space station to scoot back unaided to a handhold. Another jet pack had been available since 1984, but it was bulky and so not suitable for routine use.

Autumn shuttle missions. In October, the second mission of the Space Radar Laboratory was carried out by a crew of six aboard the shuttle Endeavour. Using radar instruments built by the U.S., German, and Italian space agencies, the astronauts made images of forests, deserts, and other features on Earth's surface.

The National Aeronautics and Space Administration (NASA) had hoped to launch the mission during the summer. Scientists wanted observations that would provide a seasonal contrast with images made on the first Space Radar Laboratory flight, in April. But computers halted the first launching attempt, on August 18, two seconds before liftoff when they detected an engine problem. The shuttle finally went into orbit for an 11-day flight on September 30.

The delay proved fortunate in one way, though. Just hours after the shuttle was launched, a volcano on Russia's

Adrift in space without a tether
Astronaut Mark C. Lee floats free of the space shuttle Discovery in September 1994, during a test of a new jet pack device. The jet pack was designed to permit astronauts to work outside a space station without a tether with no fear of drifting away from the station. A National Aeronautics and Space Administration engineer, wearing a space suit, *inset,* demonstrates the hand control for the jet pack, which attaches to the back of the suit beneath the life-support system.

Toward a New Era in Space

In February 1995, the United States space shuttle Discovery and a crew of six flew a historic mission. One of the Discovery astronauts, Air Force Lieutenant Colonel Eileen M. Collins, was the first woman shuttle pilot. And another crew member, physician Bernard A. Harris, Jr., became the first black astronaut to walk in space.

But those firsts were just footnotes to the mission. The larger importance of the flight, which included a rendezvous with the Russian space station Mir, was that it marked the dramatic beginning of what may be a new era in human space flight—an era in which the United States and Russia will cooperate rather than compete. The showpiece of that new spirit will be an international space station, scheduled to be built in the late 1990's. The station will be constructed by American astronauts and Russian cosmonauts, together with astronauts from other nations. The Discovery mission gave the partnership its flying start.

After launching from the Kennedy Space Center at Cape Canaveral, Fla., Discovery spent three days racing toward the Russian space station. Eventually, the shuttle approached to within 11 meters (37 feet) of Mir. For 10 minutes, the two spacecraft held a tight formation, flying along together at some 28,000 kilometers (17,500 miles) per hour. At about 100 metric tons apiece, they were by far the two largest spacecraft ever to rendezvous.

The astronauts and cosmonauts were moved by the historic significance of the event. Here were the two superpower rivals of the Cold War coming together in space, the most visible arena in which they had competed for more than three decades.

For years, the two nations' human space flight programs had been intertwined with political one-upmanship and technological muscle-flexing. The competition was best typified by the race to land the first humans on the Moon. But even after the Moon race was over—won by the United States in 1969—the perceived need of both countries to demonstrate their technological prowess persisted. It was that need that provided the main justification for the huge expenditure of sending people into space.

The military implications of the American and Soviet human spaceflight programs, though rarely mentioned publicly, were obvious. The first space launch vehicles were converted intercontinental ballistic missiles, and much of the technology developed in conquering space was directly applicable to both conventional and nuclear warfare.

Of course, science was always mentioned as a reason for going into space, and, clearly, science has been advanced by the many experiments that astronauts have conducted. But scientists, more often than not, have opposed sending men and women into space, arguing that the cost was too high for the knowledge to be gained.

In both the United States and the Soviet Union, politics and the military continued to propel manned spaceflight programs through the 1980's. However, once the Soviet Union collapsed in 1991 and the Cold War came to an end, the rationale for those programs began to crumble.

By the mid-1990's, economics had also entered the equation. The United States and Russia were both experiencing budgetary woes that made it difficult to finance ambitious space programs. Russia's problems, which were especially severe, stemmed from its struggle to create a free-market economy atop the ruins of the old Communist system.

The cash crunch in the United States led to the plan for building a space station with Russian involvement. Originally, the National Aeronautics and Space Administration (NASA) had wanted to construct a large international space station with the help of just the European Space Agency, Japan, and Canada. NASA developed an ambitious design for a station, but because of its high cost, the project never got off the drawing board.

Shortly after he took office in 1993, President Bill Clinton ordered NASA to redesign the space station. Eventually, he agreed to a plan that called for building a smaller station and bringing Russia into the venture. Clinton hoped this plan would both save the station from being terminated by deficit cutters in Congress and help Russia move toward a free-market economy.

Officials of both countries realized that before the assembly of the space station could begin in 1997, the two nations must learn to work and fly together. They agreed to put NASA astronauts on Mir and cosmonauts on U.S. space shuttles. They also agreed that the shuttles would fly 7 to 10 missions to Mir, where they would connect with the Russian station and some crew members would be exchanged.

Discovery's February 1995 flight was a prelude to those events. The crew of six included Russian Air Force Colonel Vladimir G. Titov, who became the second cosmonaut to ride on a U.S. spacecraft. The mission had three primary goals: to test the new communications links and decision-making procedures that would be required in a joint program; to let a NASA shuttle crew practice flying close to Mir; and to make sure the exhaust from the shuttle's *thrusters* (maneuvering jets) would not contaminate the Russian station or damage its delicate solar-power arrays.

Getting together in orbit
Russian cosmonaut Valery Polyakov peers through the window of the Russian space station Mir, *left,* during a January 1995 rendezvous with the U.S. space shuttle Discovery. In March, cosmonaut Yelena Kondakova, *above,* greets U.S. astronaut Norman E. Thagard with a kiss as he joins the Mir crew for a three-month stay at the station.

The mission tested NASA's skills, beginning with the countdown. In order to rendezvous with Mir, the shuttle had to lift off during a five-minute "window of opportunity" as the space station passed high above Cape Canaveral.

Soon after Discovery reached orbit, one of its thrusters was found to be faulty. The astronauts dealt with the malfunction by taking the fuel line that feeds the thruster out of service, though doing so made two other thrusters unusable as well. The malfunction had the Russians reconsidering whether to allow the shuttle to approach closely to their station.

The Russians were especially concerned that exhaust gases from the shuttle's thrusters might contaminate sensors on two Russian spacecraft that were docked at Mir. A dirty sensor could have prevented a spacecraft from returning to Earth successfully.

The Russians also had an unhappy memory of the only other time U.S. and Russian spacecraft had met. In 1975, as Apollo and Soyuz spacecraft joined in orbit, the U.S. vehicle bumped the Soviet craft in what engineers later described as a "hard dock." Eventually, though, the Russians approved the rendezvous with Discovery, and both sides said that having to work out the problem together was good for the new relationship.

As the Discovery mission was unfolding, two U.S. astronauts—physician Norman E. Thagard and biomedical engineer Bonnie J. Dunbar—were training in Russia to fly on Soyuz spacecraft to Mir. On March 14, 1995, Thagard lifted off with two Russian cosmonauts from the Baikonur space center in Kazakhstan to begin a three-month stay at the station.

But the new U.S.-Russian relationship has had a few bumps along the way. One set of experiments that NASA had wanted on board Mir when Thagard arrived missed the intended launching, because they were held up by Russian customs officials. And in May 1995, NASA postponed the planned launching of the shuttle Atlantis' first mission to dock with Mir, because the launching of a new module to Mir had been delayed.

Even bigger bumps could lie in the future. In Russia, the fragile economy, a growing organized-crime problem, and the specter of political upheaval have placed the space program in jeopardy. In the United States, Congress could choose to end the American-Russian partnership to retaliate for some unrelated action by Russia. That looked possible in late 1994 when Russian troops began fighting in the breakaway republic of Chechnya. Moreover, Congress, even though it is now controlled by the generally "pro-space" Republican Party, could still cancel the space station to save money. But if all these pitfalls are avoided, the coming years may bring a renaissance in the human exploration of space. [James R. Asker]

Kamchatka Peninsula erupted. Later, an earthquake struck off the Japanese island of Hokkaido. Those events provided unexpected opportunities for testing the capabilities of the radars. Geologists say radars in space could conceivably help predict such violent phenomena.

The shuttle Atlantis and a crew of six, including a French astronaut, Jean-François Clervoy, made an 11-day flight in November. The mission was the third in a series called Atlas, for *At*mospheric *L*aboratory for *A*pplications and *Sci*ence. The Atlas observations alternated between studying Earth's atmosphere and the sun's. Although scientists were disappointed when one of the seven Atlas instruments failed, they declared the mission a success.

Endeavour mission sets record. Two astronomers joined five career astronauts for the flight of Endeavour in March 1995. It was the second flight for both the astronomers and the Astro-2 observatory, which is a package of three telescopes.

The Astro-2 telescopes, mounted on a special platform in the shuttle's cargo bay, gathered light in the ultraviolet portion of the spectrum—light just beyond the violet end of the visible spectrum. Most ultraviolet light is filtered out by Earth's atmosphere, making such observations impossible for Earthbound telescopes.

The observations by the Astro-2 instruments complement those made by satellites such as the Hubble Space Telescope, the International Ultraviolet Explorer, and the Extreme Ultraviolet Explorer. By combining data obtained from these various sources, scientists can learn more about the evolution of the universe and the composition of stars and galaxies.

When Endeavour touched down on March 18, it had set a record for the longest shuttle mission. The crew spent 16 days and 15 hours in space.

Observing the Jupiter impacts. The Hubble Space Telescope, along with countless large and small telescopes on Earth, were trained on Jupiter in July 1994 to observe the bombardment of the giant planet by Comet Shoemaker-Levy 9. Over a period of six days, 20-odd pieces of the fragmented comet slammed into the giant planet at 209,000 kilometers (130,000 miles) per hour. The collisions created enormous explosions. (In the Special Reports section, see WHEN WORLDS AND COMETS COLLIDE.)

A view of the sun's poles. The Ulysses spacecraft, a joint project of the European Space Agency (ESA) and NASA, went into orbit around the poles of the sun in late 1994 and passed directly under the sun's south pole on September 13. Neither pole of the sun had ever been seen by human instruments before. Scientists had long wanted to take a look at the sun's poles to add to their knowledge of the sun and of the great effect it has on our planet.

Although Ulysses' orbit is twice as far as Earth's from the sun, its unique vantage point enabled it to obtain the valuable data that scientists had been waiting for. Ulysses is expected to continue relaying information on the sun at least through the year 2000. The probe will pass over the sun's north pole for the first time in July 1995.

The Magellan spacecraft, which successfully mapped Venus with its radar, performed one last task in 1994. In a "suicide plunge" on October 13, Magellan entered Venus' carbon-dioxide atmosphere. The spacecraft's arrays of solar power cells were set in a windmill position. As it flew toward its fiery death, data about how it tumbled provided scientists with information about the planet's cloudy atmosphere.

New rockets. In June 1994, The U.S. Air Force and the McDonnell Douglas Corporation conducted another test of the Delta Clipper (DC-X), a one-stage reusable rocket. The experimental rocket could lead to the development of a larger one-stage launch vehicle that could fly into orbit and be used over and over. NASA was also investigating the possibility of developing reusable launch vehicles. The aim of these projects is to make space flight much more routine and drastically lower its cost.

In 1995, the ESA neared completion of its new Ariane-5 rocket, which will be capable of lifting the largest commercial communications satellites two at a time. Since the 1980's, Ariane rockets, launched from Kourou, French Guiana, have cornered most of the international market in commercial satellite launches. Before then, the United States had offered the world's only commercial satel-

New views of the moon

Images relayed to Earth by the lunar orbiter Clementine and released in December 1994 provide new information about the moon. Circling in a polar orbit, Clementine produced the first complete view of the moon's south polar region, *left*. Views of the moon in various wavelengths of light resulted in a false-color composite image revealing the nature of the lunar surface, *below*. The green areas show old highland terrain, red denotes fresh highland craters, and blue marks areas where lava once flowed. An image of the Aristarchus plateau, *below left*, shows evidence of ancient volcanic activity.

lite launching services. In August 1994 and March 1995, Japan successfully launched the first big rocket it has developed on its own, the H-2, on its second and third flights.

Japan's space program is still relatively small, but it is growing rapidly. Japan remains the most steadfast partner in the project to develop an international space station. And while Europe has all but abandoned its effort to develop a small piloted space shuttle, Japan in 1995 moved ahead with a project to create a small unmanned spaceplane known as Hope.

Japan also made progress on a broad array of unmanned science-oriented spacecraft to be launched later in the 1990's. They included Adeos, an advanced Earth-observing satellite; Muses-B, a radio-astronomy spacecraft that will be operated in conjunction with observatories on the ground; Lunar-A, which will fire three probes into the moon for geologic studies; and Planet-B, Japan's first mission to Mars.

Spy satellite pictures released. In February 1995, U.S. intelligence agencies publicly released several spy satellite photographs for the first time. Officials said the 4 images were just the first of some 800,000 vintage satellite photographs that would be made available. The pictures were produced by photoreconnaissance satellites between 1960 and 1972. The images were declassified to make them available to environmental scientists and historians.

Typical equipment on those early spy satellites included a camera, long rolls of film, and two bucketlike return capsules. After a roll of film was exposed, it was loaded automatically into a capsule and ejected. As the capsule fell toward the Earth, it released a parachute. A cargo airplane would pluck the capsule from the sky with a hook that grabbed the parachute.

Film that was successfully retrieved would be rushed for processing, and the most important pictures were usually on the President's desk a few days later. This system was punctuated by many failures, but eventually it was made to work most of the time.

Although the Soviet Union developed similar capabilities, the United States had been first to come up with the scheme, and American spy agencies

Zoology

See Biology

maintained a technological edge in satellite reconnaissance. That margin gave U.S. arms negotiators and the military a distinct advantage in many critical episodes of the Cold War.

Satellite TV gains viewers. Americans began subscribing in large numbers in 1995 to new satellite services that beam television signals directly to their homes. This system, known as direct broadcast satellite (DBS), had already been available for several years in Europe. What makes DBS different from previous satellite television systems is that it competes head-to-head with local cable TV providers.

Large dish antennas to receive satellite signals have been a fixture on the American landscape for years. And local cable television companies have long used satellites to receive the programming they relay to homes.

But the large receiving dishes that have been used in such systems are expensive and, many people think, ugly. Moreover, those receivers sometimes must be pointed at different satellites in the sky to pick up various programs. These inconveniences have existed because the television industry has never been organized to sell programming by satellite.

Newer, higher-powered satellites have made it possible to shrink the size and cost of receiving equipment. The antennas for direct-to-home satellite TV measure only 45 centimeters (18 inches) across—about the size of a large pizza. With their boxes of electronics, which are necessary to decode or descramble the satellite TV signals, the antennas retailed for about $700, though that price was expected to come down as the technology becomes more widespread.

Subscribers still had to pay monthly fees comparable to cable TV charges. But the companies offering DBS services in the United States were banking on their systems' ability to transmit hundreds of channels with greater clarity than is typically provided with cable. One system, DirecTV, was offering 150 channels and planning to offer more after another satellite was launched. By early 1995, DirecTV had 500,000 subscribers, and it was expecting to top 1.5 million by year-end.   [James R. Asker]

In WORLD BOOK, see SPACE EXPLORATION; SPACE TRAVEL.

Science You Can Use

In areas selected for their current interest, *Science Year* presents information that the reader as a consumer can use in understanding everyday technology or in making decisions—from buying products to caring for personal health and well-being.

CD-ROM's: Multimedia Computing on a Silver Platter

Just a few years ago, buying computer software meant purchasing magnetic storage devices called floppy discs. Today, computer store shelves are also lined with shiny compact discs that hold encoded graphics, audio, video, animations, and text.

These discs, which take advantage of CD-ROM (compact disc, read-only memory) technology, have rapidly become one of today's most popular computer products. With a computer equipped with a special CD-ROM drive or player, a consumer can use the discs to play games, learn foreign languages, study music, or research topics.

Electronics industry analysts expect that by the end of 1995, more than 8 million United States households will own computers equipped to read CD-ROM discs. That represents a stunning increase since February 1990, when only 500,000 CD-ROM drives existed in the entire world.

CD-ROM's are increasingly present in schools as well. In 1994, almost 21,000 U.S. public schools—25 percent of the total—had CD-ROM-equipped computers in their classrooms.

The increase in the number of computers capable of reading CD-ROM's has resulted in an equally dramatic jump in the number of titles available in the compact disc format. Some industry experts estimate that there are more than 7,000 CD-ROM products available on the market today, with the number of titles expected to reach 10,000 during 1995.

Why the surge in popularity? In part, it's because CD-ROM discs can hold more data than floppy discs. But CD-ROM technology has also ushered in multimedia computing, which gives computer users access to pictures, video, and music as well as text. A student using a multimedia CD-ROM encyclopedia, for example, can look up an entry on a great composer and find not only an article to read but also pictures to look at and a snippet of the composer's music to listen to.

CD-ROM discs look exactly like the familiar audio CD's that have all but replaced vinyl records for the storage and distribution of music. And audio CD's and CD-ROM's work in much the same way. Both discs store information using the *digital* (numerical) code used by computers. Information in any format—words, pictures, or sounds—is encoded on the disc using the binary numeration system. The system comprises only two digits: 1's and 0's. Each digit is called a *bit*.

Combinations of bits represent a single unit of information, such as a letter of the alphabet, the color of a miniscule portion of a photograph, or the tones in a fraction of a second of a musical arrangement. The numerical code for the letter A, for example, is 1000001.

A series of eight bits is called a *byte*. A sentence of text may require 15 bytes of information. Encoding the information in a color photograph could require about 900,000 bytes, depending on the resolution of the image. And a 10-second clip of sound and motion video could require 1.5 million bytes, also depending on the resolution.

The discs that carry all this code are made of a hard plastic coated with metal, usually aluminum. A layer of protective plastic covers the metal, and the binary code is etched in the metal layer on the disc's bottom side.

If you looked at the surface of a CD-ROM with a microscope, you would see millions of tiny indentations known as *pits*. The smooth areas between the pits are called *lans*. The pits represent the 1's of digital code, and the lans represent the 0's.

To "read" a CD-ROM disc, a computer needs a CD-ROM drive or player. A motor in the drive spins the disc as a tiny laser beam shines on the disc's alternately pitted and smooth surface. The speed at which the disc spins varies as the laser moves along the pits and lans, from the center of the disc to the outer edge.

How CD-ROM's store data

CD-ROM technology stores words, sounds, and pictures in the form of digital code, a computer "language" that consists of series of 1's and 0's. The code is etched in a blank CD-ROM disc during the manufacturing process. A CD-ROM player or drive "reads" the code on the disc and transmits the information to the user's computer.

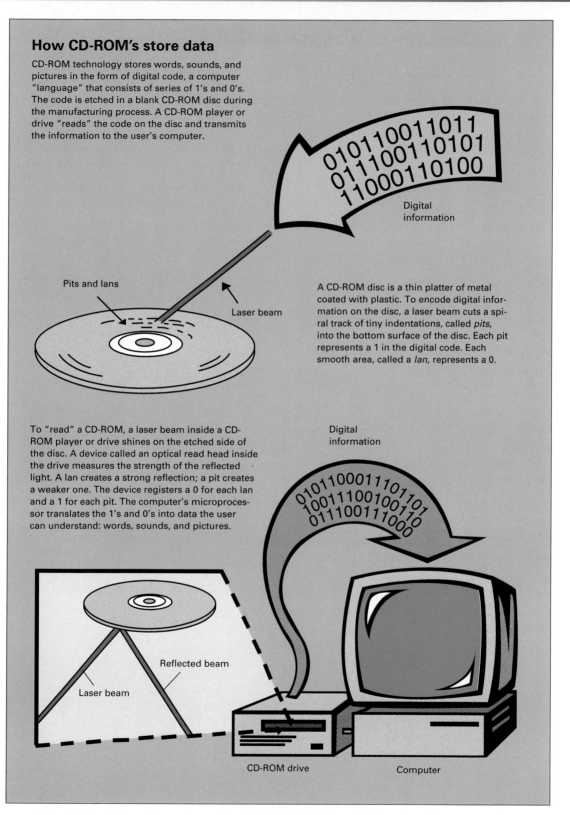

Digital information

Pits and lans

Laser beam

A CD-ROM disc is a thin platter of metal coated with plastic. To encode digital information on the disc, a laser beam cuts a spiral track of tiny indentations, called *pits,* into the bottom surface of the disc. Each pit represents a 1 in the digital code. Each smooth area, called a *lan,* represents a 0.

To "read" a CD-ROM, a laser beam inside a CD-ROM player or drive shines on the etched side of the disc. A device called an optical read head inside the drive measures the strength of the reflected light. A lan creates a strong reflection; a pit creates a weaker one. The device registers a 0 for each lan and a 1 for each pit. The computer's microprocessor translates the 1's and 0's into data the user can understand: words, sounds, and pictures.

Digital information

Reflected beam

Laser beam

CD-ROM drive

Computer

The metal layer of the disc reflects the laser light back to a device called an optical read head inside the drive. The optical read head deciphers patterns in the intensity of the reflected light. A lan's smooth surface delivers a strong reflection, but a pit delivers a weaker one. The optical read head registers a 1 for the weak reflections and a 0 for the strong ones.

The binary code then travels as electronic signals to the computer's microprocessor—the "brains" of the computer. The microprocessor contains millions of tiny transistors, which are electrical switches that either stop an electric current or allow it to flow. A transistor's "on" position corresponds to the 1 of the digital code, and the "off" position corresponds to a 0.

To process the code from the CD-ROM, the microprocessor performs hundreds of thousands, and in some cases millions, of on-off operations per second. When the information is decoded, the result appears on the computer screen in its familiar form—words, numbers, and images.

CD-ROM discs offer an enormous increase in storage capacity over magnetic floppy disks. Typical floppy disks can hold up to one or two *megabytes* (million bytes) of information. A CD-ROM disc, on the other hand, can hold more than 600 megabytes of information. This is the equivalent of 250,000 pages of text.

The more bytes a disc can hold, the more suited it is for video and other media that require large amounts of digital code. A floppy disk, for example, can store several hundred pages of text, but only a few seconds of music, spoken words, or video. A CD-ROM, on the other hand, can store hundreds of times as much information.

CD's cannot hold limitless amounts of data, however. A video CD can store a maximum of 75 minutes of film on a standard disc. A CD-ROM running at double speed can hold 58 minutes of video and audio.

New high-density CD's that carry more digital information than standard discs are expected to be marketed toward the end of 1995. Unfortunately, reading the new high-density discs will require special players or drives.

CD-ROM technology brings other trade-offs. Floppy disks can be used over and over again, with old information erased and new information added in its place. But CD-ROM discs cannot be written to after they are created—which explains why the acronym for *read-only memory* is part of their name. Today's CD-ROM technology is thus seen as primarily a publishing or storage medium.

Research is under way, however, to create CD's that can be erased. One approach to creating recordable discs would be to develop a device that melts the surface of the CD, eliminating the existing pits and lans so that the disc can have new pits etched into it. The

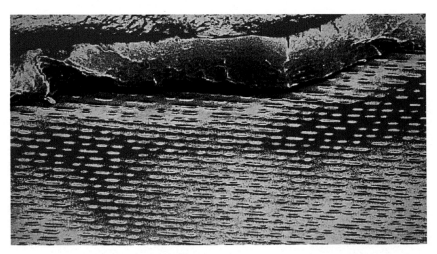

In a photomicrograph of the bottom of a CD-ROM disc, the information storing pits and lans are visible as a pattern of grooves under the protective layer of plastic.

Computer equipment you need to play multimedia CD-ROM's

- An 80486, Pentium, PowerPC, or 80480 microprocessor
- At least four megabytes and preferably eight megabytes of random access memory (RAM)
- A 400-megabyte or larger hard disk
- Double-speed CD-ROM drive
- Sound card
- Speakers
- Color monitor

first erasable CD-ROM drives are expected to be in general use before the end of the century.

Until then, most computer owners will have to be content with using CD-ROM's to read data and using floppies to record it. Indeed, most new computers contain both kinds of drives, giving users the best of both worlds: Information can be accessed on the CD-ROM, and then copied to the floppy disk and in some cases altered.

Industry experts say that owners of older computers who want to get on the CD-ROM bandwagon should consider several factors before buying a separate CD-ROM drive or add-on kit. The most important question is whether their old-

er computer is capable of handling the vast amounts of data on CD-ROM's.

Text-only CD-ROM's can run on less powerful computers, but multimedia CD-ROM's work best on computers with fast processors. For personal computers, that means 80486 chips or their successor, the Pentium processor. Their cousins in Macintosh computers are the 80480 family of processors and the PowerPC chip. All these processors are fast and sophisticated enough to manage the millions of operations required each second by multimedia programs.

The next item to consider is whether the computer contains sufficient random access memory (RAM) to temporarily store the results of the microprocessor's translations and calculations. Many computers designed for multimedia software have four megabytes of RAM, but experts say that eight megabytes are needed to provide smoother operations.

The computer will also need a sizable *hard disk*, a built-in device that stores data magnetically. Many multimedia programs are designed to transfer some of their data from the CD to the hard disk. That speeds up operations, because the computer can access information stored on a hard disk much faster than it can reach data on a CD-ROM. Computer experts recommend a 400-megabyte or larger hard disk for running multimedia CD-ROM's.

The CD-ROM drive itself should be labeled *double speed*. Such drives can find information on a disc more quickly than standard players can. The faster access time is required for most of today's CD-ROM products.

Owners of IBM-type personal computers rather than Macintosh computers also should find out if the CD-ROM drive meets Multimedia PC Council (MPC) standards, the computer industry's own standards for multimedia performance. Drive speed and MPC compatibility typically are identified on the drive's packaging.

The final items a multimedia computer needs are a color monitor, speakers, and a sound card. The sound card is a device that must be placed inside the computer casing, in a slot designed for such additional hardware.

Many CD-ROM add-on kits contain sound cards and speakers as well as the drive itself. Typical CD-ROM upgrade kits cost between $200 and $500, depending upon the capabilities of the drive and sound system.

Installing the kit may be difficult, however. And once the computer casing is open, the delicate components can be easily damaged. For these reasons, computer owners who are unfamiliar with the interior workings of a computer may prefer to have a technician install the add-on kit.

Add-on kits are not necessary for consumers purchasing new home computers. Many computer models on the market today include a built-in double-speed CD-ROM drive, color monitor, hard disk, and sound system. Typical multimedia-ready computers cost between $1,200 and $2,000.

Once the hardware is in place, consumers should be sure that they buy software in a matching format—for example, the MPC standard or the Macintosh CD-ROM. The format for CD-ROM games depends upon the type of machine used to play the game, such as Sega CD and 3DO. The CD-ROM's designed for use on one system will not play on others.

The discs are sold in a variety of places, including software specialty stores, bookstores, and department stores, as well as through mail-order catalogs. Prices for CD-ROM's range from around $25 to more than $300. Most CD-ROM games cost around $50, with multimedia encyclopedia prices somewhat higher.

Many CD-ROM's are for children, but other titles may contain material that is best suited for older or adult audiences. Many CD-ROM's today bear ratings labels identifying the suggested age of their audience and warning that the CD-ROM contains violent or suggestive material.

For consumers who want to try before they buy, some companies offer sampler discs. These discs typically contain only a small portion of a huge product. Sampler discs are available in software stores and often are included as promotional items with CD-ROM related magazines. Some sampler discs are free, while others cost a few dollars.

Consumers can expect to find a growing selection of CD-ROM titles at the corner software store as more and more media companies begin using the new format. In 1995, several motion picture companies were developing CD-ROM titles using famous actors and directors. Many book publishers were busy translating their print works into CD-ROM titles by including animation, video, and author interviews.

Software reviewers encourage consumers to be on the lookout for products created specifically for the new technology, rather than being translated from another medium. These CD-ROM's may combine sound, pictures, and words in satisfying new ways, as their creators attempt to turn multimedia into an art form for the 21st century and beyond.   [Keith Ferrell]

Selecting Athletic Shoes, Scientifically

Is it the shoes that make the athlete a star? Probably not. But a little bit of science and a lot of advertising dollars have elevated yesterday's lowly sneaker into today's pumped up, gel-filled, neon-striped, flash-lit marvels of athletic footwear.

Since the mid-1980's, athletic shoes have become a multibillion-dollar industry. The Athletic Footwear Association estimates that in 1994, Americans spent almost $12 billion on athletic footwear (excluding cleated shoes and hiking boots). Athletic shoes have become such a part of American fashion that many junior high school and high school students wouldn't consider putting their feet into anything else.

Despite the glitzy image, today's athletic shoes aren't all fluff and no stuff. The original purpose of athletic shoes was to protect and support the feet when high levels of stress are placed on them during play. Good athletic shoes are still designed primarily to do two things: prevent injuries and enhance athletic performance.

The workmanship and technology that goes into the best athletic shoes have made many sports safer, faster, and more competitive. True, new world records cannot be attributed only to better shoes. But many experts agree that athletes suffer fewer injuries today than they would if they were wearing the shoes of 20 years ago.

The stress that sports activities put on feet is a result of the laws of physics. Any sport that involves jumping or hopping on the ground puts stress on the feet because gravity pulls the body downward with a force that is proportional to the height of the jump.

The bones of the feet absorb much of the force of the landing—which may be three to five times the body weight. The jarring forces can lead to such injuries as torn ligaments, shin splints, and even broken legs.

To prevent injury, an athletic shoe should incorporate three basic features. First, the shoe should limit the impact

It's in the shoes

Athletic shoes consist of an *outsole,* which provides traction and durability; a *midsole,* which cushions the foot; and an *insole,* which improves fit. Some shoes also contain an additional cushioning layer between the outsole and midsole. The shoe's *upper* is the part that wraps around the foot. Upper features such as stability straps and high tops improve stability and support.

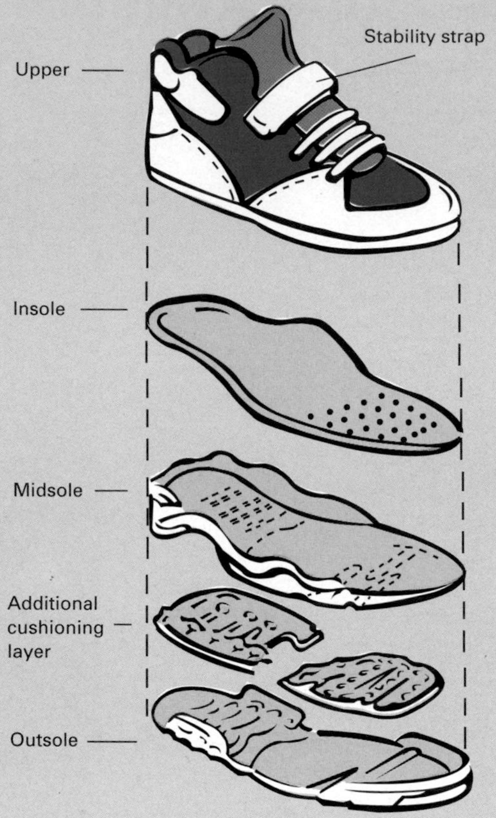

Upper

Stability strap

Insole

Midsole

Additional cushioning layer

Outsole

of the foot striking the ground by slowing the foot—and the rest of the body—as much as possible before it comes to a complete stop. That can be accomplished with firm cushioning for the foot to sink into during landings. Second, the athletic shoe should support the foot, and in some cases the ankle, while the foot is on the ground. Finally, the shoe should help guide the orientation of the foot and keep it stable within the shoe as it moves.

A shoe that does all three of these things may prevent injury, but enhancing performance is another matter. Generally, the lighter a shoe is, the more it improves the wearer's athletic performance.

Unfortunately, a lightweight shoe may not have enough structure and padding to prevent injuries. For example, the lightest basketball shoe can allow a player to jump higher because it's less heavy, but it does not provide

enough support to stand up to the demands of playing the game.

Choosing the shoe that suits not only consumers' needs but also the rigors of their sport has become almost a science in itself. But if sport enthusiasts understand a few basics about shoes, go to a reputable store specializing in athletic footwear, and spend some time trying on a variety of shoes, they should be able to find the right shoe.

First, a few general hints about selecting footwear. Fit is everything. During the jumping and landing motions of many sports, feet elongate and spread, expanding by as much as half a size. For that reason, consumers should never buy tight athletic shoes.

If the shoes feel tight in the store, they likely will squeeze the feet during a workout. Shoe shoppers should make sure there is a space the width of their thumb between the tip of the shoe and

Pros and cons of new coolants

Substitute coolants pose less harm to ozone than CFC's. But the substitutes have other environmental, economic, and safety drawbacks.

Coolant	Advantages	Disadvantages
HFC-134a	▪ Contains no chlorine. ▪ Appears to be harmless to ozone.	▪ For use in auto air conditioners, requires design changes such as less-permeable hoses and more-powerful compressors. ▪ For use in refrigerators and air conditioners, requires new lubricants to avoid plugging narrow tubes. ▪ Contributes to *global warming*, the predicted climate change due to rising levels of heat-trapping gases in the atmosphere.
HCFC-123	▪ Less harmful to ozone than CFC's.	▪ By law, its use must be phased out by 2030.
Blended hydrocarbons	▪ Contains no chlorine. ▪ Appears to be harmless to ozone.	▪ Highly combustible. ▪ Banned in 13 states and Washington, D.C.

ozone layer over much of Antarctica each year. Researchers since have found smaller holes in the ozone layer in the Arctic during the winter months.

Most atmospheric scientists attribute the gaps to the increasing concentrations of CFC's they observe in the upper atmosphere. By 1987, most of the world's industrialized nations had signed the agreement, known as the Montreal Protocol, requiring a complete halt to CFC production after 1995.

The CFC ban has caused appliance manufacturers to switch to refrigerants that are less harmful to the ozone layer. But while they may be kinder to ozone, many of the CFC substitutes have environmental, economic, and safety drawbacks of their own.

For example, appliance manufacturers have replaced a CFC refrigerant known as CFC-12, which was widely used in home refrigerators and automobile air conditioners, with a hydrofluorocarbon (HFC) compound called HFC-134a. HFC-134a molecules contain atoms of carbon, hydrogen, and fluorine but lack the chlorine that has been blamed for ozone destruction. As a result, scientists believe HFC-134a is harmless to ozone.

But replacing the CFC-12 refrigerants with HFC-134a requires some modifications in cooling equipment. Because HFC-134a molecules are smaller than CFC-12 molecules and require higher operating pressures for efficient cooling, they are more apt to leak from the hoses in auto air conditioners designed for CFC's. Therefore, changing to HFC-134a requires a switch to less permeable hose materials.

Also, more powerful compressors must be used in HFC-134a cooling systems to achieve the needed higher operating pressures. This means that an appliance must be redesigned before switching to HFC-134a. Finally, HFC-134a tends to react with lubricants designed for CFC-12 systems, causing gummy deposits to plug the narrow tubes within appliances. Therefore, a switch to HFC-134a also requires a change in lubricant formulations.

Another drawback of HFC-134a and other HFC's is that they are greenhouse gases. In the atmosphere, greenhouse gases help keep Earth warm enough to support life by trapping solar heat as it radiates back from the surface of the Earth. Greenhouse gases such as methane, water vapor, and carbon dioxide occur naturally, but human activity has increased their concentrations.

Many scientists fear that increasing amounts of greenhouse gases are leading to a rise in Earth's average surface temperature. This scenario, called *global warming*, could shift weather patterns to produce drought, move prime farmland farther north, and melt some polar ice, flooding coastal regions. As a result of these concerns, the EPA has said it may consider future restrictions on some applications of HFC's.

Meanwhile, manufacturers are replacing the CFC refrigerants traditionally used in air conditioning systems for large office buildings and factories with HCFC-123, a hydrochlorofluorocarbon (HCFC). Like CFC's, HCFC's are made up of carbon, hydrogen, chlorine, and fluorine atoms. But they are far more resistant to decomposition in the atmosphere and therefore release fewer ozone-destroying chlorine atoms.

Because HCFC's still deplete ozone, the Montreal Protocol requires that they be phased out gradually over the next 35 years. In the United States, the EPA will permit production of HCFC-123 refrigerants until the year 2030.

More friendly to ozone are other non-CFC refrigerants consisting of blends of hydrocarbons (compounds containing only carbon and hydrogen). Because hydrocarbons contain no chlorine, they pose no threat to ozone when they drift into the upper atmosphere. Several firms in Germany have built small refrigerators and freezers that use hydrocarbon refrigerants. In the United States, blends of the hydrocarbons butane and propane are sold in some states as refrigerants for auto air conditioners.

A great drawback to hydrocarbon refrigerants is the ease with which they combust. Because of the risk of fires and explosions, legislators have banned hydrocarbon refrigerants in Arkansas, Connecticut, Idaho, Indiana, Kansas, Louisiana, Maryland, North Dakota, Oklahoma, Texas, Utah, Virginia, Washington state, and Washington, D.C.

New household air conditioners typically employ an HCFC refrigerant known as HCFC-22. But this agent is less stable in the atmosphere than its chemical relative HCFC-123 and therefore is more harmful to ozone. As a result, the EPA plans to limit HCFC-22 production by the year 2010.

One innovative technology that requires no chemical refrigerants is thermoacoustic refrigeration, which uses high-intensity sound waves to produce cooling. A thermoacoustic refrigerator being developed in 1995 by Steven L. Garrett and his colleagues at the Naval Postgraduate School in Monterey, Calif., directs the sound waves from a loudspeaker into a U-shaped tube filled with pressurized helium and xenon gas.

The sound waves cause the gas in the tube to compress and expand in regular cycles. Each time the gas expands, it cools slightly. Each time the gas is compressed, it heats up again, but the heat is drawn away by a heat-absorbing material inside the tube. Repeated cycles of compression, expansion, and heat loss lower the temperature of the gas, and the tube becomes cold enough to chill the contents of a small refrigerator.

Long before consumers ever see a thermoacoustic refrigerator, however, they will have to deal with the impact of the new chemical refrigerants. In the case of home refrigerators designed to work with the new HFC refrigerants, consumers will probably see little change in price, performance, or operating cost compared with older models.

If you own a CFC refrigerator—the coolant information should be listed on the back of the appliance—the best policy is to let it live out its lifetime, discard it properly, and then replace it with one of the newer HFC models.

New auto air conditioners designed to use HFC refrigerants should cost little more than older units that use CFC's. But problems will arise for drivers of the roughly 140 million cars on U.S. roads that use CFC-based air conditioning systems. With CFC refrigerants soon to be unavailable and CFC-based systems unable to use HFC's without modifications, drivers who need their air conditioners recharged will face unpleasant options: They can have their air conditioners converted to work with HFC's, at a cost of $200 to $800; they can do without air conditioning; or they can buy a new car equipped with the HFC system.

Engineers advise against using non-CFC refrigerants advertised as compatible with CFC-based air conditioners. Such formulations, experts say, may damage a car's air conditioner. To provide cooling, non-CFC refrigerants require greater compression than CFC's. A CFC-based air conditioner probably could not provide such compression, and could fail if non-CFC's are used.

The switch to new refrigerants is an easier way to make refrigeration less of an environmental burden. The next—and harder—steps will be to make refrigerators and air conditioners more energy efficient and to learn to recycle their components.   [Gordon Graff]

The Chemistry of Cosmetics

Few people would whip out a chemistry set, uncork the vials, and slap the compounds on their face. Yet, millions of women and girls essentially do that every day when they unzip their makeup bags and apply lipstick, mascara, and other makeup. Like the compounds in a chemistry set, makeup consists of chemicals. Although the chemicals in cosmetic products are intended to improve the appearance of skin, lips, and lashes, some can cause adverse effects.

Brushing up on makeup chemistry isn't hard: If you can read a label, you are halfway there. The U.S. Food and Drug Administration (FDA) requires cosmetics manufacturers to put labels on makeup listing ingredients in descending order of weight. Ingredients that make up less than 1 percent of the makeup item, such as fragrance or colorants, are listed after other ingredients, not in descending order of weight.

The payoff from even a little bit of learning can be big. A savvy makeup user reduces her chances of developing rashes, eye infections, acne, and other health problems linked to cosmetics. She also is less likely to waste money on expensive cosmetics with formulas similar to those of less costly brands.

The first lesson in cosmetic chemistry is that most makeup ingredients are intended to give the product its color and consistency. A few basic classes of ingredients—coloring agents, bases, bulking agents, sunscreens, and additives—are common to many kinds of makeup.

Coloring agents. Color is probably what first comes to mind when you think of makeup—ruby lips, dusky eyelids, and rosy cheeks. To produce the rainbow of shades on today's makeup racks, chemists derive dyes and pigments from a variety of compounds that may sound more like they belong in a miner's cart than on a beauty queen's brow.

Coal tar, chromium oxide, aluminum powder, manganese, iron oxide, and mica flakes are just a few examples of mineral ingredients used to add color to our faces. Other pigments and dyes, such as beet powder, come from plants. Those derived from animals include carmine, a crimson pigment made from the ground-up, dried bodies of a cacti-eating bug called the cochineal insect.

By far the most common coloring agents in makeup are the coal tar colors. Coal tar is a sticky, black liquid produced by heating a kind of coal, called bituminous coal, in large ovens from which air is absent. Coal tar colors are formed from ring-shaped carbon- and hydrogen-containing compounds called *aromatic hydrocarbons*, which are purified from coal tar.

Coal tar colors are the only makeup ingredients the FDA requires to undergo safety testing for every product batch. That is because many of the compounds have been shown to cause cancer when they are injected into the skin of mice.

As a result of lawsuits filed over safety concerns, some coal tar colors are banned, some are approved for external uses only, and some are approved for external and internal uses. Once the compounds pass safety tests, they are given one of two designations. The term *FD&C* (Food, Drugs & Cosmetics), means that the color is safe for in-

Decoding a makeup label

A close reading of a makeup label can tell a chemistry-savvy shopper exactly what's in the product and give her clues to any side effects.

The term **noncomedogenic** means that the product—in this case, a blush—does not cause pimples by blocking pores. **Hypoallergenic** means it is less likely than other products to cause allergic reactions. The phrase **dermatologist tested**, on the other hand, is meaningless, since the label doesn't say whether the product passed—or failed—the physician's test.

Bulking agents allow the blush to go on smoothly. They include **talc,** which absorbs moisture and prevents caking. Prolonged inhalation can cause lung problems, however. **Oat flour** and **kaolin,** or china clay, improve covering and absorb oil.

Several terms describe bases, which hold the product together and help it cling to the skin. The bases in this blush include **isoarachidyl neopentanoate, mineral oil,** and **zinc stearate.** If the latter is inhaled, it may cause lung problems. **Acrylates copolymer** is a thickening agent that can be a strong irritant.

Noncomedogenic • Hypoallergenic • Dermatologist tested

Ingredients: Talc, oat flour, mineral oil, zinc stearate, isoarachidyl neopentanoate, kaolin, acrylates copolymer, lysine, methylparaben, imidazolidinyl urea, propylparaben, iron oxides, D&C red no. 6 barium lake, mica, bismuth oxychloride.

Additives include preservatives, such as **methylparaben**, which in rare cases can cause allergic reactions; **imidazolidinyl urea**, which can cause dermatitis, and **propylparaben**, which in rare cases also can cause dermatitis. A further additive is **lysine**, an essential amino acid used to boost the blush's protein quality. Manufacturers commonly claim that products containing protein benefit the skin.

Coloring agents include **mica**, which can cause irritation if inhaled; **bismuth oxychloride**, which may cause allergic reactions; and **iron oxides,** which are made from a combination of iron and oxygen. **D&C red no. 6 barium lake** is safe only for external use—it should never be applied near the eyes or lips, where it can be absorbed by the body. It is a lake colorant, meaning it does not dissolve in water. The colorant is made from coal tar and the element barium, which can irritate skin.

---

ternal and external use. The term *D&C* or *Ext. D&C* means the compound is safe only for external use. Safety studies have found internal use of *D&C* colors can cause cancer in animals and, in at least one instance, have caused blindness in humans. Coloring agents designated *D&C* or *Ext. D&C* should never be applied where they can be absorbed, such as near the eyes and on the lips.

Girls and women who spread face foundation on their lips or eyelids before applying lipstick or eye shadow should pay close attention to labeling information. In addition, coal tar dyes occasionally trigger allergic or irritant reactions such as rashes or inflammation, with yellow and red hues posing the most problems.

Bases. Developing alluring colors is not the only challenge facing makeup chemists. Another task is finding ways to

make those colors stick to the female face for several hours and through tears, perspiration, drinking, eating, and even kissing. Enter makeup's second major ingredient class: bases.

Almost every type of makeup—from blush to eyeliner—requires some sort of oily or waxy mixture, which makeup manufacturers call a base, to hold the colors together in a cake or tube and help those colors cling to the face. (In this case, *base* is a manufacturing term, not the chemical term for a substance that can react with an acid to decrease or neutralize acidity.)

The type of base used depends on where the product is supposed to be applied. For example, in lipsticks, about half the weight of the product is accounted for by a thick, insoluble mixture of waxes and castor bean oil that will not dissolve when a woman licks her lips or drinks a beverage. A lipstick base must balance the properties of the oil ingredients with those of wax. The oil in the lipstick makes it *viscous* (thick and sticky), so that the color clings to the lips. The waxes are *thixotropic* (becoming fluid only when stirred), so that the lipstick retains its shape and doesn't smear or melt in heat.

Other key ingredients of a lipstick base are slippery chemical compounds called esters, which are formed by reactions between alcohols and acids. Esters are added to make a lipstick shine and make the rather dry oil-and-wax mixture glide onto lips more smoothly.

Like lipstick, mascara relies on relatively heavy bases, such as paraffin and carnauba palm wax, not only to keep lash-darkening pigments stuck to the eyelashes through water and tears, but also to thicken and separate the lashes. On the other hand, eye shadow, blush, and other powdery products are bound together by lighter bases, often mineral oil, because they aren't constantly under assault by makeup-dissolving liquids.

Most of the bases used in face foundations are composed of water and mineral oil. Because water and oil do not dissolve in one another, any mixture of the two is an *emulsion*, in which tiny drops of one liquid are suspended in the second liquid. To help keep them mixed, emulsifying agents such as sodium stearate are added to form a creamy mixture.

Additional ingredients that fall into the base category include isopropyl lanolate, also referred to as wool alcohol; myristyl lactate; and octyl hydroxystearate. These are oillike, nontoxic compounds called fatty esters.

Bases cause relatively few allergic reactions. Lanolin products (which are derived from sheep's wool) or beeswax are the most likely to do so. However, the oils and waxes in makeup can aggravate a medical condition that frequently afflicts teen-agers and young women—acne. The greasy compounds promote the development of whiteheads, blackheads, and pimples because they clog skin pores. Acne-prone women should choose water-based or oil-free cosmetics.

Bulking agents. A third class of ingredients, bulking agents, play an important role in products requiring even coverage, such as face powder and eye shadow. One of the most common bulking agents is talc or French chalk, a powder made from the mineral magnesium silicate. Talc has long been used in makeup because it absorbs perspiration and has a smooth, slippery texture that makes cosmetics easier to apply.

Women should never inhale deeply when applying products containing talc, such as face powders, eye shadows, and powder blush. Repeated inhalation of talc can cause lung problems, according to medical researchers.

Recently, more-exotic bulking agents have been added to makeup, including silk powder in eye shadow, and nylon and silk fibers in mascara. Dermatologists warn makeup users to be careful when selecting products with those glamorous-sounding ingredients: Silk powder can trigger severe allergic reactions, and fiber-containing mascaras may irritate sensitive eyes.

Sunscreens. Relative newcomers to the ranks of makeup ingredients are sunscreens, which filter out most of the sun's burning rays. In the late 1970's and early 1980's, many makeup manufacturers added sunscreens to their products in response to consumer concerns about skin cancer and other skin-damaging effects of excessive sun.

Compounds that screen out harmful ultraviolet B light include para-aminobenzoic acid (PABA) and its derivatives, as well as benzophenones such as oxybenzone and dioxybenzone. However, both PABA and the benzophenones are common causes of allergic reactions.

Additives. The final class of makeup ingredients, additives, accounts for the lion's share of allergic and irritant reactions. Additives include fragrances and preservatives.

Fragrances are added to makeup to add a pleasing scent and hide the unappealing odor of some waxes, oils, and other makeup components. But the sweet scent comes at a price. A five-year study of 13,216 people conducted by a group of physicians formed by the American Academy of Dermatology found that more than one-third of allergic reactions to cosmetics were triggered by fragrance additives.

Increased public awareness of the allergy-causing potential of fragrance additives, along with a consumer move toward lighter scents, prompted manufacturers to develop alternative products. Products labeled *fragrance-free* contain no fragrance. Those labeled *unscented* carry no noticeable scent but still contain enough fragrance additives to mask the smells of other ingredients.

Preservatives that kill microbes are the second major type of additive in makeup. Many bacteria and other microorganisms reproduce rapidly in moist, warm solutions. Without preservatives, mascara, foundation, and other makeup may become an ideal culture medium for harmful microbes.

Manufacturers add a variety of chemicals known to kill microorganisms or stunt their growth. The most common preservatives in makeup are the parabens. The paraben family, which includes butylparaben, ethylparaben, and methylparaben, are rarely allergenic. But preservatives called quarternium-I5, formaldehyde, and sorbic acid are the source of many allergic reactions.

A separate class of chemical preservatives called antioxidants, which are listed on product labels as butylated hydroxyamisole (BHA) and butylated hydroxytoluene (BHT), are added to prevent ingredients from combining with oxygen, a process called oxidation that can ruin makeup's color or texture.

So, what's a girl to do after she's learned about the ingredients that go into her makeup? Why, head for the store! It's there that you can really put your knowledge of makeup chemistry to the test, tailoring your makeup needs to your skin type and budget.

First, let's consider price. Do buyers really get what they pay for? According to experts from the FDA and the Cosmetic, Toiletry, and Fragrance Association, the answer lies in what a customer wants. If you demand stylish packaging, the latest rage in colors, and personal assistance, the more expensive products sold in department stores might be a good choice. But if price and performance are your main concerns, experts say you can find many relatively inexpensive makeup products at drug or discount stores with formulas nearly identical to those of more costly brands.

When comparison shopping, remember to check the label to find out how much the product weighs. Products with cheaper price tags often weigh much less than more costly items, even though they appear to be the same size.

Shoppers with an environmental bent should be aware that when it comes to makeup packaging, the words *natural* and *not tested on animals* may not mean all that they imply. Because the FDA puts no limits on what the term "natural" may describe, makeup products described as "natural" are allowed to contain preservatives. Also, dermatologists say that the allergy risk posed by natural makeup may be greater than that from other products, in part because natural plant and animal extracts inherently may contain more impurities than their synthetic counterparts.

Animal testing is another area in which makeup manufacturers often stretch the truth. Just because a makeup item is labeled *not tested on animals* doesn't mean its ingredients haven't undergone animal testing for products previously put out by the manufacturer or undergone recent animal testing in products made by other manufacturers.

Finally, women and girls with special makeup needs should get into the habit of closely reading labels, not only for ingredients but for descriptions. Oily, acne-prone skin is the most common makeup challenge facing more than three-quarters of teen-agers and young women. If you have such skin, choose products that are labeled *noncomedogenic,* meaning they don't promote the formation of whitehead or blackhead pimples, or *nonacnegenic,* meaning they don't contribute to the formation of any kind of pimple. Select products labeled *oil-free,* but check the label to see if the product contains other greasy substances such as lanolin, carnauba, petrolatum, or emollient esters.

Although experts agree that acne outbreaks should be treated with medications rather than makeup, some skin foundations try to prevent further flare-ups with such ingredients as salicylic acid, which fights microbes, and benzoyl peroxide, which acts as a drying agent. Both of these agents are inherently drying to the skin, but a large number of people are allergic to benzoyl peroxide.

Dry skin is often a problem of older women, but it may also trouble younger African-American women. Ingredients to avoid include simple alcohols such as ethanol, methanol, and isopropyl, which dry the skin. It's also a bad idea to use foundations or cover sticks that have added powder, which is a drying agent.

Fatty alcohols, such as cetearyl and stearyl, actually help moisturize dry skin. Other desirable ingredients include lactic acid, glycolic acid, and urea. Although these nonoily compounds, called *humectants,* do not add moisture to the skin, they cover it with a protective film that prevents water already present in the skin from evaporating.

Sensitive skin and allergic reactions affect people of all ages, and many makeup products are targeted at this group. Such products are marked *hypoallergenic,* meaning they are less likely to cause allergies than regular products. Hypoallergenic products usually lack fragrances, preservatives, and other common causes of irritation and allergic reactions. However, women should remember that the products are not 100 percent allergy-proof, and most contain ingredients that trigger some allergic reactions.

The terms *allergy tested, sensitivity tested,* and *dermatologist tested* on makeup labels are of little practical importance, because the label doesn't say whether the product *passed* the test. If you are allergy prone or have sensitive skin, it may be a good idea to test new makeup on your arm for several days before putting it on your face.

Contact-lens wearers should take special care in selecting and using mascara, eye shadow, and other eye makeup. Products to avoid include mascara that contains silk or nylon fibers, as well as water-based mascara that easily flakes and falls into the eye. Frosted eye shadow may be a bad idea because the iridescent particles may fall into your eye and stick to the contact lens, possibly scratching the eye's own lens, the cornea. To reduce the risk of bacterial infection and contaminating particles, wash your hands and put in your contacts before applying eye makeup.

Whatever type of skin you have or line of makeup you prefer, makeup experts offer three basic safety warnings. First, never apply mascara in a car or other moving vehicle. The most common injury linked to makeup is scratching the eye with a mascara wand. It's not the scratch itself that poses the health hazard, but the sight-threatening infections that can occur if the scratch is not promptly treated.

Second, never use makeup that appears spoiled. If a product has a strange consistency, smells bad, or has changed colors, it may be contaminated with microbes that could cause serious infections. Do not attempt to add water or saliva to makeup that has dried out, because you will add potentially harmful microbes along with that liquid. When not in use, makeup containers should be kept tightly closed and out of sunlight, which can destroy preservatives.

Third, never share makeup. Passing makeup between people also passes microbes back and forth. A similar problem arises with the sharing of testers at cosmetics counters. A 1989 FDA survey found more than 5 percent of counter makeup samples were seriously contaminated with bacteria, mold, and other microbes. Always test lipstick on the back of your hand and ask for a new applicator or cotton swab to test other types of products.

By now, makeup may seem to be the last thing anyone would want to put on her face. Actually, adverse reactions to cosmetics are few and far between. The American Academy of Dermatology estimates there are only about 200 adverse reactions for every million applications.

Those are pretty good odds, but it's never a good idea to gamble with your face. So before you start experimenting with new makeup, take a few minutes to remember your chemistry.

[Rebecca Kolberg]

Windows to Keep Comfort High, Energy Use Low

Windows are among the most complex and elegant features of building design. They filter light, heat, air, and sound into and out of buildings, providing a sense of openness and communication with the outdoors. Windows also determine much of a particular building's energy requirements.

For several hundred years, window construction remained fairly simple. Improvements in glass production allowed architects and engineers to increase the size and number of windows in buildings. Yet until the 1970's, the same basic material was used to separate the indoors from the elements outside: a single pane of clear glass. As such, windows were often the weak link in an otherwise well-insulated and airtight building.

During the mid- to late-1970's, the cost of energy rose sharply as the Organization of Petroleum Exporting Countries (OPEC) raised the price of a barrel of crude oil from $2.75 in 1973 to a peak of $34 in 1981. The resulting energy price shocks forced consumers, builders, and window manufacturers to look again at windows and their energy costs. Researchers at the Lawrence Berkeley Laboratory calculated in 1990 that the amount of energy lost through windows in U.S. buildings every year is equivalent to the total energy content of the oil transported annually through the Alaska oil pipeline.

In addition to the dollar value of energy lost through inefficient windows, energy use for heating and cooling causes air pollution, which includes the emission of carbon dioxide. Scientists predict that an increase in the level of carbon dioxide in the atmosphere may cause *global warming*, a rise in Earth's average surface temperature.

In response to the energy crunch, some states changed residential building codes to restrict the size of windows built in new houses. Window manufacturers and engineers also began to look for ways to improve window efficiency.

The resulting advances have improved the energy efficiency of new windows so much that some of today's models are better insulators against heat loss than are the surrounding insulated walls. Invisible coatings allow sunlight to enter the home in winter but prevent warmth from escaping. Certain gases sealed between glass layers in a double-paned or triple-paned window sharply improve its insulation value.

To fully appreciate the technical advances since the early 1980's, it is necessary to understand the ways that energy flows through windows. Windows transfer heat by three mechanisms: conduction, convection, and radiation.

Conduction is the transfer of heat through a substance. For example, heat is conducted from the warm side of a window pane to the cooler side as each glass molecule gains energy and starts to vibrate faster. The molecule jostles neighboring glass molecules, passing the heat energy along. In general, metals conduct heat quite easily, while wood and other less-dense solids conduct heat less readily.

Conduction occurs not only through solid materials, such as window glass and frames, but also through air space. The air molecules between a window and a storm window, for example,

An infrared photograph shows heat loss through a house. The greatest amount of heat loss (red and yellow areas) occurs through windows and walls.

transfer heat by colliding with their neighbors. Some gases, such as the so-called "noble gases" are especially poor heat conductors. Noble gases include argon and krypton.

Convection is the movement of heat carried in a *fluid* (liquid or gas), such as air. Convection is responsible for the adage, "warm air rises."

When a warm part of a window heats the air next to it, the air rises. The warm air then heats the cold glass. As the air gives up its heat to the glass, it falls back down. This cyclical movement of air creates a *convection current*. Convection currents can occur on both the inside and outside of a window and between any layers of glass.

Infiltration is a type of convection that occurs when air currents pass through cracks and gaps around window frames. Because of infiltration, leaky windows can allow cold air to flow into a house and warm air to flow out. Infiltration is driven by wind, by differences in air pressure between the inside of a house and the outside, and by convection currents inside a building as warm air rises to higher floors.

Radiation describes the flow of energy through empty space. The most obvious example of radiation is the movement of sunlight—also called solar radiation—from the sun toward the Earth. When solar radiation pours through a window, energy in the form of visible light brightens the room. Solar energy also carries heat in the form of invisible infrared radiation.

All objects give off infrared radiation, but hot objects give off more energetic radiation than cooler objects. Infrared rays emitted by the sun have enough energy to pass through the glass pane of a window. The glass itself then becomes hotter and radiates more heat of its own, both inward and outward.

As the objects inside the room heat up, they too begin to give off more infrared radiation. But that radiation is less energetic than the rays from the sun, and so some cannot pass through the glass. As a result, the room warms up. Greenhouses and other passive solar heating systems take advantage of this one-way flow of heat radiation through glass windows and skylights.

Since the early 1970's, window manufacturers have combated heat loss mainly by adding layers of *glazing* (glass) to their windows. A double-glazed window, which consists of two panes of glass separated by an air space, insulates twice as well as single glazing. (A storm window is a simple kind of double glazing.) When concern over energy use rose during the 1970's, triple-glazed and even quadruple-glazed windows entered the market.

With double-glazed windows, the characteristics of the air space between the panes of glass has a big effect on energy performance. A very thin air space

Heat flow through a window

Heat flows in and out of a house through windows via three different mechanisms: conduction, convection, and radiation.

Conduction is the transfer of heat through a substance. In a window, heat moves from the warm side of a metal window frame to the cooler side as each molecule in the frame gains energy, vibrates faster, and jostles neighboring molecules. Heat is conducted easily through metal and window glass but moves less readily through wood or plastic window frames and the air space between panes of glass.

Radiation is the flow of energy through empty space. During daylight hours, infrared radiation from the sun streams through the window along with sunlight. Objects inside the room also radiate heat, and some of it passes out through the window.

Convection is the movement of heat in currents. Around a window, such currents are caused by warmed air rising and cooler air falling. Convection currents can form on the inside and outside of a window and between panes of glass. Convection currents that wick air through cracks around a window frame are called infiltration.

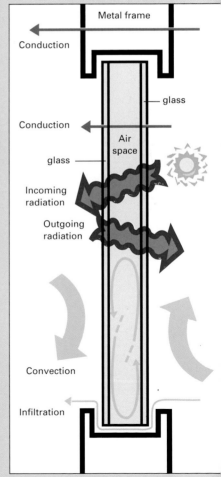

Options for energy-efficient windows

New windows come in several configurations, offering different levels of energy savings.

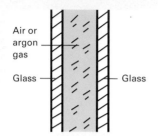

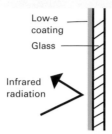

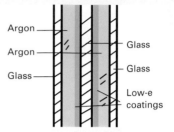

A double-glazed window consists of two panes of glass separated by an air space. This type of window insulates twice as well as a single-glazed window, because air conducts heat less well than glass. For more energy efficiency, the window may be filled with argon or another gas that conducts heat less well than air does.

A low-e coating on a window reduces heat loss by reflecting radiation rather than allowing it to pass through the window. For northern climates, the low-e coating is designed to reflect heat back into the room. For hotter climates, the coating keeps solar radiation out.

A state-of-the-art superwindow lessens heat loss by combining technologies. Such windows may contain three panes of glass with two low-e coatings. The spaces between the panes may be filled with argon gas.

---

insulates less well than a thicker air space, because heat can be quickly conducted across that small distance. An air space that is too wide, however, allows convection currents to develop between the panes of glazing. No further energy efficiency is gained when air spaces are wider than about an 2.5 cm (1 inch).

In a sealed double-pane window, heat loss through conduction is significantly reduced when the space between the panes is filled not with air but with a gas that conducts heat less well than air does. Noble gases are most commonly used for this purpose.

Argon is the noble gas used most often, though some windows contain krypton and argon-krypton mixtures. Non-noble gases used in double-glazed windows include carbon dioxide and sulfur hexafluoride.

A more important advance in window design was the development of low-emissivity (low-e) coatings in the 1980's. Low-e coatings are thin, transparent layers of silver or tin oxide that selectively reflect infrared radiation.

A variety of low-e windows are available for different climate zones and different applications. Some reduce winter heat loss by keeping more infrared radiation inside. Others keep solar heat out

to lower summertime cooling costs.

A window's solar heat gain coefficient (SHGC) measures the amount of solar energy that enters a room through the window. An SHGC of 0.8 means that 80 percent of the solar energy hitting a glazing enters the room. Typical values range from 0.4 to 0.9. Windows with a high SHGC are appropriate for northern climates. Windows with a low SHGC are appropriate in warmer climates.

The U-value of a low-e window is the rate of heat transfer through the window. The U-value is the inverse of R-value, which is familiar to many people as an indicator of how well a material insulates. That means that an R-value of 3.3 (or $\frac{3.3}{1}$) is the same thing as a U-value of 0.30 (or $\frac{1}{3.3}$). With wall insulation, the higher the R-value, the better the insulation. For a window, the lower the U-value, the better the insulation.

Different low-e glazings can be used on sides of a house with different exposures. To benefit from passive solar heating, in which the low winter sun is used to heat the house, homeowners can buy south-facing windows that contain a top-performing low-e glass with a high SHGC. For the north side, homeowners may prefer to install the lowest U-value windows they can afford.

Reading window labels

To help consumers compare window energy efficiency, new windows bear labels administered by the independent National Fenestration Rating Council (NFRC). The labels display the heat loss rating, called the *U-value*, of a particular model in two sizes. The U-values indicate the rate of heat loss through the entire window—including the glass, window frame, and the edges around it. NFRC labels also list the amount of air that leaks in through the closed window and the amount of solar heat that radiates through it.

U-values for the same window model in two different sizes. The lower the U-factor, the better the window holds in heat.

Name of the window manufacturer

The solar heat gain coefficient (SHGC) measures the amount of solar energy that enters the room through the window. The higher the SHGC value, the more solar energy passes into the room.

The model, style, and glazing of the window being evaluated

Air leakage is measured in cubic feet of air transferred per minute per linear foot of crack. The higher the value, the leakier the window.

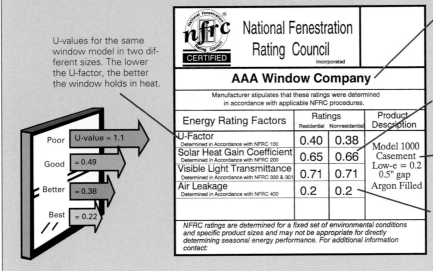

National Fenestration Rating Council Incorporated
CERTIFIED

AAA Window Company

Manufacturer stipulates that these ratings were determined in accordance with applicable NFRC procedures.

Energy Rating Factors	Ratings Residential	Nonresidential	Product Description
U-Factor Determined in Accordance with NFRC 100	0.40	0.38	Model 1000 Casement Low-e = 0.2 0.5" gap Argon Filled
Solar Heat Gain Coefficient Determined in Accordance with NFRC 200	0.65	0.66	
Visible Light Transmittance Determined in Accordance with NFRC 300 & 301	0.71	0.71	
Air Leakage Determined in Accordance with NFRC 400	0.2	0.2	

NFRC ratings are determined for a fixed set of environmental conditions and specific product sizes and may not be appropriate for directly determining seasonal energy performance. For additional information contact:

Poor — U-value = 1.1
Good — = 0.49
Better — = 0.38
Best — = 0.22

Low-e window film can also be purchased and applied to existing windows. However, the appearance of the window after the film is applied will vary with the quality of the installation.

It's important to know that the energy efficiency of a window depends on more than the kind of glazing it uses. Materials used in other parts of the window, the window's leakiness, and the window's dimensions affect efficiency.

As more energy-efficient glazings were developed, proportionately more heat was lost through the edge spacers and window frames. An edge spacer holds the panes of glass apart and provides the airtight seal in a double-pane or triple-pane window.

Edge spacers were traditionally made of aluminum. Because aluminum conducts heat easily, more energy-efficient edge spacers are made of silicone rubber or butyl rubber. In windows that contain spacers made of aluminum or thin-walled steel, the spacers usually include a strip of nonmetal material, often rubber, to act as a "thermal break" that reduces conductivity.

Wood, still the most common material used for window frames, insulates against heat loss reasonably well. Some vinyl frames insulated with fiberglass insulate better than wood.

The leakiness of windows affects a room's comfort as well as energy use, as tight windows block cold drafts and the transmission of sounds from outside. Windows vary dramatically in air leakage, usually is measured in cubic feet of air transferred per minute per linear foot of crack (cfm/ft). The tightest windows have air leak rates as low as 0.01 cfm/ft, though the industry standard is a much higher 0.37 cfm/ft. Most of the more-efficient windows leak at rates in the range of 0.01 to 0.06 cfm/ft.

The dimensions of highly efficient windows have a big impact on their total energy performance, because the glazing generally insulates better than the edge of the window. For this reason, one big window is more energy efficient than several small ones.

When buying a window, how can you make sure it's energy efficient? Before 1993, manufacturers were inconsistent in describing the energy efficiency of their windows. Those who considered only the energy performance of the glazing at the center of the glass advertised a very high insulating value. Manufacturers who factored in the energy performance of the window edges would give the same window a significantly lower insulating value. Different manufacturers used different methods to calculate energy efficiency, further complicating comparisons.

To lessen confusion, a nationwide window labeling program began in 1993, administered by the independent National Fenestration Rating Council (NFRC). The NFRC is a nonprofit collaboration of window manufacturers, building trade associations, government agencies, and consumer groups.

Windows rated by NFRC-approved testing laboratories and certified by independent inspection agencies carry labels with U-value ratings. The value measures the amount of heat that moves through a square foot of window in an hour for every degree Fahrenheit difference in temperature across the window. The U-value ratings listed on NFRC labels are whole-window values. That is, they take into account heat loss through the glass, window edge, and window frame.

After heat loss, the most important energy property of window glazings is the amount of solar heat they let in, which is measured by the SHGC. This value will be listed on NFRC window certification labels in late 1995. Windows with high SHGC's (above 0.70) are designed for colder climates, while windows with low factors are designed for hotter climates.

Air leakage is already listed by many window manufacturers in terms of cubic feet of air per minute per foot of crack. This factor will be included on NFRC labels beginning in 1995.

The window style also affects how airtight it is. In general, casement or awning windows are tighter than double-hung windows and others with panes that slide past each other.

A casement or awning window—which is hinged to the sash or window frame and opens inward or outward like a door—is more tight when closed, because it is pulled in against a gasket called a compression seal designed to prevent air leakage. Sliding windows use seals that permit one or both sashes to slide, so they are rarely as airtight.

Energy efficient windows are widely available and are often only slightly more expensive than traditional double-pane windows. Argon gas-fill adds only about 5 percent to the cost of a double-glazed window. Low-e coatings may increase the cost of a window by 10 percent to 20 percent. At least one major manufacturer now includes low-e coatings on all the products it makes.

The energy cost of single-pane windows in an oil-heated or gas-heated home in a northern climate is $0.75 to $1 per square foot of window per year. Windows on the market today can reduce those energy costs by 50 percent or more. The savings are greatest if the building takes advantage of passive solar heating in winter, for example, with several south-facing windows.

The energy savings alone are rarely sufficient to offset the cost of buying all new windows, however. But if windows are to be replaced anyway, for example, as part of a remodeling project, it makes financial sense to spend the additional 10 percent to 25 percent to get efficient windows with low-e glazings and gas-fill.

Improvements in window efficiency have enabled architects in the 1990's to design new homes filled with light, a far cry from the dark homes with smaller windows built in northern climates during the 1970's. Ongoing research may give architects even more options. For example, researchers at two U.S. Department of Energy laboratories, Lawrence Berkeley Laboratory in Berkeley, Calif., and the National Renewable Energy Laboratory in Golden, Colo., are developing electrochromic windows. These windows allow different degrees of light and heat to be transmitted, depending on the outdoor conditions and level of sunlight desired indoors. Such "smart" glazings may one day turn us all into people who live in glass houses.

[John Morrill]

World Book

Supplement

Three new or revised articles reprinted
from the 1995 edition of
The World Book Encyclopedia

Scanning electron microscope with display screen

© Lawrence Migdale, Photo Researchers

Electronic encyclopedia

WORLD BOOK Information Finder

Compact disc player

WORLD BOOK photo by Ralph Brunke

Laser scanner at checkout counter

© David R. Frazier, Photo Researchers

Electronics has revolutionized such fields as communications, education, medicine, entertainment, and business and industry, The photographs above and on the next page show some of the many uses of electronics.

Electronics

Electronics is a branch of physics and engineering that involves controlling the flow of electric charges in certain devices for a useful purpose. Electronic *components* (parts) are used in a broad range of products, including radios, television sets, computers, videocassette players, hearing aids, medical instruments, and many other products. Today, people rely so heavily on electronic products that the age we live in is often called the *electronic age.*

Thomas Edward Wade, the contributor of this article, is Professor of Electronics Engineering and Associate Dean for Research at the University of South Florida.

Electronics is part of the broad field of electricity. Electricity includes two important elements: (1) *electric current* and (2) *electric voltage.* Electric current is the flow of electric charges. Electric voltage is a type of "pressure" or force that causes the charges to move in the same direction. Familiar uses of electricity include the furnishing of energy in homes and businesses to provide light and heat, and to drive motors.

Electronics deals chiefly with the use of current and voltage to carry *electric signals.* An electric signal is an electric current or voltage modified in some way to represent information. A signal may represent sound, pictures, numbers, letters, computer instructions, or other information. Signals can also be used to count objects, to measure time or temperature, or to detect chemicals or radioactive materials.

Electronics depends on certain highly specialized

Johnson Space Center's Mission Control Center in Houston

components, such as transistors and integrated circuits, that serve as part of almost all electronic equipment. The value of such devices lies in their ability to manipulate signals extremely fast. Some components can respond to signals billions of times per second.

The field of *microelectronics* is concerned with the design and production of miniature components, chiefly integrated circuits, and of electronic equipment that uses such components. Manufacturers can create millions of microscopic electronic components on a piece of material—called a *chip*—that is no larger than a fingernail.

This article provides a broad overview of the basic tools and functions of electronics and the electronics industry. Separate *World Book* articles give detailed information on many of the topics. For a list of these articles, see the *Related articles* at the end of this article.

Uses of electronics

Electronics has changed the way people live. People have come to depend on electronic products in almost every part of their daily lives.

In communications. Electronic communication systems link people throughout the world. Radio can transmit a voice around the world in a fraction of a second. People in different countries communicate almost instantly through telephones and computers. A television viewer can watch events on another continent as they are taking place. Cellular telephones enable a person to call another person while riding in a car or walking down the street. Fax machines send and receive copies of documents over telephone lines in minutes.

Processing information. Electronic computers are used in business, schools, government, industry, scientific laboratories, and the home. People depend on computers to handle vast amounts of information with in-

credible speed and to solve complex mathematical problems in a fraction of a second. On-line services provide computer users instant access to a wide variety of information and features through telephone lines.

Medicine and research. Physicians use a variety of electronic instruments and machines to diagnose and treat disorders. For example, X-ray machines use radiation produced in a special type of electronic vacuum tube to take pictures of bones and internal organs. Physicians analyze these pictures to detect injuries and diseases. Radiation therapy, or *radiotherapy,* uses X rays and other forms of radiation as a powerful weapon against cancer. Many hearing-impaired people depend on electronic hearing aids to *amplify* (strengthen) sound waves.

Computers and other electronic instruments provide scientists and other researchers with a clearer understanding of nature. For example, computers help scientists design new drug molecules, track weather systems, and test theories that describe how galaxies develop. Electron microscopes can magnify specimens by 1 million times.

Automation. Electronic controls improve the operation of many common home appliances, such as refrigerators, sewing machines, toasters, and washing machines. People can program coffeemakers, lawn sprinklers, and many other products to turn on and off automatically. Electronic devices control video games. Microwave ovens heat food quickly by penetrating it with short radio waves produced by a vacuum tube.

Industries use computers to control other machines. Electronic robots perform a wide variety of tasks that are boring, difficult, or dangerous for people. For example, some automobiles are painted by robots using spray paint that would harm people who breathed it.

Air, sea, and space travel depend on navigation by

radar, radio, and computers. Many automobiles have electronic controls in their engines and fuel systems. Also, electronic devices control the inflation of *air bags,* safety devices that inflate to protect a driver or a front-seat passenger in a head-on collision.

How an electronic system works

To provide a basis for understanding electronics, this section describes how a common product, a handheld electronic calculator, works. A calculator has a small keypad with keys for numbers and operations, and a display screen that shows results. Most calculators are powered by a small battery or by a panel of solar cells.

Beneath the keypad, tiny *circuits* operate the calculator. A circuit is a set of connected parts through which current flows. Pressing a key creates a pulse of electric charge representing a number or operation—in other words, a signal. The signals travel through wires to the circuits.

Each circuit has a job. Some circuits store signals temporarily, awaiting further instructions. Others change signals according to instructions. For example, a circuit might multiply two numbers together. Finally, circuits send signals that light up or darken certain areas on the display screen to show the result of a calculation.

The operations of a calculator, like most electronic systems, can be divided into three stages: (1) the *input* stage, in which information enters the system as signals; (2) the *processing* stage, in which the signals are manipulated in some way; and (3) the *output* stage, in which the processed signals are changed into a form that the user can understand. Systems use various types of input and output devices that produce or respond to signals. For example, radio and television broadcasting require such devices as microphones and loudspeakers. From the time signals leave the input device until they reach the output device, the signals can go through a number of changes. The electronic components working within circuits make these changes.

Electronic circuits

In any electronic device, a circuit provides a pathway for the electric current that operates the device. A calculator has a complex circuit. Many of the parts of this complex circuit are actually smaller subcircuits that perform particular jobs. Not all of the circuits necessarily work at the same time. Certain components act as electronic "switches," turning circuits "on" and "off" as needed. When a switch allows current to pass through a circuit, the circuit is on. When a switch blocks current, the circuit is off.

How a circuit works. To understand how an electronic circuit works, one must know something about atoms. Every atom has one or more *electrons*—particles that carry a negative electric charge. Atoms also contain *protons*—particles that carry a positive electric charge. Opposite charges attract each other. Like charges *repel* (push away from) each other. Circuit operation is based on the attraction between charges.

The flow of electrons in one direction at a time forms an electric current. Voltage, also known as *electromotive force,* is the "pressure" or force that drives the electrons. In circuits, voltage is the electrical attraction caused by the difference in the charges between two points in the circuit. A power source provides voltage. One side of the power source supplies a negative voltage, and the other end supplies a positive voltage. Batteries are a common power source. Systems that plug into an electric outlet receive power from a commercial power plant.

Electrons flow from the negative voltage end of a circuit to the positive voltage end. This movement of electrons creates an electric current. Scientists, however, traditionally describe the direction of an electric current

---

Terms used in electronics

Amplification is the strengthening of a weak signal.

Amplitude is the strength of a signal. Amplitude can be measured in terms of current, voltage, or power.

Binary code is used by computers to represent information. It consists of the 0's and 1's of the binary numeration system.

Charge carriers are electrons that can flow from atom to atom and so conduct electric current.

Conductor is a material that can carry an electric current.

Digital signals represent all information with a limited number of signals. Under the binary code, only two signals are used.

Diode is a component that blocks current from flowing through it in one direction but allows current to pass in the other.

Doping is the process of adding impurities to a semiconductor. The impurities, known as *dopants,* add positive or negative charge carriers to the material, thereby increasing its ability to conduct current.

Free electron is an electron that can move from atom to atom and so conduct electric current. Free electrons are also called *charge carriers.*

Frequency is the number of times a second that a signal vibrates—that is, changes its direction of flow.

Hole is the absence of an electron bond in a crystal.

Insulators are materials that block electric current.

Integrated circuit is a tiny *chip* (piece) of semiconductor material, usually silicon, that contains a complete electronic circuit. One integrated circuit can do the work of thousands of individual electronic components.

Logic gates are small groups of circuits designed to imitate a logic function, such as counting or comparing information.

Microprocessor is an integrated circuit that contains memory, processing, and control circuits on one chip.

Oscillation vibrates an electric signal to a desired frequency.

P-N junction is the area where a p-type semiconductor meets an n-type semiconductor within a continuous crystal.

Rectification changes alternating current into direct current.

Resistor is a circuit component that decreases current flow.

Semiconductor is a material that conducts electric current better than an insulator but not as well as a conductor. Semiconductors are important because their conductivity can be altered by doping and precisely controlled by signals.

Signal is an electric current or voltage modified to represent information, such as sound, pictures, or letters.

Solid-state components control a signal flowing through a solid semiconductor material.

Switch is a component that directs the path of a current. A switch can turn a circuit on or off.

Transistor is a component that uses a small signal to control a strong current. A transistor is an arrangement of p-n junctions that can be used to amplify a signal or switch a circuit on or off.

Vacuum tube is a component that controls a signal in a container from which most of the air has been removed.

Voltage is a type of "pressure" or force that drives charges through a circuit.

Parts of an electronic system

Electronic components work together to operate a system. In the calculator below, the parts are attached to a printed circuit board. Thin wires connect the parts. A chip called the *central processing unit* carries out most calculations. It contains thousands of microscopic parts that form logic, memory, and control circuits. Other chips also help process signals. Individually made components, such as transistors, diodes, and resistors, direct and control the flow of current.

Hewlett Packard

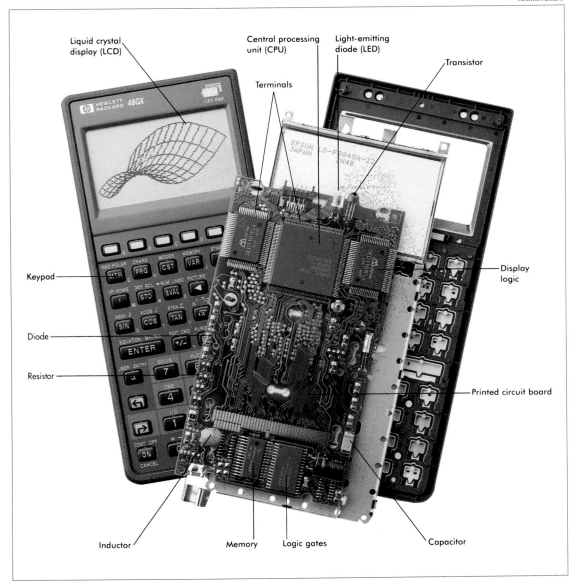

Liquid crystal display (LCD)

Central processing unit (CPU)

Light-emitting diode (LED)

Transistor

Terminals

Keypad

Diode

Resistor

Display logic

Printed circuit board

Inductor

Memory

Logic gates

Capacitor

as flowing from positive to negative. Until the late 1800's, scientists mistakenly believed that an electric current flowed in that direction.

Wires and certain other parts of circuits are made of materials called *conductors,* which can carry an electric current. In conductors, which include metals, each atom has one or more electrons that can move from atom to atom. These electrons are called *free electrons* or *charge carriers.* Circuits also contain *insulators,* materials that block current because they have no mobile charge carriers.

As electrons move through a conductor, they collide with the atoms of the material. Each collision hinders the flow of electrons and causes them to lose some energy as heat. Opposition to electric current, which changes electric energy into heat, is known as *resistance.*

A build-up of heat can damage a circuit. A calculator uses so little current that there is no danger of overheating. However, some computers generate so much heat that their circuits must be continually cooled. The whirring noise a desktop personal computer makes comes from a small fan that cools the system.

Types of electronic circuits. Manufacturers make two types of electronic circuits: (1) conventional and (2) integrated. A calculator, like most electronic devices, has both kinds.

Conventional circuits consist of separate electronic components connected by wires and fastened to a base. In most cases, manufacturers attach the components to a *printed circuit board,* a thin piece of plastic or other insulating material upon which copper "wires" are printed by a chemical process at the time of manufacture. In a calculator, all the electronic parts of the main circuit are connected on a printed circuit board.

Integrated circuits have components and connectors formed on and within a chip—a tiny piece of *semiconductor* material, usually silicon. A semiconductor is a substance that conducts electric current better than an insulator, but not as well as a conductor. The chip serves not only as the base but also as an essential part of the circuit. Most chips are no larger than a fingernail. Integrated circuits often serve as components of conventional circuits.

To make an integrated circuit, a technician prepares a large master design of the circuit with the help of a computer. A photographic process reduces the master design to microscopic size. Chip manufacturers treat silicon to alter its conductive properties by adding small amounts of substances called *dopants,* such as boron and phosphorus. The treated regions form the chip's electronic components. One chip can contain millions of microscopic parts connected by thin "lines" of metal. Chip makers arrange the parts and connections in complex patterns in several layers. Finished circuits are mounted in casings that plug into a printed circuit board.

The small size of an integrated circuit gives it several advantages over a conventional circuit. For example, an integrated circuit works faster because the signals have less distance to travel. Integrated circuits also need less power, generate less heat, and cost less to operate than conventional circuits. In addition, integrated circuits are more reliable because they have fewer connections that might fail. But strong currents and high voltages can damage integrated circuits because of their small size.

A type of integrated circuit called a *microprocessor* can perform all of the mathematical functions and some of the memory functions of a large computer. Microprocessors control many products, including video games, microwave ovens, robots, and some telephones. A microprocessor serves as the "brain" of every personal computer. Larger computers have several microprocessors that can work together at the same time.

Electronic devices use two basic types of components within circuits to control and modify signals. The two types are (1) electron tubes and (2) solid-state devices.

Electron tubes

Electron tubes control the flow of electric signals through a gas or a near-vacuum. *Vacuum tubes* are the most common type of electron tube. A vacuum tube is a glass or metal container from which most of the air has been removed. Various metallic elements within the tube produce and control beams of electrons.

From the 1920's to the 1950's, all electronic equipment used vacuum tubes. Some equipment still uses special types of such tubes. For example, the screen of a typical TV set is the end of a large vacuum tube called a *cathode-ray tube.* Other types of vacuum tubes produce radio and radar signals, X rays, and microwaves. For more information about the various kinds of vacuum tubes and how they work, see **Vacuum tube.**

Solid-state components

Transistors and certain other electronic components are called solid-state components because the signals flow through a solid semiconductor material instead of through a vacuum. Solid-state devices use less power, last longer, and take up less space than vacuum tubes. Engineers developed the first successful solid-state devices during the 1940's. Since that time, semiconductors have replaced vacuum tubes for most uses.

Most solid-state components are made of the semiconductor silicon. Silicon and other similar semiconductors are useful because scientists can precisely adjust their resistance and thus control the flow of current through them.

To be used for electronic devices, the atoms of a semiconductor must form a crystal structure. In these crystals, each of an atom's outer electrons pairs with an outer electron of a neighboring atom to form linkages known as *electron bonds* or *covalent bonds.* Ordinarily, the outer electrons are tightly bound to the atoms of the crystal, and the material acts as an insulator, resisting the flow of charges.

Scientists *dope* (treat) pure silicon crystals with extremely small amounts of dopants to increase the silicon's ability to conduct current. There are two types of doped semiconductors: (1) p-type, which contain mostly *p*ositive charge carriers; and (2) n-type, which contain mostly *n*egative charge carriers.

To create p-type semiconductors, scientists add dopants whose atoms have one less outer electron than a silicon atom. Aluminum, boron, indium, and gallium are p-type dopants. Each impurity atom creates a *hole*—that is, the absence of an electron bond—in the crystal structure. A hole acts as a positive charge, attracting electrons from neighboring atoms. Thus, a hole can move from atom to atom.

To create n-type semiconductors, scientists add dopants whose atoms have one more outer electron than a silicon atom. Arsenic, phosphorus, and antimony are n-type dopants. At room temperature, the extra electron is free to move within the crystal and acts as a negative charge carrier.

Manufacturers make various electronic devices by forming different combinations of p-type and n-type semiconductors within a continuous crystal. The place where the two types of semiconductors meet is called a *p-n junction.* The number and arrangement of p-n junctions, as well as the type and amount of dopants, determine how a device works.

Diodes are electronic components that prevent current from flowing in one direction but not the other. A semiconductor diode consists of a piece of p-type semiconductor joined to a piece of n-type semiconductor. A diode has two *terminals* (metal parts for making electrical connections). The terminals connect the end of each type of semiconductor material to the circuit. A diode can be built into an integrated circuit, or can form a *discrete* (separate) component of a conventional circuit. A discrete diode is enclosed in a protective casing.

How semiconductor components work
All semiconductor active components contain at least one *p-n junction*. The number of charge carriers near the junction determines if a current can flow through the junction. What a component does depends on how many junctions it has and how the circuit is arranged.

WORLD BOOK illustrations by Garri Budynsky, Artisan

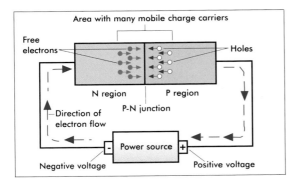

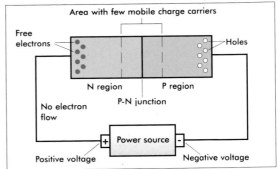

A diode has one p-n junction that can either conduct or block current, depending on the *bias* (direction) of a voltage applied to the diode's two terminals. A forward-biased diode, *left,* conducts current because charge carriers are attracted toward the junction. A reverse-biased diode, *right,* blocks current because charge carriers move away from the junction.

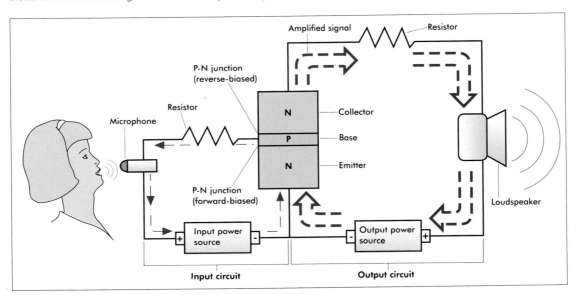

An amplifying transistor circuit can strengthen a voice signal. *Above,* a bipolar junction transistor is connected to an input circuit and an output circuit. A microphone picks up sound waves and changes each wave into a voltage signal. The voltage is applied across the transistor's forward-biased junction. As a result, free electrons from the emitter enter the base, overcoming the ability of the reverse-biased junction to block current. A strong current—fluctuating according to the pattern of the sound waves—flows through the output circuit and operates the loudspeaker.

How a diode works. A diode is basically a switching device that allows current to flow in only one direction. The current is carried by the flow of holes and electrons. The *bias* (direction) of the applied voltage determines if the p-n junction blocks current or allows it to flow.

A *forward bias* allows current to flow through the junction. To create a forward bias, a battery or other voltage source applies a negative voltage to the n-type material and a positive voltage to the p-type material. The negative voltage repels the free electrons in the n-type material toward the p-n junction. Likewise, the positive voltage repels the holes in the p-type material toward the junction. The electrons move across the junc-

tion into the p-type semiconductor. For each electron that crosses into the p-type material, the voltage source pumps one electron into the n-type material and pulls one electron out of the p-type material. As a result, electrons flow through the circuit. A small increase in the strength of the voltage causes a large increase in the current flowing through the diode. When the voltage is removed, electron flow stops.

A *reverse bias* prevents most current from flowing through the p-n junction, though a small *leakage current* gets through. To create a reverse bias, a voltage source applies a negative voltage to the p-type semiconductor and a positive voltage to the n-type semiconductor.

As a result, holes and electrons are attracted away from the junction. This creates an area on either side of the junction with no mobile charge carriers. The junction area acts as an insulator.

Uses. Diodes are used as switches and also as *rectifiers.* A rectifier circuit can change *alternating current* into *direct current.* Alternating current reverses its direction of flow many times each second. Direct current always flows in the same direction. A terminal connected to a source of alternating current gets a voltage that constantly changes from positive to negative and back again. If an alternating current is sent to a diode, the device will pass current only when the n-type semiconductor has a negative voltage. Thus, current flows through the diode in only one direction.

Almost all commercial power plants supply alternating current. Most electronic equipment requires direct current. Devices that run on commercial power use diodes as rectifiers. Devices powered by batteries do not need rectifiers because batteries produce direct current.

Transistors are arrangements of p-n junctions that can be used to amplify signals or switch a circuit on and off. Just as a small movement of a mechanical switch can turn a powerful motor on and off, a transistor uses a small input signal to control the flow of a strong current. A transistor can turn a current all the way on, all the way off, or partially on. Transistors are the most important components of integrated circuits.

How a transistor works. There are several types of transistors that work in different ways. One important type is the *bipolar junction transistor* or *bipolar transistor.* The component consists of an extremely thin layer of one type of semiconductor sandwiched between two thicker layers of the opposite type. For example, if the middle layer is n-type, the outer layers must be p-type. The middle region is called the *base.* The outer regions are the *emitter* and the *collector.*

A bipolar junction transistor has two p-n junctions and three terminals. Usually, two of the terminals connect the emitter and collector to an output circuit. The third terminal connects the base to an input circuit. Each circuit has a power source. The power sources are arranged so that one p-n junction is forward biased and the other junction is reverse biased.

Normally, the transistor prevents current from flowing through the output circuit. However, a small increase in voltage on the base terminal enables a large number of electrons to enter the base through the forward-biased junction. The number of electrons entering the base varies with the strength of the voltage. Because the base region is extremely narrow, the voltage source in the output circuit is able to attract the electrons through the reverse-biased junction. As a result, a large current flows through the transistor and through the output circuit. In this way, a small signal supplied to the base controls the flow of a strong current through the output circuit.

Another major type of transistor is the *field effect transistor,* which works in a different way than the bipolar transistor. For more information on both types of transistors and how they work, see **Transistor.**

Uses. Transistors perform three main electronic functions: (1) amplification, (2) switching, and (3) oscillation.

Amplification is the strengthening of a weak, fluctuating signal. The current that flows through the transistor and the output circuit is basically a duplicate of the input signal—but much stronger. A transistor can react to signal fluctuations billions of times per second.

Most electronic equipment would not work without amplifiers. Amplifiers are used in equipment designed to transmit or process *audio* (sound) or *video* (picture) signals. Most signals must be amplified so that they can drive an output device, such as a loudspeaker, a TV set, or a computer printer.

Amplifiers are also used to detect information. For example, special instruments record and amplify the weak electric signals given off by the human heart and brain. Physicians study these signals to diagnose certain injuries and diseases.

Switching is another important function of a transistor. As a switch, a transistor turns a circuit on or off or directs the path of signals. For a transistor to function as a switch, the strength of input signals must vary widely, so that the transistor simply turns the main supply current all the way on or off.

Oscillation converts a direct current signal to an alternating current signal of a desired *frequency* (number of vibrations per second). Transistor circuits that do this are called *oscillators.* An oscillator is actually a kind of amplifier that strengthens a signal and then feeds part of the amplified signal back into itself to produce its own input. Various circuit arrangements enable a transistor to act as an oscillator.

Oscillators serve many purposes. For example, they produce the radio waves that carry sound and pictures through space. They also produce timing signals that control the internal operations of computers and that operate certain types of automatic machinery. In medicine, an oscillator called a *cardiac pacemaker* produces carefully timed electric pulses similar to the natural pulses that make the heart beat regularly. Surgeons implant cardiac pacemakers inside the chest of certain patients to correct an irregular heartbeat.

Passive components

Electronic components may be divided into two categories: (1) active and (2) passive. *Active components* are those that can amplify, switch, or oscillate signals. Most electronics experts classify electron tubes, transistors, and certain diodes as active components. *Passive components* either change electric energy into heat or store electric energy internally. Passive components include *resistors, capacitors,* and *inductors.*

Resistors change electric energy into heat. Resistors are used to reduce the amount of current flowing through a circuit. The larger the resistor, the smaller the amount of current that flows through it.

Capacitors and inductors store electrical energy. Electronic circuits use capacitors to store information as the presence or absence of a charge. Capacitors are also used to block the flow of a direct current. Inductors, on the other hand, block the flow of alternating current but allow direct current to pass. See **Capacitor; Inductance.**

In integrated circuits, manufacturers can adjust the semiconductor chip to create areas that act as resistors and capacitors, but not as inductors. Inductors can be created only through complex circuitry. Inductors can also be attached to integrated circuits as discrete components.

Electronics and light

Many electronic devices make use of the ability of electrons to absorb and give off energy as light. Such *optoelectronic devices* include light-sensing devices, light-emitting devices, and liquid crystal displays.

Light-sensing devices, also known as *electric eyes,* use light energy to produce or control an electric current. The heart of such devices consists of a light-sensing diode, or *photodiode,* usually made of silicon. A photodiode resembles an ordinary diode but has a window or lens that lets light fall onto the p-n junction. The light knocks some electrons out of their crystal bonds, producing pairs of free electrons and holes that can flow. Some photodiodes, such as *solar cells,* generate current. Panels of solar cells power most artificial satellites and many smaller electronic devices, such as calculators. Other photodiodes are used to switch an external power supply on and off. See **Light** (diagram: Photoelectric effect of light).

Light-emitting devices use electric current to produce light. Most *light-emitting diodes* (LED's) are made from gallium arsenide or other semiconductor compounds that give off energy in the form of light instead of heat. As current flows through an LED, free electrons and holes near the p-n junction combine. When a free electron "falls" into a hole, the process releases a tiny packet of light energy called a *photon.* With a strong enough current, the junction area of the chip glows brightly. Groups of LED's are used in many displays.

Semiconductor lasers are special diodes that produce an extremely narrow, powerful beam of light. Lasers have many uses in communications, industry, medicine, and science. For example, with fiber-optic communication, a laser beam transforms the electric signals of a telephone call or TV picture into pulses of photons. The photon signals travel at great speeds through hair-thin strands of glass called *optical fibers* without losing much strength or clarity.

Liquid crystal displays (LCD's) are commonly used in calculators, digital watches, and laptop computers. A thin layer of liquid crystal is sandwiched between two sheets of glass. Normally, the display reflects light. A voltage signal causes portions of the display to darken. These portions form the shape of a number or letter. See **Liquid crystal.**

How electronic circuits process information

Circuits process information by combining inputs to produce new information according to instructions. The way a circuit processes information depends on the type of signals it works with.

Electronic circuits work with two basic types of signals: (1) digital and (2) analog. Digital signals represent all information with a limited number of voltage values. Each signal has a distinct value. Analog signals vary continuously in voltage or current, corresponding to the input information. A fluctuating voltage can stand for changes in light, sound, temperature, pressure, or even the position of an object.

Digital circuits process information by counting or comparing signals. Many digital circuits can process information much faster than analog circuits. The majority of processing is done by digital circuits.

In digital processing, all input data—words, numbers, and other information—are translated into *binary* numbers, which are groups of 1's and 0's. The code is called *binary* (consisting of two) because only two digits are used. Any binary number can be represented by a combination of circuits or devices that are in one of two states. For example, a circuit can be on or off. One state corresponds to a binary 1 and the other to a 0. Each 1 or 0 is called a *bit,* a contraction of *bi*nary digi*t.* Many systems work with bits in groups called *words.* A word that consists of 8 bits is called a *byte.*

Digital processing requires three basic elements: (1) *memory circuits,* which store data; (2) *logic circuits,* which change data; and (3) *control circuits,* which direct the operations of the system. Wire channels called *buses* link the elements to each other as well as to the entire system. A microprocessor combines these elements on one chip.

Memory circuits store bits permanently or temporarily. A common type of memory circuit contains thousands of capacitors arranged in rows. The capacitors hold bits as an electric charge or the absence of a charge. A metal conductor connects each capacitor to the system. Transistors or diodes act as switches between the capacitors and conductors. When a signal opens a switch, bits can travel along the conductor. Other circuits then restore the bits by recharging the capacitors with the same sequence of charges.

There are two basic kinds of memory circuits—*random-access memory* (RAM) and *read-only memory* (ROM). The information in RAM can be erased or added to. RAM circuits store data only as long as the power is on. When the power is turned off, all the stored charges are wiped out. RAM circuits are used in such devices as computers and certain calculators, which need to store large amounts of information for brief periods.

A researcher at an electronics laboratory wears special clothing designed to help protect the tiny silicon chips being tested. A single particle of dust can damage the chips.

A ROM circuit permanently stores information installed at the time of manufacture. This information can be neither erased nor added to. ROM generally contains instructions, or *programs,* for operating the system.

Not all memory is stored in circuits. For example, computers also use external memory devices, such as magnetic disks and magnetic tapes. Users input such memory into the system. Another type of memory device is a *compact disc,* also called a *CD,* which stores information on a plastic platter. A *CD-ROM* can store data, pictures, and sound as well as programs.

Logic circuits, also called *processors,* manipulate data according to instructions. In a processor, the bits go through a sequence of switches that change them in some way. For example, a group of switches may add two numbers together. Such a group is called an *adder.* An adder may involve hundreds of switches. During processing, bits are stored temporarily in areas called *registers,* awaiting the next instruction.

Another combination of switches can compare two bits and generate a particular output based on a set of rules established for the processor. Such circuits use binary digits to stand for such ideas as "true" or "false," instead of 1 or 0.

Designers create areas on chips that can count or compare signals by combining small groups of circuits that make simple changes in just one or two bits. These groups are often called *logic gates.* Three basic gates are (1) the *NOT-gate,* (2) the *AND-gate,* and (3) the *OR-gate.* If combined in large enough numbers, these gates can solve complex mathematical or logical problems.

A NOT-gate, also called an *inverter,* changes a bit from a 1 to a 0, or from a 0 to a 1. Such a function has many uses. For example, addition involves changing 0's to 1's and 1's to 0's.

Both AND- and OR-gates generate one output signal from two or more inputs. An AND-gate requires that all inputs be true—often represented by a 1—to produce a true output, or a 1. An OR-gate requires only one true input to produce a true output.

Control circuits direct and coordinate the work of all other parts of the system according to instructions stored in the memory circuits. One of the main jobs of the control circuit is to control the movement of bits through the system. To do this, an oscillator called the *clock* generates continuous pulses. The bits move through the circuit according to the rhythm of the clock.

Analog circuits solve problems by measuring continuously varying quantities, such as temperature, speed, and pressure. Many familiar devices, including speedometers and thermometers, work as analog computers. Small analog circuits are parts of many electronic systems that control the operations of other machines. Analog circuits are also used in navigation equipment. For more information on analog processing, see **Analog computer.**

Digital-analog conversion. Some circuits can convert analog signals into digital signals, and digital into analog. In digital sound recording, for example, the *amplitude* (strength) of the sound wave is measured thousands of times every second and converted into a digital code signal made up of rapid bursts of current. To play the resulting digital signals, a sound system converts them back to analog signals that drive a loudspeaker.

Digital signals produce better sound quality with less background noise and distortion than analog signals.

The electronics industry

The development, manufacture, and sales of electronic products make up one of the largest and most important industries in the world. The electronics industry is also one of the fastest-growing of all industries.

Research and development. Engineers and scientists at research laboratories work to add new knowledge about electronics and to develop new electronic devices. In the United States, a number of universities and electronics companies maintain research laboratories. In 1982, many large manufacturers and users of computer chips formed a nonprofit organization called the Semiconductor Research Corporation to support basic research on electronics at universities.

The U.S. government sponsors electronics research through such agencies as the National Science Foundation, the National Aeronautics and Space Administration, and the Department of Energy. The government also sponsors research through its military branches. In addition, the electronics industry and the government combine research efforts through the Semiconductor Manufacturing Technology Institute, better known as SEMATECH. The government and 14 electronics companies founded SEMATECH in 1987 to help U.S. chip makers become more competitive in manufacturing.

Manufacturing and sales. The United States and Japan are the world's largest producers of electronic components and assembled electronic products. In the early 1990's, electronics companies in the United States employed more than $1\frac{1}{2}$ million workers. The sales of United States electronics companies totaled about $300 billion each year. During the same period, electronics companies in Japan employed about 2 million workers. The Japanese firms had total sales valued at about $190 billion. Other leading producers of electronic equipment include Canada, Germany, the Netherlands, Singapore, South Korea, Taiwan, and the United Kingdom.

Careers in electronics can be divided into two main groups. They are (1) engineering and scientific careers and (2) technical careers.

Engineering and scientific careers range from developing new electronic devices to designing computers. Most of these careers require a college degree in engineering or physics. The *World Book* articles on **Engineering** and **Physics** discuss the requirements for becoming an electrical engineer and a physicist.

Most engineers and physicists who specialize in electronics work for electronics companies. Some of these companies do most or all of their work on military projects. Other engineers and physicists find jobs with the federal government, at colleges and universities, and in communication, medicine, or transportation.

Technical careers in electronics usually involve installing, operating, maintaining, or repairing electronic equipment. Many technical jobs require training in a trade school or community college. Such technical careers include automation control, computer programming, television repair, and X-ray technology.

Other technical jobs require only on-the-job training. Such jobs include operating certain types of electronic equipment in factories and offices. Some highly skilled technical jobs in the aerospace and communications industries require a college degree. Many people receive technical electronics training in the armed forces.

The development of electronics

Early experiments. During the mid-1800's, scientists experimented with *gas-discharge tubes*—that is, tubes from which some of the air had been removed, leaving a thin mixture of gases. Most of these tubes contained a combination of such gases as hydrogen and nitrogen at low pressure. Scientists discovered electric current could pass through the gas from one metal *electrode* (terminal) to another. When a battery was connected to the two electrodes, the tube glowed with bright colors. Scientists believed that the *cathode*—the negative electrode—gave off invisible rays that caused the colors. They named the rays *cathode rays.* As scientists removed still more air from the tubes for their experiments, the tubes became vacuum tubes.

In 1879, Sir William Crookes, a British scientist, developed a tube to study cathode rays. The Crookes tubes were forerunners of television picture tubes.

In 1895, German physicist Wilhelm C. Roentgen discovered X rays while studying cathode rays in a Crookes tube. By the end of the 1800's, many doctors were using X-ray photographs to diagnose internal diseases and injuries in their patients.

In 1897, the British physicist Joseph J. Thomson proved that cathode rays consist of negatively charged particles, later named *electrons.* Thomson's discovery led to the first practical electronic devices.

During the early 1900's, electrical engineers developed vacuum tubes that could detect, amplify, and create radio signals. In 1907, the American inventor Lee De Forest patented a three-electrode, or *triode,* vacuum tube. The triode tube became a key element in radio broadcasting and reception because it could amplify signals. Commercial radio broadcasting began in 1920, and the electronics industry was born. By 1927, more than 5 million American homes had radios.

The vacuum tube era lasted from the 1920's to the 1950's. During this period, vacuum tubes made possible such electronic inventions as television, radar, and computers.

As early as 1875, American scientist G. R. Carey had built a *photoelectric cell,* a device that produced an electric current when light shone on it. Carey's invention operated on the same principle as a TV camera, but it was not put to practical use until the early 1920's. In 1923, a Russian-born American scientist named Vladimir K. Zworykin made the first successful television camera tube. Using a cathode-ray tube as a model, Zworykin also developed a workable television picture tube during the 1920's. Experimental telecasts began in the late 1920's, but TV broadcasting did not begin on a large scale until the late 1940's.

In 1921, Albert W. Hull, an American engineer, invented a vacuum tube oscillator called a *magnetron.* The magnetron was the first device that could efficiently produce microwaves. Radar, which was developed gradually during the 1920's and 1930's, provided the first widespread use of microwaves.

The vacuum tube era reached its peak with the completion of the first general-purpose electronic computer in 1946. This huge machine, called ENIAC (*E*lectronic *N*umerical *I*ntegrator *A*nd *C*omputer), was built by two engineers at the University of Pennsylvania, J. Presper Eckert, Jr., and John W. Mauchly. The computer contained about 18,000 vacuum tubes and occupied about 1,800 square feet (170 square meters) of floor space. ENIAC worked 1,000 times faster than the fastest nonelectronic computers then in use.

The solid-state revolution. Three American physicists—John Bardeen, Walter H. Brattain, and William Shockley—invented the transistor in 1947. Transistors revolutionized the electronics industry, dramatically reducing the size of computers and other equipment. Transistors were used as amplifiers in hearing aids and pocket-sized radios in the early 1950's. By the 1960's, semiconductor diodes and transistors had replaced vac-

Brown Bros.

The Crookes tube was developed in 1879 by Sir William Crookes, *above.* The tube produced cathode rays. It became a model for TV picture tubes.

Brown Bros.

The electron was discovered in 1897 by Joseph J. Thomson, *above.* The discovery led to the first practical electronic components.

Brown Bros.

The vacuum tube amplifier was patented in 1907 by Lee De Forest, *above.* This tube led to the development of the radio industry.

uum tubes in much equipment.

Integrated circuits developed from transistor technology as scientists sought ways to build more transistors into a circuit. The first integrated circuits were patented in 1959 by two Americans—Jack Kilby, an engineer, and Robert Noyce, a physicist—who worked independently. Integrated circuits caused as great a revolution in electronics in the 1960's as transistors had caused in the 1950's. The circuits were first used in military equipment and spacecraft and helped make possible the first manned space flights of the 1960's.

The first microprocessors were produced in 1971 for desktop calculators. By the mid-1970's, microprocessors were being used in handheld calculators, video games, and home appliances. Business and industry began to use microprocessors to control various types of office machines, factory equipment, and other devices.

Electronics today. Scientists and engineers continue to search for ways to make electronic circuits smaller, faster, and more complex. Developing technologies include superconductors and photonics.

Superconductors are materials that lose all resistance to the flow of current at low temperatures. Superconductor devices operate extremely fast and produce almost no heat. Scientists are testing superconducting switching devices to control computer circuits.

Photonics is the science of building circuits that use photons—tiny packets of light energy—as signals instead of electrons. Photonic circuits use pulsed beams of photons to transmit data and commands through optical fibers. Photonic circuits can carry huge amounts of information, and they produce no heat. Today, the enormous information-carrying capacity of optical fibers is opening a new era in home entertainment, communications, and computer technology.

Display techniques in electronics are also rapidly changing. Manufacturers are developing flatter display panels to replace the bulky cathode-ray tubes used in television and many computer screens. One new design, introduced in 1993, uses thousands of tiny tubes side by side to form a picture. The screen is less than 4 inches (10 centimeters) thick. Another technology relies on even flatter LCD panels. These lightweight, energy-saving screens could hang on a wall like a picture. Today, portable computers such as laptop and notebook computers commonly use flat LCD screens.

In the early 1990's, manufacturers began to use a new type of liquid crystal display called the *active matrix LCD* in portable computers, video games, and other electronic products. In these displays, thousands of transistors on the inner surface of the glass control the signals that activate the liquid crystal.   Thomas Edward Wade

Related articles in *World Book* include:

Biographies

Armstrong, Edwin	Roentgen, Wilhelm C.
Bardeen, John	Shockley, William
Brattain, Walter H.	Thomson, Sir Joseph J.
De Forest, Lee	Zworykin, Vladimir K.

Additional resources

Level I
Chipmakers. Rev. ed. Time-Life Bks., 1990.
Encyclopedia of Computers and Electronics. 1983. Reprint. Checkerboard Pr., 1989.
LeBlanc, Wayne J., and Alden, R. C. *Modern Electronics.* Watts, 1986.
Leon, George D. *Electronics Projects for Young Scientists.* Watts, 1991.
Rowh, Mark. *Opportunities in Electronics Careers.* VGM Career, 1992.

Level II
Clifford, Martin. *Master Handbook of Electronic Tables and Formulas.* 5th ed. TAB, 1992.
Gibilisco, Stan, and Sclater, N. J., eds. *Encyclopedia of Electronics.* 2nd ed. TAB, 1990.
Horn, Delton T. *Basic Electronics Theory.* 4th ed. TAB, 1994.
Markus, John, and Sclater, N. J. *McGraw-Hill Electronics Dictionary.* 5th ed. McGraw-Hill, 1994.
Truxal, John G. *The Age of Electronic Messages.* MIT Pr., 1990.
Veley, Victor F. *The Benchtop Electronics Reference Manual.* 2nd ed. TAB, 1990.

RCA

Vladimir K. Zworykin, *above,* developed the TV camera tube and picture tube during the 1920's.

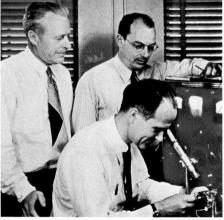

Bell Laboratories

The transistor was invented in 1947. Its inventors were William Shockley, *seated,* Walter H. Brattain, *left,* and John Bardeen, *right.* Transistors greatly reduced the size of electronic equipment.

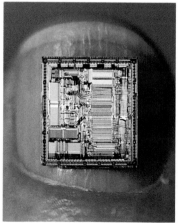

Thomas Edward Wade

The microprocessor was first developed in the 1970's. This tiny, powerful chip can perform most of the functions of a large computer.

Norvia Behling

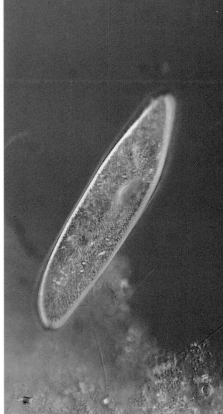
Brian Parker, Tom Stack & Assoc.

Heredity affects all living things. Heredity explains why human mothers always have human children and cats always have kittens, *left.* The process of heredity also occurs among all plants and even among one-celled organisms, such as a paramecium, *right.*

Heredity

Heredity is the passing on of biological characteristics from one generation to the next. The process of heredity occurs among all living things—animals, plants, and even such microscopic organisms as bacteria. Heredity explains why a human mother always has a human baby and why a mother dog has puppies—not kittens. It is also the reason offspring look like their parents.

Through heredity, living things inherit characteristics, often called *traits,* from their parents. You resemble your parents because you inherited your hair color, nose shape, and other traits from them. All organisms consist of cells. Tiny biochemical structures inside each cell called *genes* carry traits from one generation to the next. Genes are made of a chemical called *DNA (deoxyribonucleic acid).* They are strung together to form long chains of DNA in structures known as *chromosomes.*

Genes are like blueprints for building a house, except that they carry the plans for building cells, tissues, organs, and bodies. They have the instructions for making the thousands of chemical building blocks in the body. These building blocks are called *proteins.* Some proteins are responsible for the size, shape, and structure

The contributors of this article are Robert F. Weaver, Professor of Biochemistry at the University of Kansas, and Philip W. Hedrick, Professor of Zoology at the University of Arizona. They are coauthors of Basic Genetics *and* Genetics.

of the parts making up your body. Other proteins, known as *enzymes,* make possible the thousands of chemical reactions that occur constantly in your body and in all other living things. The process by which the cell makes a protein according to the instructions carried by a gene is known as *gene expression.*

Genes have powerful effects, but they do not control all of life. Most characteristics result from a combination of heredity and environment. For example, you may have inherited a talent for playing the piano. But you will not be able to play unless you take lessons and practice. The talent is hereditary. The lessons and practice are environmental.

The basic laws of heredity were formulated during the mid-1800's by an Austrian botanist and monk named Gregor Mendel. Mendel based his laws on his studies of the inheritance patterns of garden peas. Although Mendel published the results of his experiments in 1866, his work went unnoticed until 1900.

Mendel's experiments laid the foundation for the scientific study of heredity, called *genetics.* Through the years, *geneticists*—that is, people who study heredity—have learned much about why human beings and other living things look and behave the way they do. These scientists have also begun to uncover the causes of hereditary diseases and to develop ways to treat them. Today, genetics has several specialized branches.

Molecular genetics, for example, involves the study of the chemical nature and activities of genes. For more information on the various branches of genetics, see Genetics.

Chromosomes and genes

The structure of chromosomes and genes. In human beings and most other organisms, chromosomes are found in the part of a cell known as the *nucleus.* Chromosomes are tiny threadlike structures made largely of DNA and proteins. Chromosomes generally occur in pairs. The two chromosomes in a pair resemble each other in size and shape. They also contain similar hereditary information.

Each species of animal and plant has a characteristic number of chromosomes in its *body cells.* Body cells, often called *somatic cells,* are the cells that make up such body parts as muscles and bones. Body cells differ from *sex cells.* In male animals, the sex cells are sperm; in plants, pollen. In female animals and plants, the sex cells are eggs. Human beings typically have 46 chromosomes, arranged in 23 pairs, in their body cells. Dogs have 78 (39 pairs), and corn has 20 (10 pairs). The fruit fly *Drosophila melanogaster,* which is widely used in genetic research, has only 8 chromosomes (4 pairs).

Genes are the basic units of heredity. Each gene consists of a section of an extremely long DNA molecule found in a chromosome.

Every species of plant and animal has a certain number of genes on its chromosomes. For example, scientists estimate that human beings have from 50,000 to 100,000 different genes. The fruit fly has about 5,000 different genes, dogs have from 50,000 to 100,000, and corn has about 60,000. A set of all the genes a species has on its chromosomes is called its *genome.*

Sex cells and reproduction. There are two general types of reproduction, *asexual* and *sexual.* Asexual reproduction involves only one parent. The offspring have chromosomes identical to those of the parent. When a worm called a planarian reproduces asexually, for example, its body divides into two sections. One has the head, and the other has the tail. Each section grows the parts that are missing and becomes a new individual that is genetically identical to its parent.

Sexual reproduction generally involves two parents, each of which contributes half the chromosomes to the offspring. Sexual reproduction starts with the production of specialized sex cells that are called *gametes.* Gametes—that is, sperm, pollen grains, and eggs—are produced in a process of cell division called *meiosis.* Meiosis results in the sex cells' having half the number of chromosomes found in the body cells. In human beings, therefore, meiosis produces sperm and egg cells that have 23 chromosomes each. In dogs, the number of chromosomes in each sex cell is 39.

The uniting of an egg cell and a sperm cell, called *fertilization,* restores the full number of chromosomes. In human beings, the resulting cell, known as a *fertilized egg,* has 46 chromosomes, 23 pairs. One chromosome of each pair comes from the mother's egg, and the other from the father's sperm. After the egg has been fertilized, it begins to divide and produce exact copies of itself by a type of cell division called *mitosis.* Each of the new cells, known as *daughter cells,* has the same num-

Heredity terms

Alleles are different forms of the same gene.
Chromosomes are tiny threadlike structures inside each cell. Chromosomes carry the genes.
DNA stands for *deoxyribonucleic acid.* It is the substance within the chromosomes that carries the hereditary instructions for producing proteins and RNA's.
Gene expression is the process by which a cell makes a protein or RNA according to the instructions carried by a gene.
Genes are tiny biochemical structures inside each cell that determine particular hereditary traits, such as eye color and blood type. Each gene is a segment of DNA that carries instructions for producing the chainlike molecules that make up proteins.
Genetic variation refers to the differences in inherited traits that exist among the members of a species.
Genetics is the scientific study of heredity.
Genome is a set of all the genes a species has on its chromosomes. The human genome consists of 50,000 to 100,000 genes.
Genotype is the underlying genetic makeup of a trait or the overall genetic makeup of an individual.
Mutation is a change in a gene. It may produce a new trait that can be inherited.
Phenotype is the observable appearance of a trait or the overall appearance of an individual.
Protein is a chemical building block in the body. Proteins exist in every cell.
RNA stands for *ribonucleic acid.* Similar to DNA, it plays a key role in the production of proteins.
Trait is a characteristic, such as hair color.

How chromosomes are inherited

WORLD BOOK diagrams by Mark Swindle

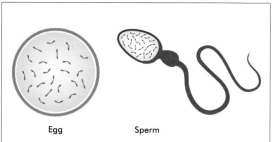

Egg   Sperm

The sex cells—that is, eggs in females and sperm in males—are produced in a process called *meiosis.* As a result of this process, mature sex cells, such as those shown above, have half the number of chromosomes found in other cells in the body. Each human egg and sperm cell thus has 23 chromosomes.

Fertilized egg

When a sperm unites with an egg, the resulting *fertilized egg* has the 46 chromosomes of a normal body cell. The chromosomes are arranged in 23 pairs. One chromosome in each pair comes from the mother, and the other comes from the father.

How a person's sex is determined

WORLD BOOK diagrams by Mark Swindle

Chromosomes known as X and Y chromosomes determine whether a fertilized egg will become a girl or a boy. An immature female sex cell has matching X chromosomes. An immature male sex cell has an X chromosome and a Y chromosome.

When an immature female sex cell divides, each resulting mature egg cell receives a single X chromosome. When an immature male sex cell divides, half the resulting mature sperm cells receive an X chromosome, and half receive a Y chromosome.

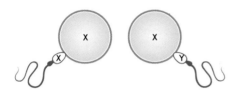

An egg fertilized by a sperm cell containing an X chromosome has two X chromosomes, *left.* It will develop into a girl. An egg fertilized by a sperm with a Y chromosome has one X and one Y chromosome, *right.* Such an egg will develop into a boy.

ber of chromosomes as the original cell. For more information on meiosis and mitosis, see **Cell** (Cell division).

Chromosomes and sexual determination. In human beings, chromosomes known as X and Y chromosomes determine an individual's sex. Eggs always have an X chromosome, but sperm may have either an X or a Y chromosome. When a Y-carrying sperm fertilizes an egg, the baby will be a boy (XY). If the sperm has an X chromosome, then the baby will be a girl (XX). Males produce sperm with an X chromosome in numbers equal to sperm with a Y chromosome. As a result, about half of all babies are boys, and half are girls.

Patterns of heredity

Dominant and recessive genes. Most genes occur in pairs. Each pair of genes is contained in a pair of matching chromosomes, with one copy of a gene in each chromosome. Some hereditary traits are determined by a single pair of genes. For example, a chemical called *phenylthiocarbamide* (PTC) tastes extremely bitter to some people. Other people cannot taste PTC at all. The difference between tasters and nontasters is due to a single pair of genes. But many other traits, called *polygenic traits,* are influenced by a number of pairs of genes. Tens or hundreds of pairs of genes are involved in the inheritance of such traits as height, weight, and intelligence.

The two genes in a pair may differ in the effects they produce. Different forms of the same gene are called *alleles.* Some alleles are *dominant,* and others are *reces-*

sive. A dominant allele masks the effects of its recessive partner. In other words, the dominant allele is expressed, and the recessive allele is not. A trait that results from a recessive allele is evident only in an individual that has two recessive alleles for that trait. For example, Mendel showed that in pea plants the allele that produces violet flowers (symbolized by *V*) is dominant over the one that causes white flowers *(v).* Pea plants that have two dominant alleles for violet flowers *(VV)* or one allele for violet flowers and one for white flowers *(Vv)* will have violet flowers. Only those with two recessive alleles *(vv)* will have white flowers.

Sex-linked genes. Genes that lie near each other on the same chromosome are called *linked genes* because they tend to be inherited together. Genes on the sex chromosomes are called *sex-linked genes.* Human beings have more than 250 genes on the X chromosome— called *X-linked* genes—that can cause hereditary disorders. These disorders include hemophilia and a type of muscular dystrophy. Most of these disorders are recessive. They typically occur only in males because males have only one X chromosome. Females have two X chromosomes. Generally, at least one of the two X chromosomes has the dominant normal allele. This allele deter-

The transmission of albinism

Albinism is a hereditary condition in which an organism cannot produce pigment. Albinism occurs in human beings and in many species of plants and animals.

WORLD BOOK diagram

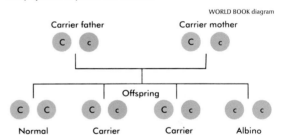

Different forms of the same gene are called *alleles.* The allele that produces pigment is *dominant* and masks the effects of the albinism allele, which is *recessive.* As a result, albinism occurs only in individuals who have two alleles for that trait. In the chart above, each parent carries one normal allele (C) and one albinism allele (c). Individuals who inherit the albinism allele from only one parent are not albinos. But they may transmit the allele to their young, as shown in the photograph below of a multicolored mother rabbit and her albino offspring.

Norvia Behling

mines the trait, and the harmful gene on the other X chromosome does not.

Sources of genetic variation

Individual members of a species differ widely from one another in their genetic makeup and therefore in their traits. You may look like your parents, but you are not an exact duplicate of either of them. You inherited half your genes from your father and half from your mother. Nor do you look exactly like your classmates, even though you and your classmates are all human beings. Scientists refer to the differences among members of a species as *genetic variation.* This section discusses the main sources of diversity among individual members of a species—mutation and genetic recombination. The next section, *Heredity and natural selection,* describes how entire species and certain groups within species change over time.

Mutation is a permanent change in the amount or the structure of the DNA in an organism's cells. It can result in alterations in gene expression and therefore in traits.

Kinds of mutations. Mutations can occur in sex cells or in body cells. A *germinal mutation* affects the DNA in the gametes and is therefore passed on from an organism to its offspring. A *somatic mutation* occurs in body cells. In human beings and other animals, somatic mutations do not affect the gametes. Consequently, the changes are not inherited by succeeding generations. However, the changes are passed along to the daughter cells of the original mutant cell.

Many mutations affect entire chromosomes. In some cases, an organism has too many or too few chromosomes. For example, people with a condition called *Down syndrome* have an extra copy of chromosome 21, one of the 23 pairs of chromosomes. Sometimes the structure of a chromosome is abnormal. For example, a mutation called *translocation* occurs when a piece of one chromosome breaks off and attaches to another.

Some mutations affect only one or a few of the chemical units making up the DNA molecule. There are several kinds of these *point mutations* or *gene mutations.* For example, a *missense mutation* changes a single pair of chemical units, thereby altering the instructions carried by that segment of DNA.

Causes of mutations. Some mutations result from mistakes that occur when copies of DNA are made during cell division. Others are caused by agents called *mutagens.* Mutagens include certain chemicals and various forms of radiation.

Genetic recombination. When organisms mate, new combinations of traits appear in their young. These combinations occur by (1) independent assortment of the genes on different chromosomes, and (2) crossing over.

Independent assortment refers to the way in which chromosomes and their genes are distributed when a sex cell divides to form eggs or sperm. An immature sex cell contains two of each chromosome—one from the individual's father and one from the mother. During meiosis, each pair of chromosomes separates, and each egg or sperm receives one chromosome from each pair. Because the chromosomes separate in a random manner, each egg or sperm receives some chromosomes

from the individual's mother and some from the father. This reshuffling of chromosomes and genes can result in new combinations of traits in offspring.

Crossing over is the exchange of genes between two partner chromosomes. Genes on separate chromosomes are inherited in a random and independent manner. But genes located close to each other on the same chromosome are generally inherited together. In other words, genes that are closely linked on a parent's chromosome largely remain linked in offspring.

Sometimes, however, linked genes are not inherited together. This situation arises because of crossing over. Just before immature sex cells divide to form sperm or eggs, each chromosome of a pair lines up side by side with its partner chromosome. During a crossing-over event, groups of genes from one chromosome change places with groups of genes from its partner chromosome. As a result, different sperm or eggs may carry different combinations of linked genes.

Heredity and natural selection

Mutation is one of the chief sources of new genetic material for a species or a *population*—a group of individuals of the same species living in the same area. Genetic recombination provides new combinations of mutations. As these two sources of genetic variation work together with a process called *natural selection* over time, the genetic makeup of a species or population changes.

Natural selection. Many mutations that alter traits are harmful, but some mutations and combinations of mutations make certain individuals better able to survive, mate, and reproduce in a given environment. These individuals will likely have more offspring that survive than individuals without the particular genetic variation. The young of the better-suited parents inherit the genes for the favorable characteristics that enabled their parents to improve their chances of surviving, mating, and reproducing. They then pass the genes along to their own offspring. As this process is repeated through many generations, more and more members of the species or population come to have the favorable genes. In this way, the process of natural selection changes the genetic makeup and therefore the traits of organisms through time.

Generally, evolution by natural selection takes place slowly and is not noticeable in a human lifetime. However, a species may change quickly in response to a major alteration in the environment, such as pollution or the introduction of a pesticide.

An example of a rapid genetic change occurred in Britain during the 1800's with a species of moth called the peppered moth. Peppered moths rest on light-colored lichens that grow on tree trunks. During the early 1800's, nearly all peppered moths were light-colored, and only a few moths carried a mutation that made them black. In the mid-1800's, however, factories burned so much coal that soot settled over the countryside, killing the lichens and blackening the tree trunks. Light-colored moths on dark-colored trees were easily seen and eaten by birds. But the birds could not see the black moths well. As a result, more of the black moths survived and produced offspring. Within 50 years, most moths in heavily polluted areas were black. After air pollution laws were passed in the mid-1900's, the tree trunks became lighter as lichens again grew on them, and the number of light-colored moths increased.

Gene pools and allele frequency. The genes of all the individuals of a population are called a *gene pool.* The degree to which a particular allele is present in a population is called the *allele frequency.* The level of diversity in a gene pool is important because genetic variation is necessary for a population to adapt to changes in the environment. For example, an insect population that has a genetic variant for resisting a new pesticide in its environment will be more likely to survive. There will be strong selection for that variant, and its frequency in the gene pool will increase. On the other hand, an insect population that does not have such a variant will die off.

Several factors besides natural selection may influence the frequency of particular alleles in a gene pool. These factors include *gene flow* and *genetic drift.*

Gene flow is the transfer of genes from one population to another. When separate populations come into contact and interbreed, new genes or combinations of genes are introduced into each group. Consequently, the gene pool of each group comes to include genes from pools of the other populations. In this manner, the allele frequencies of populations may change over time.

Genetic drift refers to chance increases or decreases in allele frequencies of a population from generation to generation. The genes of each generation represent only a sample of the previous generation's gene pool. As a result, the allele frequencies of each generation of individuals tend to vary randomly within the limitations of the preceding generation's gene pool. Such changes will probably have little effect on each generation in large populations. But they can lead to major genetic changes in small ones in a short period.

For a more detailed discussion of the factors involved in genetic variation among human populations, see Races, Human (How human populations develop and change).

Hereditary disorders

Many diseases and disorders are caused by such agents as viruses and bacteria. In other cases, however, the cause of the problem is hereditary—that is, the organism has inherited one or more abnormal genes from its parents. Because genes carry chemical instructions for the formation of proteins, defective genes can affect the production and function of proteins. For example, hemophiliacs are born with a defective gene, and thus they are unable to produce a protein crucial for blood clotting. As a result, they suffer prolonged bleeding when they are injured because their blood clots slowly.

Genes are arranged in an exact order along the length of the chromosomes. Researchers use a process known as *gene mapping* to locate and identify genes on a chromosome. This process has helped scientists determine which genes are responsible for some hereditary conditions. For example, Huntington's disease, a severe disorder of the nervous system, is caused by an abnormal gene on chromosome 4.

Many diseases, such as diabetes and rheumatoid arthritis, are common in certain families. These diseases are therefore believed to have a hereditary basis. People inherit a tendency to develop these conditions, but not the diseases themselves. Environmental factors may play a role in whether the conditions actually develop. For example, people with a genetic tendency toward diabetes may increase their chance of getting the disease by overeating and not getting enough exercise.

Scientists have developed methods of treating some hereditary disorders. For example, hemophilia can be treated by injections of the clotting factor that is missing from the blood of people who have the condition.

A technique known as *gene therapy* may offer a way

Inherited disorders

This table lists the symptoms and treatment of several hereditary disorders. As scientists learn more about genes, they are discovering that certain diseases have a genetic basis. For example, defective genes are responsible for some cases of breast cancer and of the brain disorder called Alzheimer's disease.

Name	Symptoms	Treatment
*Cystic fibrosis	Lung, pancreas, and liver damage due to abnormal mucus production	Drugs, physical therapy; experimental gene therapy; no cure
†Duchenne muscular dystrophy	Progressive weakening of the muscles	Drugs, physical therapy; no cure
*Hemophilia	Uncontrolled internal and external bleeding	Controlled by injections of missing blood-clotting factor
*Huntington's disease	Loss of muscle control and mental ability, usually in midlife	None
*Phenylketonuria	Mental retardation	Special diet to prevent onset of symptoms
*Retinoblastoma	Cancer of the eye in childhood	Radiation, drugs, surgery; usually curable if caught early
*Sickle cell anemia	Anemia, blood clots, damage to organs and nervous system	Drugs to ease symptoms; no cure
*Tay-Sachs disease	Severe brain damage in infancy	No treatment or cure

*Has a separate article in *World Book.*
†See Muscular dystrophy.

of treating hereditary disorders and certain other diseases. Such therapy involves identifying the gene that causes a genetic disease and then supplying patients with a normal copy of that gene. The normal genes come from another individual or organism and are usually inserted into a patient's cells outside the body. The altered cells are then returned into the patient's body. See **Gene therapy.**

Couples who are planning to have children can be tested to see if they carry certain potentially harmful genes. These tests are usually done as part of a process called *genetic counseling.* This process enables couples to understand their chances of bearing children with hereditary disorders. It also helps them learn ways of dealing with their situation. See **Genetic counseling.**

Heredity and environment

A gene gives only the potential for the development of a trait. How this potential is achieved depends partly on the interaction of the gene with other genes. But it also depends partly on the environment. For example, a person may have a genetic tendency toward being overweight. But the person's actual weight will depend on such environmental factors as how much and what kinds of food the person eats.

The underlying genetic makeup of a trait is called the *genotype.* The actual appearance of the trait is known as the *phenotype.* Sometimes the word *phenotype* is used to refer to the overall appearance of an individual; *genotype,* to refer to the person's overall genetic makeup.

Scientists have long debated the relationship between heredity and environment in determining a person's physical appearance and behavior. This debate is often referred to as the question of *nature versus nurture*—that is, heredity versus environment.

To try to understand the influence of genetics and the environment on phenotype, researchers have often studied identical twins, who have the same genotype. Such studies have shown that identical twins raised apart and thus in different environments tend to vary more in their characteristics than identical twins raised together. As a result, scientists have concluded that both heredity and environment play important roles in what an individual's ultimate phenotype will be.

Intelligence and other mental traits also depend on heredity and environment. Every person is born with a certain mental capacity that influences how intelligent he or she will be as an adult. The development of this capacity is influenced by the person's environment. For example, severely undernourished infants may fail to develop their natural abilities.

The flow of genetic information

Genes and proteins. Genes carry the instructions for producing proteins. Proteins are large, complex molecules made up of smaller units called *amino acids.* Twenty kinds of amino acids are commonly found in proteins. Various combinations of these amino acids are linked to form long chains known as *polypeptides.* Polypeptide chains fold into complex three-dimensional shapes.

Proteins consist of one or more polypeptide chains. These chains vary greatly in length, from only a few amino acids to thousands. They also differ according to

Grant Heilman

The effects of environment can be seen in these corn plants. All were grown from identical seeds and so have identical *genes* (units of heredity). However, the plants on the right grew in soil that lacked some nutrients needed for proper growth.

the order in which the amino acids occur. The length of the polypeptide chains and the arrangement of their amino acids determine the protein's shape and function. In most cases, one gene is responsible for making one polypeptide. The gene determines the order and number of amino acids in the polypeptide and thus the shape and function of the protein.

Proteins are found in every cell and are essential to plant and animal life. The proteins called *enzymes* speed up the chemical processes of life. Without enzymes, most of the reactions that occur in living things would happen too slowly to make life possible. These reactions include breaking down food during digestion and burning carbohydrates and fat for energy.

Many other proteins serve as building blocks for cells. Cells have different sizes and shapes—and different kinds, numbers, and arrangements of proteins—depending on where they are in an organism. Hair, nails, and part of the skin are made of a tough protein called *keratin.* The red color in blood comes from a red protein called *hemoglobin* that carries oxygen from the lungs to all parts of the body. Muscles consist largely of two proteins called *myosin* and *actin.*

The structure of DNA. The genes of all living things except some viruses are composed of DNA, which is often referred to as the *hereditary material.* DNA is a thin, chainlike molecule made up of smaller chemical units called *nucleotides.* A nucleotide in DNA is composed of a sugar known as *deoxyribose,* an oxygen-phosphorus chemical group called a *phosphate,* and a nitrogen-containing compound known as a *base.* The sugar and phosphate are the same in all DNA nucleotides, but the bases vary. There are four DNA bases: adenine (A), guanine (G), thymine (T), and cytosine (C).

DNA consists of two chains that coil around each other in a shape called a *double helix.* The double helix resembles a twisted ladder. The sides of the ladder consist of the linked sugars and phosphates of the nucleotides. Each rung is made up of two paired bases.

Base pairs. The bases of a DNA molecule are paired in a specific way to form combinations known as *base pairs.* There are A-T and G-C base pairs. Wherever there is adenine in one strand, there is thymine in the opposite strand. Wherever there is guanine in one strand, there is cytosine in the other. Other combinations are extremely rare. Because of this specific pairing of the bases, scientists say the two DNA strands are *complementary.* The sequence of bases in one strand determines the sequence of bases in the other.

DNA molecules in human beings typically have more than 100 million base pairs and measure more than 1 inch (2.5 centimeters) long when uncoiled. However, DNA is so thin it can be seen only with the aid of special microscopes called *electron microscopes.* A typical DNA molecule has a thickness of only 20 *angstroms.* One angstrom equals 0.0000001 millimeter (0.0000000039 inch).

Replication. Most of the cells in your body divide from time to time. When you get a cut, for example, the skin cells around the wound begin to divide to make new skin to repair the damage. Each of the new daughter cells produced by cell division has the same DNA as the old cells. The process by which exact copies of DNA are made during cell division is called *replication.* The accurate replication of DNA is one of the essential characteristics of the hereditary material. Without it, daughter cells would be genetically different from each other and from the parent cell. Your genetic makeup, and therefore your physical characteristics, would be constantly changing as your cells divided.

The complementary nature of the two DNA strands enables a cell to make exact copies of its DNA. Before the cell divides, sections of the two original joined strands of a DNA molecule split lengthwise, separating the base pairs. This process is similar to what would happen if a ladder split down the middle, separating its rungs. Each of the DNA strands, which resembles a half ladder, then picks up free nucleotides from the cell nucleus. The bases in the free nucleotides, with their attached sugars and phosphates, pair with the matching bases on the original DNA strands. A's pair with T's, T's with A's, G's with C's, and C's with G's. In this way, two double-stranded DNA ladders are produced that have exactly the same base sequence as the parent DNA. When the cell divides, each of the new daughter cells receives identical DNA molecules.

How proteins are made. The *genetic code* is a code formed by the sequence of the bases in DNA. This code tells the cell how to put amino acids together in the right order to make a specific polypeptide.

A group of three bases in a certain order forms a unit of the genetic code called a *codon.* Most codons specify a certain amino acid. The order of codons on DNA determines the sequence of amino acids in a protein—and the protein product that is made.

A total of 64 three-letter codons, often called *triplets,*

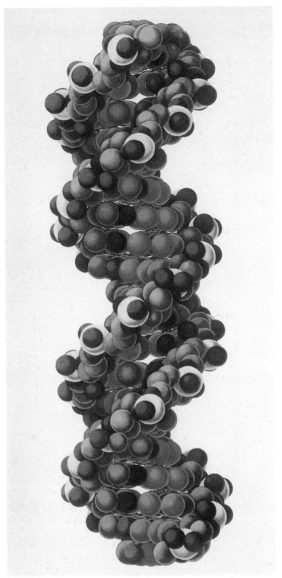

Ryland Loos from Francis H. C. Crick, the Salk Institute

A model of a DNA molecule shows that DNA is shaped like a twisted ladder. The colored spheres represent the various types of chemical units that make up DNA. This model was proposed in 1953 by biologists Francis H. C. Crick and James D. Watson.

can be formed from the four letters of the DNA bases. Because there are only 20, not 64, amino acids, there is more than one codon for most amino acids. In addition, with only minor exceptions, the same three-letter codons specify the same amino acids in all organisms that have been studied. Therefore, the genetic code is nearly universal.

Gene expression, the process by which the cell makes a protein according to the instructions carried by a gene, takes place in two steps. These steps are known as (1) *transcription* and (2) *translation.*

Transcription involves a close chemical cousin of

Studying heredity

The purpose of this activity is to study the interaction of heredity and environment in determining *phenotype*—that is, the observable characteristics—of organisms. The project looks at how various environmental factors influence the development of potato plants. *Eyes* (buds) that grow out of the same potato have the same *genotype*—that is, the same genetic makeup. Eyes can grow into new potato plants. By planting the eyes of a potato and changing such environmental conditions as light, water, and temperature, you can see how environmental factors influence characteristics.

What you need

An old potato with several eyes

A knife

Several wax paper or plastic cups

Potting soil, sand, water, plant food, and other materials you decide to use

WORLD BOOK illustrations by Mark Swindle

Activity procedure

Cut the potato so that each eye has about the same amount of potato attached to it.

Fill several of the wax paper or plastic cups with the same mixture of potting soil, sand, and water. (Potato plants grow best in slightly sandy soil and at temperatures that range from 60 to 70 °F [16 to 21 °C].)

Plant the potato pieces so the eyes are just above the surface of the soil. Provide one of the eyes with everything you think it needs to grow well, such as sufficient light and water. This eye will be your *control* for the experiment—that is, it will be the standard to which you compare the other eyes.

Alter one condition for each of the eyes other than the control. For example, place one of the eyes in a dark closet. Give one only half as much water as the others. Give another one plant food, following the directions on the package. Put one in the refrigerator to see how it is affected by the cooler temperature. Except for the one condition that you change for each plant, try to keep other environmental factors the same as much as possible. Label each container so you know which factor is different. Observe the eyes for several weeks to see how they grow. Keep a record of the plants' development. You may want to include drawings of the plants with this record.

Results and questions

After several weeks have passed, analyze the material you have collected. Are there differences in the way the individual plants have grown? Does any one environmental factor seem more influential than others in determining the plants' development? Do individuals with the same genetic makeup necessarily have the same observable characteristics? What relationship can you now conclude exists between genotype and phenotype?

Extending the activity

Think about genotype and phenotype in terms of human beings. Consider such factors as food and shelter as being part of a person's environment. Do you think you would look and act differently if you had the same genotype but grew up in another kind of home and ate different types of food? How would you be different? Can you think of other factors that are part of your environment?

DNA called *RNA (ribonucleic acid)*. Like DNA, RNA is a nucleic acid and is composed of nucleotides. But the sugar in RNA is ribose instead of deoxyribose, and RNA contains the base *uracil* (U) instead of thymine. Like thymine, however, uracil base-pairs with adenine.

During transcription, a cell makes an RNA copy of one of the DNA strands of a gene. Part of the twisted DNA ladder unwinds and splits. One of the half ladders then serves as a *template* (mold) for lining up the RNA bases. The bases of the free nucleotides pair with the exposed DNA bases. For example, the RNA bases CUACAG pair with the DNA bases GATGTC. An RNA strand called *messenger RNA* (mRNA) is formed, and it is a complementary copy of the DNA blueprint.

As transcription proceeds, the mRNA copy of the gene peels off the DNA template. It then carries the instructions for making the gene's protein product to the cell's protein factories, which are structures known as *ribosomes*. The ribosomes are outside the nucleus in a part of the cell called the *cytoplasm*. The mRNA acts as a guide to line up the amino acids in the order called for by the gene, forming the correct protein chain.

Translation. In the translation step of gene expression, the ribosomes "read" the code in the mRNA and link amino acids in the order the mRNA codons dictate. Another type of RNA, called *transfer RNA* (tRNA), plays a key role in translation. Transfer RNA brings amino acids to the ribosomes from other parts of the cytoplasm.

A molecule of transfer RNA has two sites with important roles in translation. One site contains an *anticodon*, which consists of three nucleotides. The bases in the nucleotides of each tRNA anticodon are complementary to those in an mRNA codon and can therefore base-pair with them. The other important site is at one end of the tRNA molecule. The tRNA binds to a specific amino acid at this site. For example, tRNA with the anticodon CGU binds to the mRNA codon GCA, which codes for the amino acid alanine. The end of the tRNA binds to alanine. Thus, this tRNA can deliver alanine to the ribosome.

The mRNA moves through a ribosome one codon at a time. After a codon arrives at the decoding center of the ribosome, a tRNA molecule brings in the appropriate amino acid. In this way, the polypeptide grows, one amino acid at a time, until the ribosome reaches the end of the message in the mRNA. The last codon of the message signals that the chain is complete and tells the ribosome to stop production.

After the ribosome reads the stop codon, the finished polypeptide chain is released. The ribosome can then begin producing another polypeptide. In most proteins that consist of more than one polypeptide chain, the chains are manufactured separately, and then they combine to make the protein.

History of the study of heredity

Early ideas about heredity. One of the oldest known theories of inheritance was proposed by the Greek philosopher Aristotle, who lived during the 300's B.C. Aristotle taught that traits are inherited through the blood. This theory was wrong, but it was generally accepted for more than 1,000 years.

A correct theory of inheritance could not be formulated until after sex cells had been discovered and their functions determined. The discovery of eggs and sperm occurred during the late 1600's. At that time, many biologists thought that either the egg or the sperm contained a tiny but fully formed embryo that merely increased in size inside the mother. In the late 1700's, Caspar Friedrich Wolff, a German scientist, proved embryos are not preformed. He showed that an embryo grows from a fertilized egg, and he argued that the sperm and the egg contribute equally to the embryo.

During the early 1800's, a French biologist and nobleman, the Chevalier de Lamarck, suggested that traits acquired during the lifetime of an organism could be passed on to its offspring. Later genetic discoveries showed that transmission of such acquired characteristics from one generation to the next does not occur.

However, Lamarck's theory was basically accepted by the British biologist Charles Darwin, who proposed the theory of natural selection in his book *The Origin of Species* (1859). Darwin believed each part of the body produced tiny particles that moved through the bloodstream into the eggs or sperm. These particles supposedly influenced hereditary traits. The British scientist Francis Galton, a cousin of Darwin's, disproved this idea. Galton transfused blood from black rabbits into white rabbits to see if the white ones would have black babies. But the white rabbits still produced white offspring.

Mendel's laws. During the mid-1800's, Gregor Mendel, an Austrian botanist and monk, conducted a series of experiments on inheritance. Working in his monastery garden, he studied traits in pea plants. The results of these experiments led Mendel to formulate the first correct theory of heredity. This theory consisted of two principles called *Mendel's laws of heredity.*

Mendel's first law, the Law of Segregation, has three parts. (1) Hereditary characteristics are determined by separate units (now called genes). (2) These units occur in pairs. (3) The genes in a pair *segregate* (separate) during the division of sex cells, and each sperm or egg receives only one member of the pair.

Mendel's second law is called the Law of Independent Assortment. This law states that each pair of genes behaves independently of all other pairs during the production of sex cells. Therefore, each pair of genes is inherited independently of all other genes. Geneticists now know that independent assortment applies only to genes that are on different chromosomes or far apart on the same chromosome. Genes that are linked, or near each other on the same chromosome, tend to be inherited together.

The birth of genetics. Mendel published a report of his work in 1866. But it went unnoticed until 1900. Then, three European botanists studying heredity each rediscovered Mendel's work. These three scientists were Hugo de Vries of the Netherlands, Carl Correns of Germany, and Erich von Tschermak of Austria. They conducted plant-breeding experiments and independently got results similar to those Mendel had obtained.

Many important genetic discoveries quickly followed the rediscovery of Mendel's principles. During the early 1900's, a group of scientists directed by Thomas Hunt Morgan at Columbia University in New York City discovered many important aspects of heredity. These researchers included Calvin B. Bridges, Hermann J. Muller, and Alfred H. Sturtevant. Morgan and his co-workers

Mendel's experiments on heredity

In the mid-1800's, Gregor Mendel, an Austrian botanist and monk, studied traits in pea plants. The diagrams below show the main steps in Mendel's experiments on seed color.

WORLD BOOK diagrams by Mark Swindle

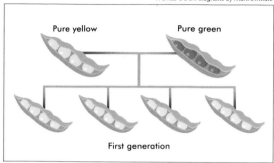

First generation

Mendel first experimented with purebred strains of pea plants—one with yellow seeds and one with green seeds. He crossed these strains, and all the resulting hybrid seeds were yellow. He concluded that yellow seed color was the dominant trait.

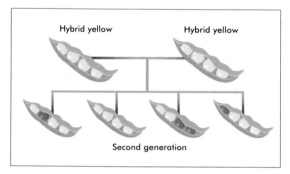

Second generation

Plants grown from the hybrid yellow seeds produced yellow and green seeds in a ratio of about 3 to 1. The inheritance patterns Mendel discovered in this experiment and similar ones led him to formulate the first correct theory of heredity.

studied the inheritance of such traits as eye color and wing shape in fruit flies. They showed that genes were on chromosomes, made the first genetic map, demonstrated the inheritance of genes on sex chromosomes, and discovered crossing over. In 1931, the American geneticist Barbara McClintock demonstrated that crossing over involves the physical exchange of chromosomal material.

The chemistry of genes became the focus of much research in genetics after 1940. By the early 1950's, scientists had proved that genes control chemical reactions in cells by directing the production of enzymes and other proteins. They had also determined that DNA is the hereditary material.

Two scientists, James D. Watson of the United States and Francis H. C. Crick of the United Kingdom, proposed a model of the ladderlike chemical structure of DNA—the double helix—in 1953. Their model was a breakthrough because it suggested for the first time how DNA can be replicated faithfully. Watson and Crick suggested that DNA replicates by splitting down the middle and building two ladders by matching complementary halves. They also proposed that mutations result from a

change in the sequence of bases along the ladder. In 1958, the American geneticists Matthew S. Meselson and Franklin Stahl demonstrated experimentally that DNA replicates just as Watson and Crick had proposed.

In 1961, scientists working at the California Institute of Technology reported their discovery of messenger RNA. That same year, the American biochemist Marshall W. Nirenberg and his colleagues at the National Institutes of Health (NIH) identified the first word of the genetic code—UUU. By 1967, the entire code had been broken.

The era of genetic engineering. Since the early 1970's, much of the study of heredity has involved the use of techniques known as genetic engineering or recombinant DNA technology. Recombinant DNA technology alters the genes in organisms to produce molecules called *recombinant DNA.*

Scientists produce recombinant DNA by first using enzymes called *restriction enzymes* to cut the chromosomal DNA from a plant or animal into pieces. They then make a recombinant DNA molecule by chemically attaching these smaller pieces to special DNA molecules called *vectors.* Vectors have the ability to enter cells and replicate. Next, scientists transplant the recombinant DNA into a bacterial or yeast cell. When these cells reproduce, researchers can obtain a huge number of identical cells that contain the recombinant DNA. A group of genetically identical cells is known as a *clone.*

Experiments with recombinant DNA have revealed much about the structure and function of genes. Recombinant DNA technology also has important medical applications. In 1982, genetically engineered insulin for diabetics became the first recombinant DNA drug approved by the United States Food and Drug Administration (FDA) for use on people. Other genetically engineered drugs followed. They include human growth hormone (hGH), which is used to treat children whose growth is seriously below average; *tissue plasminogen activator,* used to treat heart attacks by breaking up blood clots; and *interferon,* used for halting the spread of viruses from cell to cell.

Another important medical application of recombinant DNA technology is gene therapy. In 1990 and early 1991, researchers at the NIH used gene therapy on patients for the first time. They treated two young girls who had faulty genes for the enzyme *adenosine deaminase* (ADA). The genes produced a deficiency of the enzyme, which caused the girls to have severely weakened immune systems. The researchers used a modified virus to deliver a normal copy of the ADA gene to the girls. A few months after gene therapy, both girls had properly working immune systems. However, the therapy did not cure their condition, and the girls needed to receive periodic additional treatment. In 1993, NIH researchers used gene therapy for the first time on a patient with cystic fibrosis, a hereditary disorder that causes a life-threatening build-up of thick mucus in the lungs.

By the mid-1990's, teams of geneticists had identified and cloned the genes that control several other serious genetic disorders. They include amyotrophic lateral sclerosis (ALS), Duchenne muscular dystrophy, and Huntington's disease.

Recombinant DNA technology has agricultural applications as well. Researchers are experimenting with using genetic-engineering techniques to improve cer-

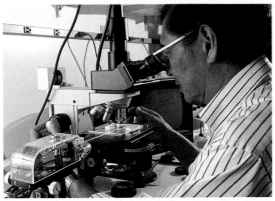

David L. Cornwell, Eleanor Roosevelt Institute

The Human Genome Project is designed to create a genetic map of the entire set of human genes. This researcher is dissecting a chromosome for study as part of the project.

tain features of crops, including the ability of plants to resist diseases and pests. In 1994, the FDA approved for sale a genetically engineered tomato that is supposed to have an improved shelf life and flavor.

The Human Genome Project. In the late 1980's, scientists in the United States and a number of other nations launched the Human Genome Project. This project is designed to create a genetic map of the entire set of human genes—the 50,000 to 100,000 genes of the human genome. Another of its goals is to determine the base sequence of the 3 billion base pairs in all the DNA in a human cell. Geneticists hope that a genetic map will help them identify more genes associated with diseases. They believe that the sooner these genes are located and identified, the sooner they can design strategies to try to cure the diseases.   Robert F. Weaver and Philip W. Hedrick

Marine biology is the study of organisms that live in the sea. It deals with all forms of life in the oceans, from viruses so small they can be seen only with the most

powerful electron microscopes to whales, the largest living animals.

Living things are found in all parts of the ocean, from the shores where waves splash onto the land to the deepest points of the ocean floor. Because people have always been able to visit the seashore at low tide and observe marine life, studies of marine biology began in shallow-water regions. Early marine biologists studied plants and animals from deep waters by using nets and other devices to collect samples. The development of scuba diving equipment has enabled biologists to observe marine organisms in their natural habitats, especially in the clear tropical waters along coral reefs. Scientists also can visit the deepest parts of the ocean in special underwater craft. Marine biologists who usually study life in deepwater regions are called *biological oceanographers.*

What marine biologists do. Marine biologists describe and classify marine organisms. They try to determine how these organisms develop, how they obtain food, how they reproduce, how they interact with other organisms, and why particular groups of organisms live in different regions of the ocean.

The work of marine biologists becomes increasingly important as people use more and more of the ocean's resources for food and recreation. Marine biologists seek to learn how extensively marine plants and animals can be harvested as food without destroying their natural populations. These scientists also investigate whether or not certain human activities, such as dumping waste products in the ocean, harm marine life.

Marine biologists try to discover what substances marine organisms produce that can be used to treat human diseases. They have found substances in sponges, soft corals, and other marine animals that appear to be effective in treating bacterial and viral infections. Other substances are being tested by drug companies as possible treatments for arthritis and various types of cancer, including leukemia.

Joe Viesti

Marine biologists study marine life in its environment. These scientists may travel long distances to an isolated area to study a particular marine animal. They collect data on the animal and on characteristics of its environment, such as water temperature and salt content.

Marine biologists have used marine animals in experiments to increase our knowledge of human life processes. For example, much of our understanding about the early developmental states of organisms has come from the study of marine animals. In experiments with the eggs of sea urchins, marine biologists have determined how chemical substances influence the development of *embryos* (developing young). Marine biologists also have used the squid's giant nerve fibers to discover how nerves work. The squid's nerve fibers are so large that scientists can place instruments inside different parts of the nerve to record mechanical, chemical, and electrical responses.

Many marine biologists do much of their work in special laboratories near seacoasts. Seawater is readily available there to maintain organisms for research. Among the most famous marine laboratories in the United States are the Marine Biological Laboratory of the Woods Hole Oceanographic Institution at Woods Hole, Mass.; Scripps Institution of Oceanography at La Jolla, Calif.; and the University of Washington at Seattle's Friday Harbor Laboratory, located at Friday Harbor, Calif.

Biological oceanographers usually focus on the open ocean and deepwater regions of the oceans. In addition to studying the ocean's organisms, they investigate the physical and chemical nature of the ocean, including its temperature, salt content, and oxygen content. For example, they try to learn how sunlight, nutrients, and temperature in the sea affect the growth rate of the mass of tiny marine plants known as *phytoplankton.* Phytoplankton forms the basis of the ocean *food web* (feeding interrelationships among organisms). Understanding how food webs function is important in determining how many fish can be harvested in different regions of the oceans.

Many biological oceanographers go to sea in special research vessels to study organisms in their natural environment. From these ships, they use water-sampling bottles, nets, dredges, and other collecting devices to take samples for further study. They also make use of *remotely operated vehicles (ROV's).* ROV's are small submarinelike "robots" that are controlled from research vessels on the ocean's surface. ROV's are equipped with video cameras that allow scientists to observe and record the behavior of organisms. Many ROV's also have mechanical arms to collect samples for study. Biological oceanographers visit the deepest regions of the ocean in deep-diving craft called *submersibles.*

Some of the most exciting discoveries in marine biology have come from studies in the deep ocean. In 1977, scientists used the submersible *Alvin* to study the sea bottom on the East Pacific Rise near the Galapagos Islands. To their surprise, they found large populations of bottom-dwelling organisms surrounding volcanic hot springs in the ocean crust, about 6,000 feet (2,000 meters) below the sea's surface. They did not expect to find such abundant life at that depth, where there was no phytoplankton to support the food web. Phytoplankton could not grow because light did not penetrate to that depth. Studies showed that bacteria living on chemicals in the hot springs provide the basis of the food web for this deepwater community. Some scientists now suggest that life on the earth may have started near such hot springs.

Biological oceanographers also are involved in studies of the ocean *ecosystem.* The ocean ecosystem consists of all living and nonliving things in the ocean and the relationships among them. In one such study, called the Joint Global Ocean Flux Study (JGOFS), oceanographers from throughout the world are investigating how activity of the ocean's food web might decrease the amount of carbon dioxide in the air. Many scientists believe that the amount of carbon dioxide in the atmosphere has slowly increased as people burn more coal, oil, and natural gas for energy. They worry that this increase in atmospheric carbon dioxide will prevent surface heat from escaping into space. This *greenhouse effect* could cause a gradual—and potentially disastrous— warming of the earth's temperature.

Some carbon dioxide is used by the phytoplankton at the ocean's surface waters and then transferred through the food web to the ocean's depths. JGOFS research seeks to determine whether this activity will offset the increased amount of carbon dioxide in the air.

David L. Garrison

Related articles. See **Ocean.** See also the following articles:

Marine life

Algae	Echinoderm	Seaweed
Animal (Animals of	Fish	Sponge
the oceans)	Kelp	Squid
Cnidarian	Mollusk	Turtle
Crustacean	Plankton	(Sea turtles)
Diatom	Sea urchin	Walrus
Dolphin	Seal	Whale

Other related articles

Careers (Marine science)	Scripps Institution
Cousteau, Jacques-Yves	of Oceanography
Diving, Underwater	Woods Hole Oceanographic
(Submersibles)	Institution

Dan McCoy, Rainbow

Marine biologists use laboratories to study marine life in order to better understand human life processes. The scientist above is doing research on the memory of snails.

Index

How to use the index
This index covers the contents of the 1994, 1995, and 1996 editions of *Science Year,* The World Book Science Annual.

Each index entry gives the last two digits of the edition year, followed by a colon and the page number or numbers. For example, this entry means that information on atomic bombs may be found on pages 119-120 and 127-128 of the 1996 *Science Year.*

When there are many references to a topic, they are grouped alphabetically by clue words under the main topic. For example, the clue words under **Automobiles** group the references to that topic under the main heading and five subtopics.

An entry in all capital letters indicates that there is a Science News Update article with that name in at least one of the three volumes covered in this index. References to the topic in other articles may also be listed in the entry.

An entry that only begins with a capital letter indicates that there are no Science News Update articles with that title but that information on this topic may be found in the editions and on the pages listed.

The "see" and "see also" cross references indicate that references to the topic are listed under another entry in the index.

The indication (il.) after a page number means that the reference is to an illustration only.

An entry followed by *WBE* refers to a new or revised *World Book Encyclopedia* article in the *Science Year* supplement section. This entry means that there is a *World Book Encyclopedia* article on marine biology on page 351 of the 1996 *Science Year.*

Index

A

A8 (automobile), **95:** 262-263
Abalones, **96:** 233
Abciximab (drug), **96:** 250-251
Absorption lines, **94:** 218-219
Accelerators, Particle. See **Particle accelerators**
Accidents. See **Risk assessment**
Accretion disks, **96:** 219, **95:** 22 (il.), 24, 26-27, **94:** 226-227
Acetaminophen, **95:** 322-323
Acetylcholine, **94:** 277
Acid rain, **95:** 181, 261
Acne, **96:** 322-323
Acquired immune deficiency syndrome. See **AIDS**
Acrophobia, **95:** 39-40
Actuators (engineering), **94:** 162
Acyclovir (drug), **96:** 250
Adenosine deaminase deficiency, **95:** 133-135
Adenosine triphosphate, **94:** 278
Adolescents, **96:** 291, **94:** 291
Adrenaline, **96:** 227-228
Advanced Communications Technology Satellite, **95:** 306
Advanced Photon Source (particle accelerator), **96:** 290
Advertising, **95:** 296-297
Aegean Sea (tanker), **94:** 250
Aerobics shoes, **96:** 313
Aerobraking, **95:** 308
Aerodynamics, **94:** 67
Africa
    cheetahs, **95:** 47, 59
    dinosaur fossils, **96:** 264-265
    early humans, **96:** 204-208, **95:** 208-209, 211, 220
    Ebola virus, **96:** 293
    extinctions, **96:** 174
    Goodall interview, **96:** 105-117
African Burial Ground, **94:** 117-131
Afrovenator (dinosaur), **96:** 264
Aging, **95:** 238
AGRICULTURE, **96:** 196-199, **95:** 206-208, **94:** 202-205
    ancient, **96:** 210, **95:** 218
    cloning, **95:** 93
    songbird population, **94:** 38-39, 42
    see also **Botany; Food; Pesticides**
AIDS
    cancer link, **95:** 284
    deaths, **95:** 298
    drugs, **96:** 250, **95:** 282-284, **94:** 243
    fullerene HIV block, **95:** 246-247
    Gallo case, **95:** 302
    official definition, **94:** 293
    pregnancy, **95:** 282-283
    retrovirus, **95:** 123-124, 131-132, 137
    women and minorities, **96:** 294
AIDS-like illness, **94:** 271-272, 294 (il.)
Air cleaners, **94:** 317-320
Air conditioners, **96:** 315-324, **94:** 248
Air pollution
    air cleaners, **94:** 317-320
    asthma, **96:** 260
    automobile emissions, **96:** 46-50, 53, **95:** 318, 320-321
    biomass energy, **95:** 189, 192
    extinctions, **96:** 175, 191

fine particulates, **95:** 266
    fossil fuels, **95:** 180-181
    indoor, **96:** 260-261
    risks, **95:** 161, 163
    see also **Acid rain; Ozone pollution**
Air traffic control, **96:** 242 (il.)
Aircraft. See **Aviation**
Akbar the Great, **95:** 47, 49-50
Akkadian empire, **95:** 211-213
Alaskan wolves, **96:** 244-245, **95:** 254-255
Alcohol consumption, **96:** 295, **95:** 296-297
    see also **Ethanol; Methanol**
Alfvén, Hannes, **96:** 248
Algae, **96:** 145-146, 151-153
Allergies, **96:** 323
Alligators, **96:** 37
Allosaurus (dinosaur), *WBE*, **95:** 351
Alpha AXP (microprocessor), **94:** 236
Alpha decay, **96:** 288
Alpha particles, **96:** 121, 123 (il.), 127
ALS. See **Amyotrophic lateral sclerosis**
Altai Mountains, **94:** 265
Aluminum, **96:** 58, 258, **95:** 262-263
Alyeska Trans-Alaska Pipeline, **95:** 267
Alzheimer's disease, **96:** 276-277, **95:** 274, 282, **94:** 277
Amber, **94:** 260 (il.)
Ambulocetus natans (animal), **95:** 270 (il.), 286
America Online (network), **95:** 252
Amino acids, **96:** 199
Ammonites, **95:** 78-81
Amorphous cells, **95:** 262
Amphibians
    cloning, **95:** 94-101
    deaths and extinctions, **96:** 175, **95:** 252-254, 261
    fossil studies, **96:** 263-264
    river ecosystem, **95:** 63, 70
Amur tigers, **95:** 254
Amygdalae, **96:** 227, 291-292
Amylase (enzyme), **95:** 136
Amyloid precursor protein, **96:** 277, **94:** 277
Amyotrophic lateral sclerosis, **95:** 275 (il.), **94:** 256-266
Analgesics, **95:** 322-323
Analog signals, **95:** 166-167
Analogy, and risk, **95:** 157-158
Anderson, Forrest N., **95:** 235
Andrew, Hurricane, **96:** 30, 34 (il.), 35 (il.), 37-43
Andromeda galaxy, **95:** 24, 227 (il.)
Anemia, **94:** 270
Anencephaly, **94:** 284
Anfinsen, Christian B., **96:** 248
Angioplasty, **96:** 270
Angiosperms, **95:** 271
Angkor Wat (temple), **96:** 208 (il.)
Animals
    cave, **96:** 97-103
    cloning, **95:** 93-94
    cosmetics testing, **96:** 322
    cross-species transplants, **96:** 278-279
    exotic invaders, **94:** 133-145
    ocean crust formation, **94:** 264
    rights, **96:** 112-113
    risk assessment studies, **95:** 159

river ecosystem, **95:** 63-66, 70-71
    see also **Biology; Conservation; Ecosystems; Endangered species; Prehistoric animals; Zoology**
Ankylosaurus (dinosaur), *WBE*, **95:** 351
Anning, Mary, **95:** 81-84
Antarctica
    continental drift, **96:** 275-276
    dinosaurs, **95:** 269
    global warming, **96:** 251
    ozone hole, **96:** 222, 317, **95:** 233, **94:** 253, 276
ANTHROPOLOGY, **96:** 200-202, **95:** 208-211, **94:** 205-208
    books, **96:** 234, **95:** 242, **94:** 228
Antibiotics, **96:** 198, **95:** 322
Antihistamines, **95:** 323-324
Antimatter, **94:** 187
    birth of universe, **94:** 191-192, 198
    laboratory production, **94:** 233
    quark theory, **96:** 136-137, **95:** 288
Antioxidants, **95:** 285
Antiparticles. See **Antimatter**
Antiprotons, **96:** 137, 138 (il.)
Ants, **96:** 253
Anxiety, **96:** 292-293, **94:** 292-293
Apatosaurus (dinosaur), **95:** 87 (il.), 89
    WBE, **95:** 351-352
Apolipoprotein-E, **95:** 274, 282
Apple Computer, Inc., **95:** 247-249, **94:** 235 (il.), 236-237
Apple maggots, **94:** 204
Appliances, Home, **94:** 248
Aprontin (drug), **96:** 251
Archaebacteria, **96:** 231
ARCHAEOLOGY, **96:** 203-211, **95:** 211-220, **94:** 208-216
    African Burial Ground, **94:** 117-131
    book, **96:** 234
    Moche civilization, **94:** 45-57
    see also **Native Americans**
Archaeopteryx (bird), **95:** 270, **94:** 256
Arctic, **96:** 251-252, 317, **95:** 215-218, **94:** 253
Arecibo telescope, **94:** 110-111
Argon-argon dating, **95:** 109
Ariane-5 rocket, **96:** 302
Armenia, **94:** 295
Army radiation experiments, **95:** 300
ARPAnet (network), **95:** 172
Art, Prehistoric. See **Caves**
Arthritis, Rheumatoid. See **Rheumatoid arthritis**
Asbestos, **94:** 318
Asexual reproduction, **95:** 92-93
Ash, as nutrient, **96:** 199
Aspartame, **95:** 284
Aspen trees, **94:** 231 (il.)
Aspirin, **95:** 322-323
Asteroids
    collision with Earth, **96:** 14, 20, **95:** 119, **94:** 221
    moons of, **95:** 228-229
    space probe studies, **94:** 220-221
Asthma, **96:** 260
Astro-2 observatory, **96:** 302
Astrometry, **94:** 112-113
ASTRONOMY, **96:** 211-219, **95:** 221-229, **94:** 216-227
    books, **96:** 234, **95:** 242, **94:** 228

Index

Index

Index

Index

Photonic wire, **96**: 238
Photoreceptors, **95**: 241
Photosynthesis, **96**: 145, 148 (il.), 182, 268-269, **94**: 264
Photovoltaic cells, **95**: 195-197, 262
Physical fitness. See **Exercise**
PHYSICS, **96**: 286-291, **95**: 288-292, **94**: 287-291
  books, **96**: 235, **95**: 243, **94**: 229
  Lederman interview, **95**: 138-149
  Nobel Prizes, **96**: 223-224, **95**: 234, **94**: 280-281
  science student awards, **96**: 227, **95**: 237, **94**: 298
  see also **Subatomic particles**
Physiology or medicine, Nobel Prize for, **96**: 224, **95**: 234-235, **94**: 281
Phytoplankton, **96**: 146, 149, **95**: 259, **94**: 82, 138-139, 286
Piezoelectric effect, **96**: 255, **94**: 164-166
Pigs, **95**: 218, **94**: 140 (il.)
Pinatubo, Mount. See **Mount Pinatubo**
Pine trees, **96**: 228-229
Pioneer species, **96**: 31, 42
Pitohui (bird), **94**: 302-303
Plague, **96**: 293
Planetesimals, **94**: 104-108
Planets, **95**: 221, **94**: 103-115, 180
  see also **Astronomy** and individual planets
Plants
  Antarctica, **96**: 251
  biodiversity benefits, **96**: 182
  biological clock gene, **96**: 268-269
  cave, **96**: 97-103
  cloning, **95**: 93
  electrical signals, **94**: 230
  exotic invaders, **94**: 133-145
  global warming, **96**: 149-151, **94**: 252
  insect evolution, **95**: 271
  Jurassic Period, **95**: 81
  light detection, **95**: 240-241
  ocean crust formation, **94**: 264
  river ecosystem, **95**: 63-67, 70-71
  self-pollination, **95**: 240
  see also **Agriculture; Biology; Botany; Conservation; Ecosystems; Endangered species; Forests; Wetlands**
Plaque, Dental, **94**: 314
Plasma (physics), **95**: 22 (il.), 27, 197, 290-292
Plastics, **96**: 58, 198-199, 237, **95**: 325-328
Plate tectonics
  computer model, **94**: 264
  earthquakes, **95**: 278-279, **94**: 262-263
  geothermal energy, **95**: 191
  ocean crust formation, **94**: 261-264
  satellite research, **94**: 300
  volcanoes, **95**: 276
Pleiades (star cluster), **94**: 181 (il.)
Pleistocene Epoch, **95**: 271
Plesiosaurs, **95**: 83
Plinian column, **95**: 113 (il.), 115
Pluto, **95**: 229, **94**: 18 (il.), 21
Plutonium, **95**: 300
Point bars, **95**: 62, 65 (il.)
Poisson, Roger, **95**: 302

Pollination, **95**: 240
Pollution. See **Air pollution; Environment; Water pollution**
Polyacrylamide, **95**: 206 (il.)
Polycyclic aromatic hydrocarbons, **94**: 219
Polyethylene, **95**: 326
Polyhydroxybutyrate (plastic), **96**: 198-199
Polymerase chain reaction, **96**: 84, **95**: 234
Polymers, **94**: 267
Polypropylene (plastic), **96**: 237
Pools (geology), **95**: 63, 65 (il.), 71, 75
Popper, Sir Karl, **96**: 249
Population bottlenecks, **95**: 54
Population growth, **96**: 180, **94**: 91
Positron emission tomography, **94**: 147-148, 158, 159
Positronium, **94**: 233
Possum, Brushtail, **94**: 136 (il.)
Pottery, **94**: 49-50
Poverty, **94**: 98
  see also **Developing nations**
PowerBook Duo (computer), **94**: 237
PowerPC microprocessor, **95**: 247-249
Predators, **95**: 78, 260-261, **94**: 34-35, 136-139
Pregnancy, **96**: 294, **95**: 282-283
Prehistoric animals, **95**: 268-271, **94**: 205-208
  Jurassic Period, **95**: 77-89
  see also **Dinosaurs; Fossil studies**
Prehistoric people, **96**: 200-202, **95**: 208-211, **94**: 205-208
  WBE, **94**: 337-348
  see also **Anthropology; Archaeology; Fossil studies; Native Americans; Neanderthals**
Premature birth, **96**: 294-295
Preservation of documents, **95**: 310-314
Primate, Fossil, **95**: 269 (il.)
Privacy, **96**: 296, **95**: 175-177
Probability, **95**: 152
Programs. See **Computers and electronics**
Propane. See **Liquefied petroleum gas**
Prostaglandins, **95**: 322-323
Prostate cancer, **96**: 83, 84, **95**: 284-285
Protective headgear, **95**: 265-266
Proteins, **96**: 77-83, **95**: 124-125
Protogalaxies, **94**: 195
Protons, **96**: 121, 132, 137-140, **94**: 186-187
Proxima Centauri (star), **94**: 65, 109, 112
Pseudoryx (animal), **95**: 241 (il.)
PSR 1257+12 (pulsar), **94**: 103-104, 115
PSYCHOLOGY, **96**: 291-293, **95**: 292-295, **94**: 291-293
  virtual reality systems, **95**: 39-40
  see also **Brain**
Pteranodon (animal), **96**: 65 (il.), 66 (il.), 72, 73
Pterodactyls, **96**: 60-73, **95**: 84, 89 (il.)
Ptolemy, **94**: 176-177
PUBLIC HEALTH, **96**: 293-295, **95**: 296-298, **94**: 293-295

books, **96**: 235, **95**: 243
ionizing radiation, **96**: 119-129
Pueblos, **96**: 209-210
Pulsars
  binary, **95**: 234
  Geminga, **94**: 216-217
  high-speed, **94**: 217-218
  planets around, **95**: 221, **94**: 103-104, 114-115
Pumice, **95**: 110
Pyroclastic flows, **95**: 113 (il.), 115, 120, 277

Q

Quality-control genes, **96**: 81-83
Quantum mechanics, **95**: 24-25, 290
Quarks, **94**: 187, 188
  top, **96**: 131-143, **95**: 141-144, 288, **94**: 288-289
Quasars, **95**: 24, 26, **94**: 182, 224-225
Queen Alexandra's birdwing (butterfly), **96**: 175 (il.)
Quetzalcoatlus (animal), **96**: 63-64

R

Rabbits, **94**: 306
Radar, **94**: 32
Radiation
  experiments on humans, **96**: 119-120, **95**: 300-301
  ionizing, and health, **96**: 119-129
  window efficiency, **96**: 325
Radiation era, **94**: 192
Radiation sickness, **96**: 125
Radiation therapy, **96**: 81
Radio galaxies, **95**: 227-228
Radio telescopes, **94**: 110-111
Radioactive decay, **96**: 121
Radioactivity, **96**: 120-121, **95**: 300-301
  see also **Radiation**
Radium, **96**: 120-125
Radon, **96**: 125, **95**: 161
Rain. See **Acid rain; Drought**
Rain forests, **96**: 181 (il.), 183 (il.), 188, **94**: 90-91, 94, 96 (il.)
Ramirez, Richard, **96**: 169
Ramses II, **96**: 203
Raven, Peter H., **94**: 88-101
Reality Engine (computer), **95**: 33
Re-bar steel, **96**: 256
Recombinant DNA technology. See **Genetic engineering**
Rectal cancer, **96**: 84
Recycling, **96**: 258, **95**: 328, **94**: 249
Red shift, **96**: 215, **94**: 24, 109 (il.), 114, 179, 185
Red sprites, **96**: 221
Reefs. See **Coral reefs**
Refrigeration, **96**: 315-324
Regenerative braking, **96**: 51
Relativity, **95**: 15-18, 21, 27, **94**: 178, 224
Renal cancer, **96**: 84
ReoPro (drug), **96**: 250-251
Repressed memory, **95**: 294
Reproduction (biology), **95**: 92-93
  human, **95**: 92-94, 102-105
  see also **Childbirth; Cloning**
Reptiles, **95**: 63, 70
Respiratory disease, **95**: 280

Index

Index

Acknowledgments

The publishers of *Science Year* gratefully acknowledge the courtesy of the following artists, photographers, publishers, institutions, agencies, and corporations for the illustrations in this volume. Credits should read from top to bottom, left to right on their respective pages. All entries marked with an asterisk (*) denote illustrations created exclusively for *Science Year*. All maps, charts, and diagrams were prepared by the *Science Year* staff unless otherwise noted.

2-1	Naoto Hosaka, Gamma/Liaison
2-2	George Frey, *Time Magazine*
2-3	NASA
3-1	Jean Clottes, Ministere de la Culture from Sygma
3-2	Tim D. White, Brill Atlanta
3-3	Eugene Shoemaker
4-1	Zig Leszczynski, Animals Animals
4-2	Patrick Landmann, Gamma/Liaison
5-1	Giles Bassignac, Gamma/Liaison
5-2	American Museum of Natural History
10	Ford Motor Company
11-1	Steven Kirk © The Walt Disney Co. Reprinted with the permission of *Discover* Magazine
11-2	K.R. Downey
12	Mark Gabbana*
15-1	Dennis di Cicco
15-2	Mark Gabbana*
15-3	Mark Gabbana*
16	Eugene Shoemaker
17-1	Space Science Institute
17-2	AP/Wide World
17-3	AP/Wide World
17-4	AP/Wide World
19	TASS from Sovfoto
20, 23-24	Meteor Crater, Northern Arizona Mark Gabbana*
26	Meteor Crater, Northern Arizona Mark Gabbana*
28-1	NOAA from NASA
28-2	A.E. Jugo & F.N. Scatena, Institute of Tropical Forestry, USDA
28-2	A.E. Jugo & F.N. Scatena, Institute of Tropical Forestry, USDA
28-3	A.E. Jugo & F.N. Scatena, Institute of Tropical Forestry, USDA
32	Deidre Wroblewski*
34-1	Ted Levin
34-2	Douge Perrine, Innerspace Visions
35	Joel Sartore, National Geographic Society
38-39	Robin DeWitt*
41	Ted Levin
44	Paul Miller*
47-1	Orbital Engine Company
47-2	WORLD BOOK illustration
47-3	Orbital Engine Company
48-1	General Motors Corporation
48-2	Paul Miller*
48-3	General Motors Corporation
49-1	Paul Miller*
49-2	Unique Mobility Inc.
52-1	Mazda Motor Corporation
52-2	Paul Miller*
52-3	Mazda Motor Corporation
54	Ford Motor Corporation
57	Paul Miller*
60-1	Deidre Wroblewski*
60-2	Steven Kirk © The Walt Disney Co. Reprinted with the permission of *Discover* Magazine
61	Pat Redman*
62	Deidre Wroblewski*
63-1	Peter Wellnhofer
63-2	Samuel Thomas Soemmerring, 1817
64	"Landscape of the Lias Epoch" from Figuier's *Earth Before the Deluge*, 1863
65-1	Steven Kirk © The Walt Disney Co. Reprinted with the permission of *Discover* Magazine
65-2	Sternberg Museum of Natural History, *Fort Hayes State University*
65-3	Steven Kirk © The Walt Disney Co. Reprinted with the permission of *Discover* Magazine
65-4	WORLD BOOK illustration by Atos Menaboni
66-1	WORLD BOOK illustration by Arthur Singer
66-2	Sternberg Museum of Natural History, *Fort Hayes State University*
67	Steven Kirk © The Walt Disney Co. Reprinted with the permission of *Discover* Magazine
68	Deidre Wroblewski*
69	Steven Kirk © The Walt Disney Co. Reprinted with the permission of *Discover* Magazine
71-1	Martin Lockley
71-2	Deidre Wroblewski*
71-3	Pat Redman*
74-1	AMC from Custom Medical
74-2	B.S.I.P. from Custom Medical
77-78	Barbara Cousins*
80	Barbara Cousins*
82	Barbara Cousins*
86	K.R. Downey
90	Michael Nichols, Magnum
91-1	K.R. Downey
91-2	John D. Brooks
91-3	Harold E. Wilson, Earth Scenes
92	Len Ebert*
94-1	Robert and Linda Mitchell
94-2	John Brooks, National Park Service
94-3	Robert and Linda Mitchell
94-4	John Brooks, National Park Service
95	K.R. Downey
98-1	Len Ebert*
98-2	Stoufer Productions from Animals Animals
98-3	Robert and Linda Mitchell
98-4	Robert and Linda Mitchell
99	Robert and Linda Mitchell
100-1	Superstock
100-2	Robert and Linda Mitchell
101	Michael Nichols, Magnum
104-1	Baron Hugo Van Lawick © National Geographic Society
104-2	Jane Goodall Institute
106-1	Michael K. Nichols
106-2	Ralph Brunke*
107-1	Ralph Brunke*
107-2	Baron Hugo Van Lawick © National Geographic Society
108	Jane Goodall Institute
109-1	Jane Goodall Institute
109-2	Breese, Gamma/Liaison
110	Ralph Brunke*
111	Michael K. Nichols, Magnum
112-1	Ralph Brunke*
112-2	E. Koning
115-1	Baron Hugo Van Lawick © National Geographic Society
115-2	Ralph Brunke*
116	Ralph Brunke*
118	Fermilab Visual Media Services
126-1	Fermilab Visual Media Services
126-2	Roberta Polfus*
126-3	Fermilab Visual Media Services
126-4	Roberta Polfus*
127	Fermilab Visual Media Services
129	NASA/Science Photo Library from Photo Researchers
132	Jack Kenner
136	Rose Zgodzinski*
137-1	Rose Zgodzinski*
137-2	Rose Zgodzinski*
137-3	Rose Zgodzinski*
137-4	Rose Zgodzinski*
137-5	U.S. Department of Energy from Photo Researchers
137-6	Will & Denni McIntyre, Photo Researchers
138	Rose Zgodzinski*
144	Roberta Polfus*
147-1	Jerry Irwin, Photo Researchers
147-2	Roberta Polfus*
148-1	Roberta Polfus*
148-2	Takeshi Takahara, Photo Researchers

148-3	Kenneth S. Johnson, Moss Landing Marine Laboratories
148-4	Kenneth S. Johnson, Moss Landing Marine Laboratories
149	Roberta Polfus*
153-1	NASA
153-2	Roberta Polfus*
154	Roberta Polfus*
158-1	Reuters/Bettmann
158-2	David Parker, Science Photo Library from Photo Researchers
162-163	Barbara Cousins*
165-1	Patrick Landmann, Gamma/Liaison
165-2	Jacques M. Chenet, Gamma/Liaison
165-3	Philippe Plailly Science Photo Library from Photo Researchers
167-1	John Thornton, University of California, Berkeley
167-2	David R. Frazier
167-3	Patrick Landmann, Gamma/Liaison
169	Alexander Jason, Gamma/Liaison
172-1	Zig Leszczynski, Animals Animals
172-2	Luiz C. Marigo, Peter Arnold Inc.
175-1	Gerard Lacz, Peter Arnold Inc.
175-2	WORLD BOOK illustration by John F. Eggert
177-1	Delbert Wiens
177-2	Jack Jeffery, Photo Resource Hawaii
180	Thomas Kitchen, First Light
183	Luiz C. Marigo, Peter Arnold Inc.
184	Sarah Figlio*
186	DeGolyer Library, Southern Methodist University
187	Bettmann Archive
188-1	Mark D. Phillips, Photo Researchers
188-2	Earl Roberge, Photo Researchers
191	Robert Rattner
192	IINBio
194	NASA
195-1	Australian Museum, Sydney
195-2	Warford, Sygma
196	Purdue University News Services
198	Robert Devlin, Fisheries and Oceans Canada
200-1	Tim D. White, Brill Atlanta
200-2	Sarah Figlio*
202-1	Randall L. Susman, New York University at Stoney Brook
202-2	Sarah Figlio*
203	AP/Wide World
204	Paul Tacon, Australian Museum, Sydney
205	Charles O'Rear, West Light
206-207	Jean Clottes, Ministere de la Culture from Sygma
208-1	Jet Propulsion Laboratory
208-2	Art Resource
209	Maya Research Program
212	Susan Ridgeway, University of Hawaii
213-215	NASA
216	Oter Lahav, Dwingeloo Galaxy Survey Team
218	NCSA, University of Illinois at Urbana-Champaign
221-1	Dan Osborn, Geophysical Institute, University of Alaska
221-2	Sarah Figlio*
223-1	Carlo Allegri, Sygma
223-2	Reuters/Bettmann
224-1	Shelly Katz, Gamma/Liaison
224-2	Marty Katz
226	Mathematical Association of America
228	Royal Botanical Gardens, Sydney, Australia
229	Sally Shaywitz, M.D., Yale School of Medicine
231	Sarah Figlio*
232	Australian Museum, Sydney
236	Kenneth S. Suslick, Mike Wong, Lu Anne Miller, University of Illinois at Urbana-Champaign
237	Edward Wintner, MIT
240	Almaden Research Center, IBM Corporation
242	R. MacNeil, J. Ventrellal © MIT Media Lab
243	Microsoft Corporation
245	Lawrence Livermore Laboratories
247	Ann Hilborn
248-1	Globe Photos
248-2	Mary Evans Picture Library
248-3	AP/Wide World
249-1	NYT Pictures
249-2	NYT Pictures
249-3	AP/Wide World
252	Jerry Asher, Bureau of Land Management
253	Sanford Porter, USDA/ARS
256	Millitech Corporation
257	Gilles Bassignac, Gamma/Liaison
259-1	EPIX from Sygma
259-2	Warford, Sygma
262-1	American Museum of Natural History
262-2	American Museum of Natural History
263-1	Ted Daeschler, Academy of Natural Sciences of Philadelphia
263-2	University of Chicago
266	George Frey, *Time Magazine*
267	Walter Gehring
268	Reprinted by permission from *Nature*, Vol. 372, 1 December 1994, Cover
271	Naoto Hosaka, Gamma/Liaison
274	Jet Propulsion Laboratory
275	NASA
277-1	John L. Pauly, M.D.
277-2	John L. Pauly, M.D.
279	CSIRO Australian Animal Health Laboratory
280-1	Ron Laytner
280-2	National Library of Medicine Visible Human Data Set from Vic Spitzer, University of Colorado Health Services Center
280-3	National Library of Medicine Visible Human Data Set from Vic Spitzer, University of Colorado Health Services Center
284-1	Richard A. Lutz, Rudgers University
284-2	A. Giddings, E. Kristof, W. Lange, R. Lutz & the R/V Atlantis II /DSV Alvin crew
285-1	Ed Peltzer, Woods Hole Oceanographic Institution
285-2	NASA
287	Thomas J. Watson Research Center, IBM Corporation
290	Grange-Landemann from Gamma/Liaison
294	Raveendran, Agence France-Presse
299	NASA
301	NASA
303-1	U.S. Geological Survey
303-2	U.S. Geological Survey
303-3	Image Processing by ACT Corporation
305-1	NASA/Science Source from Photo Researchers
305-2	Dan McCoy, Rainbow
307	Julie Pace*
308	J. Burgess/Science Photo Library from Photo Researcher
309	Dan McCoy, Rainbow
311	All Sport from Photo Researchers
312	Julie Pace*
315	Julie Pace*
316-1	NASA
316-2	Julie Pace*
319	Luc Novovitch, Gamma/Liaison
324	NASA/Science Source from Photo Researchers
325-327	Julie Pace*
329-1	Dan McCoy, Rainbow
329-2	Lawrence Migdale, Photo Researchers

World Book Encyclopedia, Inc., provides high-quality educational and reference products for the family and school. They include THE WORLD BOOK~RUSH-PRESBYTERIAN-ST. LUKE'S MEDICAL CENTER~MEDICAL ENCYCLOPEDIA, a 1,072-page fully illustrated family health reference; THE WORLD BOOK OF MATH POWER, a two-volume set that helps students and adults build math skills; THE WORLD BOOK OF WORD POWER, a two-volume set that is designed to help your entire family write and speak more successfully; and the HOW TO STUDY video, a presentation of key study skills with information students need to succeed in school. For further information, write World Book Encyclopedia, Inc.; 2515 E. 43rd St.; P.O. Box 182265; Chattanooga TN 37422-7265.